SPECIAL ANNIVERSARY EDITION

30th ANNUAL

Steam Passenger Service
DIRECTORY

LES MACDONALD

A guide to tourist railways, trolley operations,
railway museums, live-steam railroads, and
toy train exhibits in the United States and Canada

For Your Information

Listings: We attempt to include every tourist railway, trolley operation, railway museum, live-steam railroad, and toy train exhibit in the United States and Canada about which reliable information is available. If you know of a new operation, please contact the production manager.

Accuracy: Every effort has been made to ensure the accuracy of the contents. However, we depend on the information supplied by each operation. We cannot assume responsibility for errors, omissions, or fare or schedule changes.

1996 Directory: To be published in April 1996. Listings must include photographs (postcards are not accepted) and must be received by November 17, 1995; fares and schedules must be received by January 19, 1996. New listings are welcome; please contact the production manager for information.

Guest Coupons: Be sure to use the reduced-rate coupons provided by many operations in this edition of the *Steam Passenger Service Directory*.

Brochures: Most operations in the *Directory* offer brochures and/or timetables. Please see the symbol section for each listing.

Advertising: Advertising space for the 1996 *Directory* must be reserved by January 1, 1996. Please contact the production manager for information.

Comments: Comments and suggestions are welcome and will be answered promptly.

Front Cover: Strasburg Rail Road, Strasburg, Pennsylvania. Photo by Les MacDonald.

Production

Mark Smith
Publisher

Kathy Truax
Production Manager

Michelle Giroux
Editor

Villanti & Sons Printers, Inc.
Separations, Film Work, and Printing

ISSN-0081-542X

GEORGE A. FORERO, JR.

The 1995 *Steam Passenger Service Directory* is dedicated to
George A. Forero, Jr., who has put in great effort and traveled long
distances to capture superb images of railway preservation on film.

Symbol Key

D: Display
M: Museum
R: Ride

&#9855;	Handicapped Accessible	📷	Guided Tours
▯	Refreshments	🚂	Excursions
🏢	Restaurant	🍎	Arts & Crafts
🍴	Dining Car/Dinner Train	⛉	Picnic Area
🚗	Parking	📖	Book Shop/Museum Store
🚌🚌	Bus/RV Parking	arm	Member of the Association
⊞	Gift Shop/Souvenirs		of Railway Museums
🏠	National Register of	TRAIN	Member of the Tourist
	Historic Places		Railway Association, Inc.
✉	Send Large SASE for	▲	Memberships Available
	Brochure	»	AMTRAK Service to a City
			Nearby

ICI FREER

TOM LELL

DOYLE YODER

The mission of the *Steam Passenger Service Directory* is to recognize and celebrate the men and women who have worked tirelessly to restore old engines and electric cars and who have devised means of interpreting and running antique railway equipment against nearly impossible conditions for the education and enjoyment of the general public. . .

MARK SMITH

LES MACDONALD

STEAMSCENES

. . . A second mission of the *Directory* is to encourage a spirit of cooperation and interdependence among the various museums and steam, electric, and diesel-operated railroads.

Adapted from Edgar Thorn Mead's introduction in the first **Steam Passenger Service Directory,** *1966*

LES MACDONALD

Empire State Railway Museum, Inc.

Peter H. Tassone

On this 30th anniversary of the *Steam Passenger Service Directory*, we, the Directors of the Empire State Railway Museum, Inc., gratefully acknowledge the support of railroad museums, steam railroads and other tourist rail attractions. This support has made the *Directory* the standard reference for railroad tourist operations in North America. We also acknowledge the very high standard of quality that Great Eastern Publishing brings to this reference work to make it an outstanding publication.

We give a very special thank you to our patrons, advertisers, supporters and publisher for the continued success of the *Steam Passenger Service Directory*.

For more information, please contact:

EMPIRE STATE RAILWAY MUSEUM, INC.
P.O. Box 455
Phoenicia, NY 12464-0455
(914) 688-7501

Yes, you _can_ go home again!

Remember the depot in your home town?

The agent, working third trick, keeping the telegraph clicking as down the line number eight blows two longs, a short and a long for the highway at the city limit. Reaching across his desk, the agent flips a switch and the order board turns red, its light beaming north in the mist. Soon, the engine rounds the curve by Main Street and, bell ringing, the big locomotive comes to a halt just beyond the depot, by the water spout. The depot clock shows the train on time at 11:48 p.m. The Creole has arrived.

While the fireman fills the tender, the agent pushes the baggage float over to the mail and express car, maintaining communications with the rest of the world for another day. As he pulls the float back under the shed, you notice Mr. Wilson, owner of the local hardware store, climbing aboard the Pullman and taking his seat in section 4, a lower berth, off on a buying trip to Chicago. Back at the controls of the stoker, the fireman is building steam as the hogger acknowledges the conductor's high ball with two blasts on the Paducah three chime.

Soon all is quiet again except for the telegraph clicking out orders for a south bound freight. As you climb on your Schwinn , you notice the signal is green again, its light gleaming on the rails. This is home town, America.

The museums and railroads in this directory will take you back to those days again. As you visit them, notice the sounds, smells and peculiarities of railroading forgotten over the years. You'll feel the lurching and rocking of the coaches, the aroma of coal smoke and hot oil, the lonesome whistle and the smiling conductor.

Support these museums; their preservation of the past is your ticket to future trips back home.

*A*nd to recall the <u>real</u> glory days of railroading, stop in at the gift shop and select one of our videos. Our programs were all filmed when the great trains roamed the country by dedicated photographers who preserved the images of railroading from the 1930's to the 1960's. All transferred from film to video by studios such as Disney/MGM and narrated with sound and appropriate music to create the highest acclaimed railroad videos available. Available at better tourist railroads.

If the store you visit doesn't have our tapes,
write for a free catalog.

Over 30 titles/More coming.
Most railroads covered.

2016 N. Village Ave.
Tampa, FL 33612
(813)932-3887

Quality, the difference is on the screen.

Discover
the fascination
of railroading at the

Colorado Railroad Museum

You can ring the bell on some of Colorado's oldest steam locomotives or climb into a red caboose. See over sixty cars and engines displayed in an authentic setting at the foot of the Rocky Mountains. The museum building, a replica of an 1880 style masonry depot, houses more than 50,000 rare old photographs, papers and artifacts. There's fun for the entire family!

Touch History...

Steam Train Runs
June 3-4
July 8-9
August 26-27
October 14-15
December 2-3

Open Every Day
9 a.m. - 5 p.m.
(June, July & August)
9 a.m. - 6 p.m.

Colorado Railroad Museum
Book Store & Gift Shop

Filled with over 1,000 railroad books, video tapes, posters, prints, jewelry, magazines and other memorabilia.

The Colorado Railroad Museum publishes the biggest and best railroad book and gift catalog. For your copy, send $2 (refundable on first order) to the address listed below.

Profits from the catalog and gift shop sales help us to preserve Colorado's railroad heritage.

Become a member of the Colorado Railroad Museum, call for information. The museum is a private not-for-profit organization, it is not state owned, operated or funded.

Colorado Railroad Museum
17155 W. 44th Avenue
P.O. Box 10
Golden, CO 80402-0010
Telephone (800) 365-6263 or (303) 279-4591
Fax (303) 279-4229

SUMMER 1995

STEAMTOWN GRAND OPENING
STEAMTOWN NATIONAL HISTORIC SITE - SUMMER 1995

In July, 1995, The United States National Park Service will open Steamtown National Park. You are invited!

After nine years of planning and five years of construction, doors will open on two new museums, a Park Theater, working Roundhouse and Turntable, Visitor's Center, Excursion Boarding Depot and the Bookstore.

The excitement of the 1890's will return to the historic Delaware, Lackawanna & Western Railyard. Steam excursions, visiting railroad equipment, guided tours and living history will welcome all of America and beyond.

It's the story of coal, iron and rail - it's the story of early times in this nation, and the beginning of the industrial revolution, just the way it happened years ago in Scranton, Pennsylvania.

(81) EXIT 53 SCRANTON

For more information,
call the Visitor's Bureau at
1-800-22-WELCOME

LACKAWANNA
Heritage Valley

Preserving Yesterday For Tomorrow

NATIONAL·RAILROAD M U S E U M

Green Bay, Wisconsin

From the Fastest   *...To the Largest*

Eisenhower Train   Big Boy Engine

1995 SPECIAL EVENTS*

For brochure or more
information, write or call:

**National Railroad Museum
2285 S. Broadway
Green Bay, WI 54304
Telephone: (414) 437-7623**

RAILFEST
June 24 & 25
   Hobo Stories & Activities
   Thomas the Tank Engine activities
   New Intermodal Exhibit
   RPO Car Stamp Cancellations
   Eisenhower Re-enactment
MAGIC WORLD OF LIONEL TRAINS EXHIBIT
June 29 - July 2
AMERICAFEST TRAIN RIDES
(Off Grounds) July 4
HANDCAR RACES AT FRENCH CREEK DAYS
(Off Grounds) July 8
FALL EXCURSION (Day Trip)
Call for dates & information

* All events are subject to change. Details on daily activities and collection on Page 311 of this Directory.

THOMAS
THE TANK ENGINE
& FRIENDS
™

contact Cindy Bernstein, Head of Public Affairs, Britt Allcroft Inc
1133 Broadway Suite 1520 New York, New York 10010
Tel: 212-463-9623 Fax: 212-463-9626

RIDE INTO HISTORY!

STRASBURG RAIL·ROAD
SINCE 1832

P.O. Box 96
Strasburg, PA 17579-0096
(717) 687-7522

Climb aboard one of America's oldest steam trains for a scenic turn-of-the-century ride through the heart of Pennsylvania's Amish country.

From your seat on one of our authentic coaches, all carefully restored at Strasburg, you'll travel through immaculate farms still tilled in the same manner as a century ago. It's a return to a simpler way of life.

Open daily April to October, weekends year-round. Call or write for more information.

MISS THE TRAIN, AND YOU'LL MISS LANCASTER COUNTY.

Passage to The Past.

The weather is always beautiful for a steam train ride.

Take a seven-mile, 50-minute round trip on a former Chicago & North Western branch line built in 1903, and experience small town America in simpler times.

Smell the coal smoke and listen to the lonesome whistle against the wind.

Trains depart from a restored 1894 C&NW depot. Then visit the museum with its nationally acclaimed, restored, turn-of-the-century wooden passenger and freight cars.

There are also picnic grounds and a gift shop to enjoy.

North Freedom is near Baraboo and Wisconsin Dells in the heart of one of America's favorite tourist destination areas.

Call 608-522-4261, or write P.O. Box 55, North Freedom, WI 53951, for a brochure and schedule information.

MidContinent Railway

RIDE & HELP SAVE THE EAST BROAD TOP R.R.

The 1873 narrow gauge East Broad Top Railroad in Orbisonia, Pennsylvania, needs your help to keep operating in 1995. By purchasing special commemorative tickets you can keep the EBT running now and contribute to its future restoration. The East Broad Top Development Fund is leading this effort. All proceeds from the sale of these special tickets will go towards supporting the preservation of the EBT. Even if you can't be in Pennsylvania this summer, please support preserving this landmark piece of Americana.

$10.00 Commemorative tickets may be ordered from:

**East Broad Top Development Fund
c/o Huntingdon County Heritage Commission
P.O. Box 374, Huntingdon, PA 16652
Tel.: (814)643-5091**

CHECK/MONEYORDER/VISA/MASTERCARD ACCEPTED

1995 E.B.T.R.R. SCHEDULE

June 3 - August 27 Saturday & Sunday
September schedule to be determined,
October 7-8: FALL SPECTACULAR
Trains depart 11:00 a.m., 1:00 p.m. & 3:00 p.m.
For Group Rates, contact the EBTRR at (814)447-3011

RAIL TRAVEL CENTER

Travel Worldwide:
Rail, Air, and Sea

Tours by train: escorted and independent itineraries

Eurailpass and all other rail and rail-pass ticketing

COURTESY OF LES MacDONALD

COURTESY OF LES MacDONALD

Cruise and air ticketing

Custom individual travelservices anywhere, by any mode

Our tours visit the USA, Canada, Switzerland, Mexico, Australia, and New Zealand. Also available are "Colorado by Rail," the annual "Great Railfan Tour," New England foliage rail tours, the "Swiss Rail Tour," and VIA RAIL Canada trips coast to coast.

For details or to book:

Amtrak ▶ Tours

Rail Travel Center
2 Federal Street, St. Albans, VT 05478
(800) 458-5394 USA/Canada
(802) 527-1788 Anywhere

VIA Rail Canada

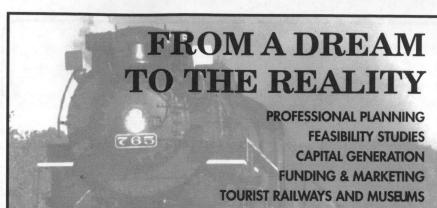

A-18

ASSOCIATION OF RAILWAY MUSEUMS, INC.

The association is the professional society for organizations having the common goal of preserving railway heritage through the acquisition, rehabilitation, restoration, operation, protection, and display of historic railroad and street railway equipment.

Since its founding in 1961, the Association of Railway Museums has been involved with helping and promoting the railway museum movement. Its publications and meetings serve this purpose.

The ARM is a professional affiliate of the American Association of Museums and, as such, speaks to the larger museum community on behalf of railway museums. The ARM is also actively working to address the special regulatory problems of operating railway museums.

The annual meetings are open to all persons interested in railway preservation. The 1995 convention will be at St. Paul, Minnesota, September 20-24, and hosted by the Minnesota Transportation Museum, which is preserving steam, diesel, and electric equipment. Convention information is available from the Association.

Join the large and small, volunteer and professional museums in the U.S. and Canada that recognize the value of membership in the Association of Railway Museums. Besides memberships, ARM offers several affiliation categories. Also, individual subscriptions are offered to the only publication devoted exclusively to the needs of railway museums.

For further information contact:

Association of Railway Museums, Inc.
P.O. Box 3311
City of Industry, CA 91744-0311
Telephone & Facsimile: (818) 814-1438

You are invited to join TRAIN
THE TOURIST RAILWAY
ASSOCIATION, INC.

TRAIN is the one trade association that is serving the growing needs of tourist rail lines, railroad museums, excursion operators, private car owners and suppliers - the multi-faceted groups that make up creative railroading.

With over 350 member organizations, and growing every month, our Roster is too long to print in the Steam Directory. Our members included in the STEAM PASSENGER SERVICE DIRECTORY may be identified by the **TRAIN** logo on their listing page.

TRAIN members receive our bi-monthly magazine- *TRAINLINE*, filled with articles relating to the tourist railway industry.

TRAIN is an action association dealing decisively in the areas of
- Legislation
- Insurance
- Mechanical-steam
- Mechanical-electric
- Advertising
- Safety
- Operations
- Mechanical-diesel
- Mechanical-passenger cars
- Promotion

For further information on this important alliance of professionals write:

The Tourist Railway Association, Inc.
Frances K. Minnich, *Corresponding Secretary*
P.O. Box 460537
Aurora, CO 80046-0537
Phone (303) 680-6217
1-800-67-TRAIN
FAX (303) 680-6231

GET MORE FROM YOUR MODEL RAILROADING . . .

JOIN THE NATIONAL MODEL RAILROAD ASSOCIATION

MEMBERSHIP APPLICATION

NMRA, INC. - 4121 CROMWELL RD. - CHATTANOOGA, TN 37421

I enclose . . . ☐ Check   ☐ Money Order   ☐ Charge

☐ **Regular,** One Year .... $24.00   ☐ **Affiliate,** One Year $13.00
☐ **Regular,** Two Years .... $48.00   (No Bulletin)
☐ **Family Member,** One Year .. $ 5.00   ☐ **Sustaining,** One Year $48.00
(Available to Spouse or Minor Child of Regular Member)
☐ **Youth,** One Year .... $16.50   ☐ **Life Membership,** Apply to Home
(Under 20 Years)   Office with date of birth for quotation.

(U.S. FUNDS ONLY) ☐ NEW ☐ RENEWAL

Date of Birth (Youth Membership Only) _____

Annual Dues of $24.00 includes $13.00 for subscription to the *BULLETIN.*

Scale & Gauge _____   Special Interests (include prototype):

Name _____   _____

Street _____   Charge to: ☐ American Express ☐ VISA
                                                       ☐ MasterCard
City _____   Exp. Date _____

State & Zip _____   **CARD NUMBER**

Introduced By _____   ☐☐☐☐☐☐☐☐☐☐☐☐☐☐☐☐☐☐☐☐

NMRA No. _____   Signature _____

REMOVE OR SEND FACSIMILE   **SP/Rev. 1-93**

A-24

ALASKA RAILROAD
Diesel, scheduled
Standard gauge

COURTESY OF THE ALASKA RAILROAD

Ride/Operation: The Alaska Railroad, established in 1914 with railroad equipment used in the construction of the Panama Canal, provides passenger service between Anchorage and Seward and between Anchorage/Denali National Park and Fairbanks. Scenic rides on 469 miles of main-line track through state and national parks offer passengers an opportunity to view wildlife such as bear, moose, beavers, and birds. Spectacular mountain terrain and optional tours are also available at stops along the way.

Displays/Exhibits: Potter Section House State Historic Park, ten miles south of Anchorage, features a museum and rail cars depicting the history of the Alaska Railroad. Small gift shops in Anchorage and Denali Depots.

Schedule: <u>Anchorage-Denali National Park/Fairbanks</u>: Daily express, May 18-September 19. <u>Anchorage-Seward</u>: Daily, May 20-September 4. <u>Anchorage-Fairbanks</u>: Weekends, September 28-May. <u>Winter Tours</u>: Weekends, September 19-May.

Fare: Call or write for information.

Locomotives: Four rail diesel cars; 48 locomotives of various types.

Passenger Cars: Three Vistadome cars; seven coaches; six new coaches constructed in 1990; five diners/food-service cars.

Rolling Stock/Equipment: 1,222 pieces of all types, including owned and leased freight cars.

Special Events: Special rates and promotional packages available in late May, June, late August, and September; available in Anchorage Depot only.

    (some routes)   (summer only)

    TRAIN (Express Train)

Contact: Janet Swanson
Customer Service Supervisor

Mailing Address:
P.O. Box 107500
Anchorage, AK 99510
Telephone: (907) 265-2494
(800) 544-0552

1

WHITE PASS & YUKON ROUTE
Steam, diesel, scheduled
36" gauge

GEORGE A. FORERO, JR.

Ride/Operation: Built in 1898 to supply the Klondike Gold Rush, the White Pass & Yukon Route is one of the most spectacular mountain railroads in the world. Declared an International Historical Civil Engineering Landmark by the American and Canadian Society of Engineers, the WP&YR offers round-trip excursions from Skagway to White Pass Summit or Lake Bennett and through rail/bus connections to Whitehorse, Yukon. Steam engine No. 73 pulls trains 1 1/2 miles to the edge of town, where it is cut off to let diesels tackle the 4-percent grade to the summit. The WP&YR carried more than 140,000 passengers during the 1994 season, breaking all previous ridership records.

Displays/Exhibits: A four-panel mural in the WP&YR depot depicts the complete history of the North and of the railroad. Next door is the visitors' center for the Klondike Gold Rush National Historical Park, which contains comprehensive displays about the 1898 Gold Rush, the railroad, and the area.

Train: Parlor cars from many narrow-gauge railroads, including the Sumpter Valley, the Pacific Coast, the Northwestern Pacific, the Utah & Northern, and the Los Angeles & Redondo, most dating from the 1880s and 1890s; nine steel cars, one built by Pacific Car & Foundry in 1935. (The newer cars retain "old" styling.)

Schedule: Daily, May 15-September 15. Excursion trains: Lv. Skagway 8:45 a.m. & 1:15 p.m. for a 40.8-mile, 3-hour round trip. Through service, northbound: Lv. Skagway 12:40 p.m. (train); arr. Fraser, B.C., 2:30 p.m. (change to bus); arr. Whitehorse, Yukon, 6:30 p.m. Through service, southbound: Lv. Whitehorse, Yukon, 8:15 a.m. (bus); arr. Fraser, B.C., 10:20 a.m. (change to train); arr. Skagway, Alaska, 12:10 p.m. Lv. Skagway 8:00 a.m for an 80-mile, 5-1/2 hour trip to Lake Bennett; box lunch included.

Fare: Summit excursion: Adults $72.00, children $36.00. Lake Bennett excursion: Adults $119.00, children $59.50. Through service: Adults $92.00, children $46.00. Reservations recommended.

Locomotives: No. 73, 1947 Baldwin 2-8-2—last White Pass steam engine; 11 General Electric 90 Class boxcab diesel locomotives; 2 Alco MLW 101 Class road diesels.

Rolling Stock/Equipment: WP&YR freight operations were suspended in 1982, but equipment remains on the property. A former Denver & Rio Grande Western narrow-frame UTLX tankcar, Oahu

railway flats, Colorado & Southern boxcars, and strings of home-built ore flats, container flats, and cabooses are stored on sidings in Skagway.

Location: Railroad Depot, 2nd & Spring streets.

Radio Frequency: 160.305

Contact: Tina Cyr
Manager, Passenger Services

Mailing Address:
P. O. Box 435
Skagway, AK 99840
Telephone: (800) 343-7373
(907) 983-2217

Alaska, Wasilla
M

MUSEUM OF ALASKA
TRANSPORTATION & INDUSTRY
Transportation museum
Standard gauge

COURTESY OF MUSEUM OF ALASKA TRANSPORTATION & INDUSTRY

Ride/Operation: The Alaska Live Steamers operate the 7 1/2-inch-gauge Alaska Central Railroad on the site.

Displays/Exhibits: Alaskan transportation and industrial artifacts are displayed outdoors and in the exhibit hall on this 10-acre site. Representing rail history are three Alaska Railroad locomotives and 25 pieces of rolling stock, as well as the last remaining U.S. Bureau of Mines Safety Car, a steam wrecker, a Jordan Spreader, a Pullman troop train, and a 1918 caboose. They are joined by 200 other industrial and transportation artifacts, including aircraft, vehicles, boats, heavy machinery, and hand tools.

Schedule: Memorial Day-Labor Day, Monday-Saturday, 10:00 a.m.-6:00 p.m. Labor Day-Memorial Day, Tuesday-Saturday, 9:00 a.m.-5:00 p.m. Alaska Live Steamers operate May to September.

Admission: Adults $3.00, students $1.50, family rate $7.00. Group rate $2.00 each.

Locomotives: No. 1000, first diesel in Alaska; No. 1500, which starred in the film *The Runaway Train.;* 1944 General Electric center cab.

Special Events: Open house with demonstrations, July 4th weekend. Antique engine show and demos, mid-August.

Location: Off mile 46.5 Parks Highway, next to airport.

Contact: Bea Adler
Director of Education

Mailing Address:
P.O. Box 870646
Wasilla, AK 99687
Telephone: (907) 376-1211

3

THE ARIZONA RAILWAY MUSEUM
Railway museum
Standard gauge

COURTESY OF ARIZONA RAILWAY MUSEUM

Displays/Exhibits: The museum building, reminiscent of an early Southwestern railway depot, houses railroad memorabilia and artifacts from railways of the Southwest and elsewhere. The museum is expanding its trackage to exhibit additional equipment.

Schedule: Weekends, 12:00-4:00 p.m. (except holidays). Please call for summer hours.

Admission: Free; donations welcomed.

Rolling Stock/Equipment: 1906 Baldwin 2-8-0 No. 2562, idler car No. 7131, steam derrick No. 7130 and caboose No. 413, all former Southern Pacific; 1943 Plymouth gas-mechanical switch engine; GRYX No. 799, three-compartment tank car; Southern Pacific tank car No. 60157, single dome; former Santa Fe pulpwood car No. 320219, caboose No. 999741, boxcars No. 600197 and No. 202493, and coach No. 2870; former Seaboard 10-6 sleeper "West Palm Beach"; SFRD No. 16811, ice bunker refrigerator car; former Rio Grande caboose No. 01469; 1950 Baldwin DRS 6-6-1500, former Magma Arizona Railroad No. 10; 1949 observation car, former Pennsylvania Railroad "Frank Thompson"; 1933 UTLX tank car.

Notes: The museum is a nonprofit volunteer organization.

Location: In Chandler at Erie and Delaware Streets, adjacent to the Southern Pacific tracks one-half mile east of state route 87. From I-10, take Chandler Boulevard east to Chandler. About 20 miles southeast of downtown Phoenix.

Contact: President

Mailing Address:
P.O. Box 842
Chandler, AZ 85224
Telephone: (602) 821-1108

4

VERDE CANYON RAILROAD
Diesel, scheduled
Standard gauge

Ride/Operation: Passengers enjoy a 4-hour narrated tour through the Sycamore Wilderness area, accessible only by rail or on foot. Red cliffs and wildlife abound along the route, which passes through a 680-foot tunnel and over the S.O.B. bridge. The trip takes in the historic town of Perkinsville, where *Where the West Was Won* was filmed.

Train: Open-air gondolas are accessible from all cars, as are deli and souvenir cars. Coach cars feature snack bars, and first-class passengers are treated to complimentary champagne and snacks.

Schedule: Wednesday-Monday, April, May, October & November; Wednesday-Sunday, January-March, September & December; 10:00 a.m. Five Moonlight Trains run during the summer months.

Fare: Adults $34.95, senior citizens $30.95, children (4-12) $19.95, children under 3 ride free. First-class fare $52.95 (includes hors d'oeuvres). All rates include tax. Special group rates, charter prices, tour operators' passes, and travel agents' passes available. Commissionable.

Locomotives: GP-7 diesel.

Passenger Cars: Three first-class cars with living-room-style seating; three coaches; three open-air gondolas; deli and souvenir cars.

Special Events: Live music and commentary on all cars. Western barbeques by the river on request. Weddings, Company parties. Jazz trains.

Location: At 300 North Broadway. Take exit 260 off I-17 and watch for signs for Clarkdale. Two hours north of Phoenix and 16 miles southwest of Sedona.

Flagstaff/Phoenix

Contact: Rita Gardner
Marketing Vice President

Mailing Address:
300 North Broadway
Clarkdale, AZ 86324
Telephone: 800-293-RAIL
(602) 639-0010

MCCORMICK RAILROAD PARK
PARADISE & PACIFIC RAILROAD
Steam, diesel, scheduled
15" gauge

Ride/Operation: Passengers ride through 30 acres of beautiful park land on a mile of 15-inch-gauge track. The train crosses four trestles, passes a scale ghost-town play area, and traverses a tunnel.

Displays/Exhibits: Maricopa Live Steam Club displays include 3/4-inch-, 1-inch-, and 1 1/2-inch-scale displays; there are also N-, HO-, O-, and LGB-gauge club displays. Static displays include former Magma Arizona Railroad 1907 Baldwin 2-6-0 No. 6; 1928 Pullman observation car "Roald Amundsen"; former Santa Fe baggage car, which contains railroad artifacts; 1894 former Santa Fe railroad depot; 1907 former Santa Fe railroad depot.

Train: Gondola cars modeled after Rio Grande Southern and Denver & Rio Grande Western cars; cattle cars after D&RGW cars; a tank car after a Colorado & Southern car; and a caboose after a D&RGW caboose.

Schedule: Daily, year-round, except Thanksgiving and Christmas, beginning at 10:00 a.m.

Fare/Admission: $1.00; children under 3 ride free. Park admission is free.

Locomotives: No. 11, 2-8-2; No. 12, 2-6-2; No. 10, 4-6-0; GP-7 and SW-8 switch engines.

Special Events: Free summer concert series, June and July. Railfair, October. Holiday Lights, mid to late December.

Notes: McCormick Railroad Park is owned and operated by the city of Scottsdale.

Location: 7301 East Indian Bend Road; three miles north of downtown, just off Scottsdale Road.

Phoenix (*Sunset Limited*)

Contact: Rose Williams
Park Coordinator

Mailing Address:
7301 East Indian Bend Road
Scottsdale, AZ 85250
Telephone: (602) 994-2312

6

OLD PUEBLO TROLLEY
Electric, scheduled

GEORGE A. FORERO, JR.

Ride/Operation: Old Pueblo Trolley's electric streetcars travel through some of the most historic, diverse areas of Tucson. Beginning in the heart of the Fourth Avenue Business District, the track passes shops and restaurants, then turns onto University Boulevard, passing the Arizona Historical Society and beautifully restored homes, boutiques, and cafes, and ends at the main gate of the University of Arizona. Streetcar service began in Tucson in 1906 and lasted twenty-four years; the nonprofit Old Pueblo Trolley was formed in 1983. Volunteers spent ten years building the current system, which they continue to operate.

Schedule: Year-round: Friday, 6:00 p.m.-12:00 a.m.; Saturday, 10:00 a.m.-12:00 a.m.; Sunday, 12:00 p.m.-6:00 p.m. Fall, winter, and spring only: Monday-Friday, 11:00 a.m.-2:00 p.m. Schedule subject to change.

Fare: One way: Adults $1.00, children (6-12) $.50. All day: Adults $2.50, children (6-12) $1.25. Educational charter trips are available to schools, youth groups, senior-citizens' groups, and child-care centers and can include a tour of the Fourth Avenue car barn. Group excursions and party charters also available.

Notes: Old Pueblo Trolley is a member of the Arizona Historical Society.

Location: From I-10, take the Speedway exit east to Fourth Avenue. Turn right and look for the trolley track in the street at the intersection of University and Fourth. Follow the track either on Fourth Avenue or University to a car stop or either end of the line.

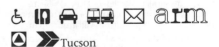

Contact: Stuart Rudick
Director

Mailing Address:
P.O. Box 1373
Tucson, AZ 85702
Telephone: (602) 792-1802

GRAND CANYON RAILWAY
Steam, scheduled
Standard gauge

JEFF BROUWS

Ride/Operation: The Grand Canyon Railway's turn-of-the century steam train operates from Williams, Arizona, to the South Rim of the Grand Canyon. Passengers ride in authentically restored 1923 Harriman coaches across 65 miles of pine forests, grassy plains, and small canyons, arriving at the 1910 Grand Canyon depot just steps from the rim. Western entertainment, strolling musicians, interpretive programs, and free refreshments combine to make this an unforgettable journey.

Rail service to the Grand Canyon originated in 1901. American's passion for the automobile ended train service to the canyon in 1968, and it was restored by the GCR in 1989. Ironically, because environmental preservation is a priority today, the auto has become the albatross at the South Rim, and the steam train is an important transportation alternative. The Grand Canyon Railway is dedicated to preserving the romance of the Old West and the pristine environment of the Grand Canyon.

Displays/Exhibits: The Williams Depot, listed on the National Register of Historic Places, was once a bustling Harvey House and depot. Today it offers visitors a free museum, a year-round engine display, a gift shop, and the Depot Cafe and Espresso Bar.

Schedule: Daily, March 15-January 1 (except December 24-25). Friday-Sunday, February. Wednesday-Sunday, March 1-14. Depart Williams 9:30 a.m., arrive Grand Canyon 11:45 a.m.; depart Grand Canyon 3:15 p.m., arrive Williams 5:30 p.m.

Fare: Adults $49.00 plus $4 National Park Service fee, children (6-12) $19.00. Club Class (pastries and coffee served in the morning; fully stocked bar): $12.00 additional. Chief Class (first-class service; complimentary continental breakfast; afternoon hors d'oeuvres; cocktails available): $40.00 additional. Rates do not include tax.

Locomotives: Nos. 18, 19 & 20, 1910 Alco SC-4 2-8-0s; No. 29, 1906 Alco SC-3 2-8-0; No. 4960, 1923 Baldwin 2-8-2.

Passenger Cars: Coach Class: 1920s-vintage Harriman-type 90-passenger. Club Class: converted 1920s Harriman 60-passenger with mahogany bar.

Chief Class: 1927 Pullman open-platform 30-passenger.

Location: Williams is on I-40, 35 miles west of Flagstaff.

Mailing Address:
123 North San Francisco, Suite 210
Flagstaff, AZ 86001
Telephone:
1-800-THE-TRAIN (843-8724)
Other Inquiries: (602) 773-1976

EUREKA SPRINGS & NORTH ARKANSAS RAILWAY
Steam, scheduled
Standard gauge

GEORGE A. FORERO, JR.

Ride/Operation: A 4-mile, 45-minute round trip through a wooded valley next to a winding creek in the heart of the Ozarks. During the "turn-around" trip, the steam engine is turned on a turntable at one end of the line and on a wye at the other end. Visitors may also ride the train, then take the city-operated trolley through downtown Eureka Springs.

Displays/Exhibits: The Eureka Springs depot, built in 1913 of locally cut limestone; operating turntable from the Frisco Lines; 1896 Smoker coach, former Central of Georgia; two steam tractors.

Train: Steel coaches, former Rock Island; wooden caboose, former Cotton Belt.

Schedule: Monday-Saturday, April 1-October 31, on the hour, 10:00 a.m.-4:00 p.m. Dining car: Monday-Saturday; lunch, 12:00 & 2:00 p.m.; dinner, 5:00 & 8:00 p.m.

Fare: Adults $8.00, children (4-11) $4.00, children under 4 ride free. Call or write for dining-car fares.

Locomotives: No. 1, 1906 Baldwin 2-6-0, former W.T. Carter; No. 201, 1906 Alco 2-6-0, former Moscow, Camden & San Augustine; No. 226, 1927 Baldwin 2-8-2, former Dierks For. & Coal.

Passenger Cars: Six commuter cars, former Rock Island.

Rolling Stock/Equipment: No. 4742, 1942 EMD SW-1.

Location: In northwest Arkansas, a short distance from the Missouri border. Take highway 23 north to the city limits.

Radio Frequency: 151.655

Contact: Robert L. Dortch, III
Depot Manager

Mailing Address:
P.O. Box 310
299 North Main Street
Eureka Springs, AR 72632
Telephone: (501) 253-9623

FORT SMITH TROLLEY MUSEUM
Electric, scheduled
Railway museum

BRADLEY MARTIN

Ride/Operation: Passengers take a 1-mile, 20-minute round trip on a restored Fort Smith Birney Safety Car from "Hanging" Judge Parker's Court Room and Gallows at the Fort Smith National Historic Site, then past the trolley museum and the Fort Smith National Cemetery. The National Historic Site is adjacent to the Old Fort Museum, which features the colorful history of Fort Smith's frontier days.

Displays/Exhibits: Original Fort Smith and Hot Springs streetcars, three internal-combustion locomotives, three cabooses, former Missouri-Kansas-Texas diner, power car. Memorabilia and photos are also displayed.

Schedule: Daily, May-October; Monday-Saturday, 10:00 a.m.-5:00 p.m.; Sunday, 1:00-5:00 p.m. Weekends, November-April; Saturday, 10:00 a.m.-5:00 p.m.; Sunday, 1:00-5:00 p.m. Group tours available at other times by special arrangement.

Fare: Adults $1.00, children $.50.

Trolleys: No. 225 (operational and on Historic Register), No. 221, No. 205, and No. 10, all former Fort Smith Light and Traction; No. 50, former Hot Springs Street Railway; No. 1545, former Kansas City Public Service.

Locomotives: General Electric 44-ton, former United States Air Force No. 1247; No. 6, 8-ton Plymouth, former Augusta Railroad; No. 7, 35-ton Vulcan.

Rolling Stock: Diner bunk car, former MKT; converted troop sleeper power car and caboose; cabooses, former Burlington Northern and Union Pacific; 5 motor cars, former Frisco.

Special Events: Annual Open House, April 30.
Location: 100 South 4th Street, 3 blocks south of Garrison Avenue in Fort Smith's historic downtown.

Contact: Bradley Martin
General Manager

Mailing Address:
2121 Wolfe Lane
Fort Smith, AR 72901
Telephone: (501) 783-0205
(501) 783-1237

10

ARKANSAS RAILROAD MUSEUM
Railway museum

BARRY ROBINSON

Ride/Operation: Steam locomotive No. 819 operates excursions several times a year.

Displays/Exhibits: The museum features a variety of railroad equipment and rolling stock, including St. Louis South Western GP-30 No. 5006, passenger and business cars, coaches, a snowplow, and other artifacts. This is a working museum; displays coexist with the locomotive- and car-repair shop.

Train: St. Louis South Western steam locomotive No. 819; tool, power, crew, and baggage cars; six coaches; commissary car; dome car; three business cars.

Schedule: Museum hours: Monday-Saturday 9:30 a.m.-2:30 p.m. No daily or weekly trips currently scheduled; please call or write for information.

Fare/Admission: Museum: No charge. Excursions: Fare varies depending on length of trip.

Locomotives: St. Louis South Western class L-1 4-8-4 No. 819; SSW No. 336; SSW GP30 No. 5006; U.S. Army Alco MRS-1 No. B-2089.

Passenger Cars: Six coaches, dome lounge, three business cars.

Rolling Stock/Equipment: Two HEP power cars; tool car; crew car; baggage car; wooden SSW caboose; U.S. Army snowplow; several motor cars.

Special Events: Yearly steam excursion to Tyler, Texas, in third week of October. Other trips are being planned. Please call or write for information.

Notes: The Museum is operated by the Cotton Belt Rail Historical Society, Inc.

Location: 1400 East 2nd Street.

Contact: Bennie Price
President

Mailing Address:
Cotton Belt Rail Historical Society
P.O. Box 2044
Pine Bluff, AR 71613
Telephone: (501) 541-1819

11

ARKANSAS & MISSOURI RAILROAD
Diesel, scheduled
Standard gauge

ARKANSAS & MISSOURI RAILROAD

Ride/Operation: Visitors can choose either a 134-mile or a 70-mile Ultimate Railway Journey, crossing over trestles and passing through Winslow Tunnel on their way to the top of the Ozark Mountains. The 134-mile round trip includes complimentary breakfast and snacks; the 70-mile trip includes snacks.

Schedule: <u>April-November</u>; most Wednesdays, Fridays & Saturdays, plus some Sundays in April & October and Tuesdays in October. <u>Reservations are taken</u> Mondays through Fridays, 8:00 a.m. to 5:00 p.m. Please call or write for complete schedule.

Fare: <u>April-September & November</u>: Wednesdays & Fridays, $33.00; weekends, $38.00. <u>October</u>: Tuesdays, Wednesdays & Fridays, $38.00; weekends, $44.00.

Locomotives: Alco 2000-horsepower C240.

Rolling Stock/Equipment: No. 102, 1899 combination coach/baggage, former Boston & Maine; No. 104, 1917 Pullman coach; Nos. 105 & 106, 1920s Harlin & Hollingsworth.

Special Events: Please call or write for information.

Location: 306 East Emma Street.

Contact: Jackie Kimbrough
Passenger Operations Manager

Mailing Address:
306 East Emma Street
Springdale, AR 72764
Telephone: (800) 687-8600

12

California, Alpine
D-R

DESCANSO, ALPINE & PACIFIC RAILWAY
Scheduled
24" gauge

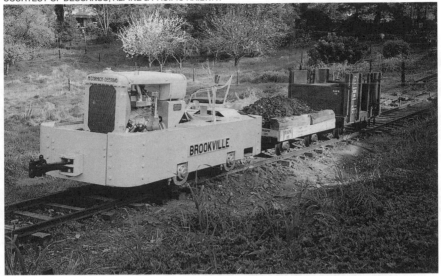

Ride/Operation: Passengers ride an industrial 2-foot-gauge railway to yesteryear among 100-year-old Engelman oaks in San Diego County's foothills. The train leaves Shade Depot and makes a 1/3-mile round trip, climbing the 6 1/2-percent grade to High Pass/Lookout and crossing a spectacular 100-foot-long wooden trestle, giving passengers magnificent views of the surrounding area.

Displays/Exhibits: At Shade Depot and Freight Shed is a display of railroad artifacts, including those of the DA&P. Mail service with mailer's postmark permit canceling is available.

Train: Gasoline-powered engine, open-type industrial/passenger cars.

Schedule. June-August. Sundays, 1.00-3.00 p.m., every half hour. September-May: Intermittent Sunday operation. Rides and tours may be scheduled at other times with advance notice; please call to arrange.

Fare/Admission: No charge.

Locomotives: No. 2, 1935 2 1/2-ton Brookville, SN 2003, powered by original McCormick-Deering 22 1/2-horsepower P-12 gasoline engine, former Carthage (Missouri) Crushed Limestone Company.

Location: Thirty miles east of San Diego. Take Tavern Road exit off I-8, travel south on Tavern 1.9 miles, turn right on South Grade Road and travel .6 mile, turn left onto Alpine Heights Road; the DA&P is the fifth driveway on the right.

San Diego

Contact: Roy Athey
Superintendent of Operations

Mailing Address:
1266 Alpine Heights Road
Alpine, CA 91901
Telephone: (619) 445-4781

California, Anaheim
R

COURTESY OF DISNEYLAND RAILROAD

Ride/Operation: All aboard an old-fashioned steam train for a grand circle tour of Disneyland! Passengers can depart at any of the four station stops within the theme park.

Displays/Exhibits: Walt Disney's live-steam locomotive, "Lilly Belle," is displayed along with photographs of Disney and his Carolwood-Pacific Railroad.

Train: Currently operating four steam engines.

Schedule: <u>Daily</u>, year round.

Fare/Admission: <u>Fare</u>: Included with park admission. <u>Regular park admission</u>: Adults $33.00, children $25.00. <u>Prices subject to change</u> without notice.

Locomotives: 1954 4-4-0 "CK Holliday," Walt Disney Imagineering; 1954 4-4-0 "EP Ripley," Walt Disney Imagineering; 1894/1968 Baldwin 2-4-4T "Fred Gurley"; 1925/1959 Baldwin 2-4-0 "Ernest S. Marsh."

Passenger Cars: Replicas of various train cars, cattle cars, excursion cars, and caboose converted to transport passengers.

Location: Disneyland Theme Park, 1313 Harbor Boulevard.

Contact: Dave Omel
Operations Manager

Mailing Address:
P.O. Box 3232
Anaheim, CA 92803
Telephone: (714) 999-4565

14

California, Berkeley

R

GOLDEN GATE LIVE STEAMERS, INC.
Steam, scheduled
2 1/2", 3 1/4", 4 3/4", 7 1/2" gauges

Ride/Operation: Established in 1936, this club promotes interest in live steam and has a stationary boiler to operate stationary steam engines. The club's Tilden Park site has steaming bays for thirty to forty engines as well as raised track in 2 1/2-inch, 3 1/4-inch, and 4 3/4-inch gauges and ground-level track in 4 3/4-inch and 7 1/2-inch gauges. Valid boiler certificates from other clubs are accepted; IBLS wheel standards are enforced.

Schedule: Sundays, year round, 11:00 a.m.-3:00 p.m., weather permitting.

Fare: Donations welcomed.

Locomotives: More than 275 locomotives are running or under construction. Weights of the locomotives range from 14 pounds to almost a ton. The club has a 1 1/2-inch Atlantic and a 1 1/2-inch Pacific. Privately owned engines range from small 4-4-0s to a big 4-8-4. Steam boats, stationary engines, and steam traction are also modeled.

Special Events: Spring Meet, May 20-21. Barbeque Days: January 8, February 5, March 5, April 9, May 7, June 4, July 9, August 6, September 3, October 8, November 5, December 3. Fall Meet, October 7-8.

Note: Monthly meetings, second Friday of each month, 8:00 p.m., at St. Christopher's Church at Hacienda and Via Toledo in San Lorenzo.

Location: Corner of Grizzly Peak Boulevard and Lomas Cantadas in Tilden Park, Oakland.

Contact: Jim Dameron
Secretary

Mailing Address:
130 Pereira Avenue
Tracy, CA 95376
Telephone: (209) 835-0263

15

REDWOOD VALLEY RAILWAY CORP.
Steam, scheduled
15" gauge

REDWOOD VALLEY RAILWAY

Ride/Operation: A 1 1/4-mile, 12-minute ride through redwoods, laurels, and the scenic wilds of Tilden Park, passing through a tunnel, over a trestle, up and down grades, and around many curves. The operation re-creates an old-time narrow-gauge atmosphere with authentically designed locomotives, wooden cars, realistic trackwork, and scale buildings.

Train: Most trains are twelve cars long plus a caboose.

Schedule: Weekends and holidays, 11:00 a.m.-6:00 p.m., weather permitting (no trains after dark). Weekdays, Easter and summer vacations, 12:00-5:00 p.m. Closed Christmas Day.

Fare: Single-ride ticket $1.50, five-ride ticket $6.00.

Locomotives: 0-4-0 No. 2, "Juniper," internal-combustion switcher; 2-4-2 No. 4, "Laurel"; 4-4-0 No. 5, "Fern"; 4-6-0 No. 11, "Sequoia."

Passenger Cars: Freight-type cars with wood bodies, truss rods, and archbar trucks. Capacity eight adults each.

Rolling Stock/Equipment: One Denver & Rio Grande Western-style eight-wheel caboose; 9 four-wheel work "Jimmies"; weed-spray car; tie-inserter car; ballast-regulator car; push car.

Note: The current project is a 2-6-2 locomotive.

Location: Tilden Regional Park.

 TRAIN

Contact: Erich Thomsen
President

Mailing Address:
2950 Magnolia Street
Berkeley, CA 94705
Telephone: (510) 548-6100

California, Bishop
M

LAWS RAILROAD MUSEUM
& HISTORICAL SITE
Railway museum

36" gauge

Displays/Exhibits: In 1960, the Southern Pacific Railroad abandoned "The Slim Princess," its famed narrow-gauge line from Keeler to Laws, which traveled over the mountains to near Carson City, Nevada. At the time of the abandonment, the railroad deeded 1909 Baldwin 4-6-0 No. 9, the Laws station building, rolling stock, and other property to the city of Bishop and Inyo County. The 1883 depot, the reception center, and the station agent's residence are open to the public. Outside is the hand-operated gallows-type turntable, used until the last day of operation. The train, headed by No. 9, includes several freight cars and a caboose. Other narrow-gauge rolling stock on display includes a rare cupola caboose, passenger and freight equipment, and a Brill self-propelled car. Also at the site are the Wells Fargo building, library and arts building, assay house, Chalfont General Store, bottle house, country store, doctor's office, carriage house, Conway house, Laws post office, farm machinery, pioneer display building, firehouse, print shop, and stove house.

Schedule: Daily, 10:00 a.m.-4:00 p.m., weather permitting. Limited schedule in winter.
Admission: Donations welcomed.

Location: From Bishop, follow U.S. Highway 6 north 4.5 miles to the junction of Silver Canyon Road, then turn right.

Contact: Alice J. Boothe
Administrator

Mailing Address:
P.O. Box 363
Bishop, CA 93515
Telephone: (619) 873-5950

SAN DIEGO RAILROAD MUSEUM
Diesel, scheduled
Standard gauge

COURTESY OF SAN DIEGO RAILROAD MUSEUM

Ride/Operation: A 16-mile, 1 1/2-hour round trip from Campo to Miller Creek through the scenic hills of San Diego back country, over the San Diego & Arizona (former San Diego & Arizona Eastern, former Southern Pacific). The museum also maintains a restored depot at La Mesa. Administrative offices and research library are located in the historic Santa Fe Depot.

Displays/Exhibits: Large collection at Campo includes: No. 11, 1929 Alco 2-8-2T, former Coos Bay Lumber Co.; No. 46, 1937 Baldwin 2-6-6-2, former California Western Railroad; No. 2353, 1912 Baldwin 4-6-0 & No. 104, 1904 Baldwin 2-8-0, both former Southern Pacific Railroad; many historic passenger cars and freight and work equipment from area railroads. Walking tours of the Campo collection are featured every weekend.

Train: Open-window coaches, former Santa Fe, Lackawanna, and Union Pacific.

Schedule: Weekends & certain holidays; train leaves the Campo depot at 12:01 & 2:30 p.m.

Fare: Adults $10.00, senior citizens $8.00, children (5-12) $3.00, children under 5 ride free. Group rates available.

Locomotives: No. 3, 1923 Lima 3-truck Shay, former Hutchinson Lumber; No. 1366, 1947 Fairbanks-Morse H20-44, former Union Pacific; No. 1809, EMD MRS-3, former U.S. Army (SD&A); No. 7485, 45-ton General Electric, former U.S. Army (SD&A); No. 2093, 1949 Alco RS-2, former Kennecott Copper.

Special Events: Specialty train rides featured monthly. Please call or write for price, destination, schedule, and reservations.

Location: Fifty miles from downtown San Diego. Take the Buckman Springs exit off I-8 east and travel south 10 miles to state highway 94, then one mile west to Campo.

Contact: Kay B. Carter
Executive Director

Mailing Address:
1050 Kettner Boulevard
San Diego, CA 92101
Telephone:
Tape: (619) 697-7762
Campo Depot: (619) 478-9937
Administrative Office: (619) 595-3030

NORTHERN COUNTIES LOGGING MUSEUM
Steam, scheduled
Standard gauge

EILEEN FAHEY

Ride/Operation: Fort Humboldt State Historic Park, in southwestern Eureka, hosts a small logging exhibit emphasizing historic steam artifacts, primarily from local redwood lumber companies. Some equipment has been restored by the Northern Counties Logging Interpretive Association and is steamed on occasion. Visitors can enjoy a short ride behind a steam locomotive, usually two round trips to the end of the 400 feet of track.

Displays/Exhibits: One and one-half acres of display area contain six steam donkeys, from a small 3-ton vertical spool to a 110-ton Washington Iron Works "Slackliner," and two small (9- and 12-ton) steam locomotives of unique design. A walkway around the grounds includes display panels that take visitors from logging's earliest days to today's modern mechanized methods.

Schedule: Park: daily, 9:00 a.m.-5:00 p.m., availability of staff permitting. Steam-ups: April 29-30, May 20, June 17, July 15, August 19, and September 16, 10:00 a.m.-4:00 p.m.

Fare: A donation of $1.00 (adults) and $.50 (children) is requested to help with equipment maintenance.

Locomotives: No. 1, 1892 Marshutz & Cantrell 12-ton 0-4-0, former Bear Harbor Lumber Company; 9-ton 0-4-0, former Elk River Mill & Lumber Co. No. 1, "Falk." The NCLIA has several other locomotives at a separate location, including No. 2, 1898 Baldwin 2-4-2T, former Bear Harbor Lumber Co.; No. 15, 1916 Baldwin 2-8-2, and No. 33, 3-truck Shay, both former Hammond Lumber Co.; No. 29, 1910 Baldwin 2-6-2, former Pacific Lumber Co.; No. 7, 2-truck Shay, former Arcata & Mad River (being restored to operating condition); No. 54, 2-ton Heisler converted to diesel, former Mutual Plywood Corp.

Rolling Stock/Equipment: At a separate location are several steam, diesel, and gasoline donkeys of various sizes, a steam sawmill (under restoration), and a Clyde track-laying machine, one of only two known to exist.

Special Events: Fourteenth Annual Dolbeer Steam Donkey Days, April 29-30, held in conjunction with Eureka's Rhododendron Festival. Other steam-ups may be scheduled for special events such as Rotary International District Conventions, Humboldt County School Day, etc.; please call for information.

Location: 3431 Fort Avenue.

Eureka (bus service)

Contact: Bill Fahey

Mailing Address:
NCLIA
3431 Fort Avenue
Eureka, CA 95501
Telephone: (707) 445-6567

COURTESY OF ROARING CAMP & BIG TREES NARROW GAUGE RAILROAD

Ride/Operation: Trains leave from the 1880 South Pacific Coast depot at Felton and make a 6-mile, 1 1/4-hour round trip from Roaring Camp to Bear Mountain in the Santa Cruz Mountains. The route, which has a maximum gradient of 8 1/2 percent, passes directly through the Welch Big Trees Grove of California Redwoods, the first grove purchased for preservation of the redwoods, in 1867. A spectacular mountainside switchback is located at Spring Canyon.

Displays/Exhibits: Steam sawmill, 1880 general store, covered bridge, red caboose saloon, chuckwagon barbecue, linotype/print exhibit, photo booth. Henry Cowell State Park is adjacent.

Train: Open excursion-type cars; side-door caboose; observation car.

Schedule: January 1-June 9 & October 2-December 31, weekends & holidays, 12:00, 1:30 & 3:00 p.m. January 1-March 31, Wednesday-Friday, 11:00 a.m. June 11-September 5, daily, 11:00 a.m., 12:15, 1:30, 2:45, & 4:00 p.m. September 5-December 31, weekdays, 11:00 a.m.

Location: Six miles north of Santa Cruz on Graham Hill Road.

Fare: Adults $12.50, children (3-12) $9.00.

Locomotives: No. 1, 1912 Lima 2-truck Shay, former Coal Processing Corp. No. 2593; No. 2, 1899 2-truck Heisler, former West Side Lumber Co. No. 3; No. 5, 1928 2-truck Climax, former Elk River Coal & Lumber No. 3; No. 6, 1912 Lima 2-truck Shay, former W.M. Ritter No. 7; No. 7, 1911 Lima 3-truck Shay, former West Side & Cherry Valley Ry. No. 7; No. 40, 1958 Plymouth diesel switcher, former Kaiser Steel Co. No. 2.

Special Events: California Gold Rush Extravaganza. 1830s Mountain Man Rendezvous. Fourth of July Frog Jump. Moonlight Steam Train Parties.

Contact: Georgiana P. Clark
Chief Executive Officer

Mailing Address:
P.O. Box G-1
Felton, CA 95018
Telephone: (408) 335-4484
Fax: (408) 335-3509

20

TEAM PASSENGER SERVICE DIRECTORY 1995 GUEST COUPONS
Savings for you and your family are shown on the back of the coupon

---

CORYDON SCENIC RAILROAD
Corydon, Indiana
Steam Passenger Service Directory
1995 Guest Coupon

LINDEN RAILROAD MUSEUM
Linden, Indiana
Steam Passenger Service Directory
1995 Guest Coupon

RAILSWEST RAILROAD MUSEUM
Council Bluffs, Iowa
Steam Passenger Service Directory
1995 Guest Coupon

TRANS-MISSISSIPPI TROLLEY
Keokuk, Iowa
Steam Passenger Service Directory
1995 Guest Coupon

ALTIMORE STREETCAR MUSEUM
Baltimore, Maryland
Steam Passenger Service Directory
1995 Guest Coupon

**NATIONAL CAPITAL
TROLLEY MUSEUM**
Wheaton, Maryland
Steam Passenger Service Directory
1995 Guest Coupon

**OLD COLONY & FALL RIVER
RAILROAD MUSEUM**
Fall River, Massachusetts
Steam Passenger Service Directory
1995 Guest Coupon

ADRIAN & BLISSFIELD RAIL ROAD
Blissfield, Michigan
Steam Passenger Service Directory
1995 Guest Coupon

IRON MOUNTAIN IRON MINE
Iron Mountain, Michigan
Steam Passenger Service Directory
1995 Guest Coupon

MICHIGAN TRANSIT MUSEUM
Mt. Clemens, Michigan
Steam Passenger Service Directory
1995 Guest Coupon

1995 GUEST COUPONS
Savings Available and Conditions for Use

LINDEN RAILROAD MUSEUM
Regular Price: Adults $2.00
With This Coupon: Adults $1.50
Valid May 1, 1995 - April 30, 1996
Maximum 1 Person Per Coupon

CORYDON SCENIC RAILROAD
Regular Price: Adults $8.00, Children $5.00
With This Coupon: Adults $7.00, Children $4.
Valid May 1, 1995 - April 30, 1996
Maximum 1 Person Per Coupon

TRANS-MISSISSIPPI TROLLEY
Regular Price: Adults $7.50, Children $6.00
With This Coupon: Adults $6.00, Children $4.00
Valid May 1, 1995 - April 30, 1996
Maximum 10 Persons Per Coupon

RAILSWEST RAILROAD MUSEUM
Regular Price: Adults $2.50, Children $1.25
With This Coupon: Adults $2.00, Children $.
Valid May 1, 1995 - April 30, 1996
Maximum 1 Person Per Coupon

NATIONAL CAPITAL TROLLEY MUSEUM
Regular Price: Adults $2.00, Children $1.50
With This Coupon: Free Admission
Valid May 1, 1995 - April 30, 1996
Maximum 1 Person Per Coupon

BALTIMORE STREETCAR MUSEUM
Regular Price: Adults $4.00, Children $2.00
With This Coupon: Free Admission with Pai
Admission of Equal or Greater Value
Valid May 1, 1995 - April 30, 1996
Maximum 1 Discount Per Coupon

ADRIAN & BLISSFIELD RAIL ROAD
Regular Price: Adults $7.50, Children $4.50
With This Coupon: Adults $7.00, Children $4.00
Valid May 1, 1995 - April 30, 1996
Maximum 6 Persons Per Coupon

OLD COLONY & FALL RIVER RAILROAD MUSEUM
Regular Price: Adults $1.50, Children $.75
With This Coupon: Adults $1.00, Children $.
Valid May 1, 1995 - April 30, 1996
Maximum 4 Persons Per Coupon

MICHIGAN TRANSIT MUSEUM
Regular Price: Adults $5.00, Children $2.50
With This Coupon: Adults $4.50, Children $2.00
Valid May 1, 1995 - April 30, 1996
Maximum 2 Persons Per Coupon

IRON MOUNTAIN IRON MINE
Regular Price: Adults $5.50, Children $4.50
With This Coupon: Two for the Price of One
Valid May 1, 1995 - April 30, 1996
Maximum 1 Discount Per Coupon

CITY OF TRAVERSE CITY PARKS & RECREATION Traverse City, Michigan Steam Passenger Service Directory 1995 Guest Coupon	**END-O-LINE RAILROAD PARK AND MUSEUM** Currie, Minnesota Steam Passenger Service Directory 1995 Guest Coupon
COMO-HARRIET STREETCAR LINE Minneapolis, Minnesota Steam Passenger Service Directory 1995 Guest Coupon	**WABASH FRISCO & PACIFIC RAILWAY** Glencoe, Missouri Steam Passenger Service Directory 1995 Guest Coupon
ST. LOUIS, IRON MOUNTAIN & SOUTHERN RAILWAY Jackson, Missouri Steam Passenger Service Directory 1995 Guest Coupon	**PATEE HOUSE MUSEUM** St. Joseph, Missouri Steam Passenger Service Directory 1995 Guest Coupon
CONWAY SCENIC RAILROAD North Conway, New Hampshire Steam Passenger Service Directory 1995 Guest Coupon	**TOY TRAIN DEPOT** Alamogordo, New Mexico Steam Passenger Service Directory 1995 Guest Coupon
CUMBRES & TOLTEC SCENIC RAILROAD Chama, New Mexico Steam Passenger Service Directory 1995 Guest Coupon	**ARCADE & ATTICA RAILROAD** Arcade, New York Steam Passenger Service Directory 1995 Guest Coupon

1995 GUEST COUPONS
Savings Available and Conditions for Use

END-O-LINE
RAILROAD PARK AND MUSEUM
Regular Price: Adults $2.00, Children $1.00
With This Coupon: Adults $1.50, Children $.75
Valid May 1, 1995 - April 30, 1996
Maximum 1 Person Per Coupon

CITY OF TRAVERSE CITY
PARKS & RECREATION
Regular Price: Adults $1.00, Children $.50
With This Coupon: Adults $.50, Children $.2
Valid May 1, 1995 - April 30, 1996
Maximum 4 Persons Per Coupon

WABASH FRISCO & PACIFIC RAILWAY
Regular Price: Adults & Children $2.00
With This Coupon: Adults & Children $1.50
Valid May 1, 1995 - April 30, 1996
Maximum 6 Persons Per Coupon

COMO-HARRIET STREETCAR LINE
Regular Price: Adults $1.00,
Children Under 5 Ride Free
With This Coupon: Adults $.75,
Children Under 10 Ride Free
Valid May 1, 1995 - April 30, 1996
Maximum 4 Persons Per Coupon

PATEE HOUSE MUSEUM
Regular Price: Adults $2.00
With This Coupon: Adults $1.00
Valid May 1, 1995 - April 30, 1996
Maximum 2 Persons Per Coupon

ST. LOUIS, IRON MOUNTAIN
& SOUTHERN RAILWAY
Regular Price: Adults $8.00, Children $4.00
With This Coupon: Adults $7.00, Children $3.
Valid May 1, 1995 - April 30, 1996
Maximum 6 Persons Per Coupon

TOY TRAIN DEPOT
Regular Price: Adults $1.50, Children $1.00
With This Coupon: Adults $1.25, Children $.75
Valid May 1, 1995 - April 30, 1996
Maximum 4 Persons Per Coupon

CONWAY SCENIC RAILROAD
Regular Price: Varies
With This Coupon: $.50 Off
Valid May 1, 1995 - April 30, 1996
Maximum 5 Persons Per Coupon

ARCADE & ATTICA RAILROAD
Regular Price: Adults $8.00, Children $5.00
With This Coupon: Adults $7.25, Children $4.50
Valid May 1, 1995 - April 30, 1996
Maximum 1 Person Per Coupon

CUMBRES & TOLTEC SCENIC RAILROA
Regular Price: Adults $32.00, Children $16.00
With This Coupon: Adults $28.80,
Children $14.40
Valid May 1, 1995 - April 30, 1996
Maximum 2 Persons Per Coupon

STEAM PASSENGER SERVICE DIRECTORY 1995 GUEST COUPONS
Savings for you and your family are shown on the back of the coupon

VERDE CANYON RAILROAD Clarkdale, Arizona Steam Passenger Service Directory 1995 Guest Coupon	**OLD PUEBLO TROLLEY** Tucson, Arizona Steam Passenger Service Directory 1995 Guest Coupon
ROARING CAMP & BIG TREES **NARROW-GAUGE RAILROAD** Felton, California Steam Passenger Service Directory 1995 Guest Coupon	**SOUTH COAST** **RAILROAD MUSEUM** Goleta, California Steam Passenger Service Directory 1995 Guest Coupon
NAPA VALLEY WINE TRAIN Napa, California Steam Passenger Service Directory 1995 Guest Coupon	**ORANGE EMPIRE** **RAILWAY MUSEUM** Perris, California Steam Passenger Service Directory 1995 Guest Coupon
SAN DIEGO **MODEL RAILROAD MUSEUM** San Diego, California Steam Passenger Service Directory 1995 Guest Coupon	**TRAIN TOWN** Sonoma, California Steam Passenger Service Directory 1995 Guest Coupon
YOLO SHORTLINE **RAILROAD COMPANY** Woodland, California Steam Passenger Service Directory 1995 Guest Coupon	**FORNEY HISTORIC** **TRANSPORTATION MUSEUM** Denver, Colorado Steam Passenger Service Directory 1995 Guest Coupon

1995 GUEST COUPONS
Savings Available and Conditions for Use

OLD PUEBLO TROLLEY
Regular Price: Adults $1.00, Children $.50
With This Coupon: Two For the Price of One
Valid May 1, 1995 - April 30, 1996
Maximum 1 Discounts Per Coupon

VERDE CANYON RAILROAD
Regular Price: Adults $34.95, Children $19.95
With This Coupon: Adults $31.50,
Children $18.10
Valid May 1, 1995 - April 30, 1996
Maximum 1 Person Per Coupon

SOUTH COAST RAILROAD MUSEUM
Regular Price: Adults & Children $1.00
With This Coupon: Free Admission
Valid May 1, 1995 - April 30, 1996
Maximum 2 Persons Per Coupon

ROARING CAMP & BIG TREES NARROW-GAUGE RAILROAD
Regular Price: Adults $12.50, Children $9.00
With This Coupon: Adults $11.25,
Children $8.10
Valid May 1, 1995 - April 30, 1996
Maximum 4 Persons Per Coupon

ORANGE EMPIRE RAILWAY MUSEUM
Regular Price: Adults $6.00, Children $4.00
With This Coupon: Adults $5.00, Children $3.00
Valid May 1, 1995 - April 30, 1996
Maximum 4 Persons Per Coupon

NAPA VALLEY WINE TRAIN
Regular Price: Adults $30.00/$24.00
With This Coupon: Adults $27.00/$21.60
Valid May 1, 1995 - April 30, 1996
Maximum 1 Person Per Coupon

TRAIN TOWN
Regular Price: Adults $3.50, Children $2.50
With This Coupon: Adults $1.75, Children $1.25
Valid May 1, 1995 - April 30, 1996
Unlimited Discounts Per Coupon

SAN DIEGO MODEL RAILROAD MUSEUM
Regular Price: Adults $3.00
With This Coupon: Two for the Price of One
Valid May 1, 1995 - April 30, 1996
Maximum 1 Discounts Per Coupon

FORNEY HISTORIC TRANSPORTATION MUSEUM
Regular Price: Adults $4.00, Children $1.00
With This Coupon: Adults $3.50, Children $.75
Valid May 1, 1995 - April 30, 1996
Maximum 1 Person Per Coupon

YOLO SHORTLINE RAILROAD COMPANY
Regular Price: Adults $12.00/$10.00,
Children $7.00/$5.00
With This Coupon: Adults $11.00/$9.00,
Children $6.00/$4.00
Valid May 1, 1995 - April 30, 1996
Maximum 4 Persons Per Coupon

TINY TOWN RAILWAY
Morrison, Colorado
Steam Passenger Service Directory
1995 Guest Coupon

SHORE LINE TROLLEY MUSEUM
East Haven, Connecticut
Steam Passenger Service Directory
1995 Guest Coupon

CONNECTICUT TROLLEY MUSEUM
East Windsor, Connecticut
Steam Passenger Service Directory
1995 Guest Coupon

VALLEY RAILROAD COMPANY
Essex, Connecticut
Steam Passenger Service Directory
1995 Guest Coupon

WILMINGTON & WESTERN RAILROAD
Wilmington, Delaware
Steam Passenger Service Directory
1995 Guest Coupon

HIGH SPRINGS STATION MUSEUM
High Springs, Florida
Steam Passenger Service Directory
1995 Guest Coupon

GOLD COAST RAILROAD MUSEUM
Miami, Florida
Steam Passenger Service Directory
1995 Guest Coupon

BIG SHANTY MUSEUM
Kennesaw, Georgia
Steam Passenger Service Directory
1995 Guest Coupon

MONTICELLO RAILWAY MUSEUM
Monticello, Illinois
Steam Passenger Service Directory
1995 Guest Coupon

VALLEY VIEW MODEL RAILROAD
Union, Illinois
Steam Passenger Service Directory
1995 Guest Coupon

1995 GUEST COUPONS
Savings Available and Conditions for Use

SHORE LINE TROLLEY MUSEUM
Regular Price: Adults $5.00,
Senior Citizens $4.00, Children $2.00
With This Coupon: One Child Admitted Free
with Each Paying Adult or Senior Citizen
Valid May 1, 1995 - April 30, 1996
Unlimited Discounts Per Coupon

TINY TOWN RAILWAY
Regular Price: Adults $2.00, Children $1.00
With This Coupon: One Child Admitted Fre
with Each Paying Adult
Valid May 1, 1995 - April 30, 1996
Unlimited Discounts Per Coupon

VALLEY RAILROAD COMPANY
Regular Price: Adults $14.00/$8.50,
Children $7.00/$4.25
With This Coupon: Adults $12.60/$7.65,
Children $6.30/$3.83
Valid May 1, 1995 - April 30, 1996
Maximum 4 Persons Per Coupon

CONNECTICUT TROLLEY MUSEUM
Regular Price: Adults $6.00, Children $3.00
With This Coupon: Adults $5.00, Children $2
Valid May 1, 1995 - April 30, 1996
Maximum 4 Persons Per Coupon

HIGH SPRINGS STATION MUSEUM
Regular Price: Adults $3.00, Children $2.00
With This Coupon: Adults $2.00, Children $1.00
Valid May 1, 1995 - April 30, 1996
Maximum 6 Persons Per Coupon

WILMINGTON & WESTERN RAILROAI
Regular Price: Adults $12.00/$6.00,
Children $5.00/$4.00
With This Coupon: Adults $11.00/$5.00,
Children $4.00/$3.00
Valid May 1, 1995 - April 30, 1996
Maximum 1 Person Per Coupon

BIG SHANTY MUSEUM
Regular Price: Adults $3.00, Children $1.50
With This Coupon: One Child Admitted Free
with a Paying Adult
Valid May 1, 1995 - April 30, 1996
Maximum 1 Person Per Coupon

GOLD COAST RAILROAD MUSEUM
Regular Price: Adults $4.00, Children $2.00
With This Coupon: Adults $3.00, Children $1.
Valid May 1, 1995 - April 30, 1996
Maximum 1 Person Per Coupon

VALLEY VIEW MODEL RAILROAD
Regular Price: Adults $3.50, Children $1.75
With This Coupon: Adults $3.00, Children $1.50
Valid May 1, 1995 - April 30, 1996
Maximum 6 Persons Per Coupon

MONTICELLO RAILWAY MUSEUM
Regular Price: Adults $5.00,
Senior Citizens & Children $3.00
With This Coupon: Adults $4.50,
Senior Citizens & Children $2.50
Valid May 1, 1995 - April 30, 1996
Maximum 4 Persons Per Coupon

STEAM PASSENGER SERVICE DIRECTORY 1995 GUEST COUPONS
Savings for you and your family are shown on the back of the coupon

RAILROAD MUSEUM OF PENNSYLVANIA Strasburg, Pennsylvania Steam Passenger Service Directory 1995 Guest Coupon	**OIL CREEK & TITUSVILLE RAILROAI** Titusville, Pennsylvania Steam Passenger Service Directory 1995 Guest Coupon
ᵃENNSYLVANIA TROLLEY MUSEUM Washington, Pennsylvania Steam Passenger Service Directory 1995 Guest Coupon	**LYCOMING COUNTY HISTORICAL SOCIETY & MUSEUM** Williamsport, Pennsylvania Steam Passenger Service Directory 1995 Guest Coupon
TRAINFEST '95 Milbrook, South Dakota Steam Passenger Service Directory 1995 Guest Coupon	**TENNESSEE VALLEY RAILROAD** Chattanooga, Tennessee Steam Passenger Service Directory 1995 Guest Coupon
USTIN STEAM TRAIN ASSOCIATION Austin, Texas Steam Passenger Service Directory 1995 Guest Coupon	**HEBER VALLEY RAILROAD** Heber City, Utah Steam Passenger Service Directory 1995 Guest Coupon
ANACORTES RAILWAY Anacortes, Washington Steam Passenger Service Directory 1995 Guest Coupon	**YAKIMA VALLEY RAIL & STEAM ASSOCIATION** Toppenish, Washington Steam Passenger Service Directory 1995 Guest Coupon

1995 GUEST COUPONS
Savings Available and Conditions for Use

OIL CREEK & TITUSVILLE RAILROAD
Regular Price: Adults $9.00,
Senior Citizens $8.00, Children $5.00
With This Coupon: Adults $8.00,
Senior Citizens $7.00, Children $4.00
Valid May 1, 1995 - April 30, 1996
Maximum 6 Persons Per Coupon

RAILROAD MUSEUM OF PENNSYLVANI
Regular Price: Adults $6.00
With This Coupon: Adults $5.00
Valid May 1, 1995 - April 30, 1996
Maximum 1 Person Per Coupon

LYCOMING COUNTY
HISTORICAL SOCIETY & MUSEUM
Regular Price: Adults $3.50, Children $1.50
With This Coupon: Adults $3.00, Child
Admitted Free with a Paying Adult
Valid May 1, 1995 - April 30, 1996
Maximum 1 Discount Per Coupon

PENNSYLVANIA TROLLEY MUSEUM
Regular Price: Adults $5.00, Children $3.00
With This Coupon: Adults $4.00, Children $2.0
Valid May 1, 1995 - April 30, 1996
Maximum 1 Person Per Coupon

TENNESSEE VALLEY RAILROAD
Regular Price: Adults $8.00, Children $4.00
With This Coupon: Adults $7.00, Children $3.50
Valid May 1, 1995 - April 30, 1996
Maximum 2 Persons Per Coupon

TRAINFEST '95
Regular Price: Adults $7.00, Children $5.00
With This Coupon: Adults $6.00, Children $4.0
Valid May 1, 1995 - April 30, 1996
Maximum 1 Person Per Coupon

HEBER VALLEY RAILROAD
Regular Price: Adults $16.00, Children $12.00
With This Coupon: Adults $14.00,
Children $10.00
Valid May 1, 1995 - April 30, 1996
Maximum 1 Person Per Coupon

AUSTIN STEAM TRAIN ASSOCIATION
Regular Price (Coach Fare): Adults $24.00,
Children $10.00
With This Coupon (Coach Fare):
Adults $12.50, Children $5.00
Valid May 1, 1995 - April 30, 1996
Maximum 1 Person Per Coupon

YAKIMA VALLEY
RAIL & STEAM ASSOCIATION
Regular Price: Adults $8.00, Children $5.00
With This Coupon: Adults $5.00, Children $3.00
Valid May 1, 1995 - April 30, 1996
Maximum 5 Persons Per Coupon

ANACORTES RAILWAY
Regular Price: Adults & Children $1.00
With This Coupon: Adults & Children $.50
Valid May 1, 1995 - April 30, 1996
Maximum 1 Person Per Coupon

STEAM PASSENGER SERVICE DIRECTORY 1995 GUEST COUPONS
Savings for you and your family are shown on the back of the coupon

LAKE WHATCOM RAILWAY
Wickersham, Washington
Steam Passenger Service Directory
1995 Guest Coupon

**HARPERS FERRY
TOY TRAIN MUSEUM
& JOY LINE RAILROAD**
Harpers Ferry, West Virginia
Steam Passenger Service Directory
1995 Guest Coupon

NATIONAL RAILROAD MUSEUM
Green Bay, Wisconsin
Steam Passenger Service Directory
1995 Guest Coupon

**CAMP FIVE
MUSEUM FOUNDATION, INC.**
Laona, Wisconsin
Steam Passenger Service Directory
1995 Guest Coupon

KETTLE MORAINE RAILWAY
North Lake, Wisconsin
Steam Passenger Service Directory
1995 Guest Coupon

WYOMING SCENIC RAILROAD
Laramie, Wyoming
Steam Passenger Service Directory
1995 Guest Coupon

**BRITISH COLUMBIA
FOREST MUSEUM**
Duncan, British Columbia
Steam Passenger Service Directory
1995 Guest Coupon

**WEST COAST
RAILWAY HERITAGE PARK**
Squamish, British Columbia
Steam Passenger Service Directory
1995 Guest Coupon

**HALTON COUNTY
RADIAL RAILWAY**
Rockwood, Ontario
Steam Passenger Service Directory
1995 Guest Coupon

**HULL-CHELSEA-WAKEFIELD
STEAM TRAIN**
Hull, Quebec
Steam Passenger Service Directory
1995 Guest Coupon

1995 GUEST COUPONS
Savings Available and Conditions for Use

HARPERS FERRY TOY TRAIN MUSEUM & JOY LINE RAILROAD
Regular Price: Adults & Children $1.00
With This Coupon: Adults & Children $.75
Valid May 1, 1995 - April 30, 1996
Maximum 2 Persons Per Coupon

LAKE WHATCOM RAILWAY
Regular Price: Adults $10.00
With This Coupon: Adults $9.00
Valid May 1, 1995 - April 30, 1996
Maximum 2 Persons Per Coupon

CAMP FIVE MUSEUM FOUNDATION, INC.
Regular Price: Adults $13.25
With This Coupon: Adults $12.75
Valid May 1, 1995 - April 30, 1996
Maximum 1 Person Per Coupon

NATIONAL RAILROAD MUSEUM
Regular Price: Adults $6.00, Children $3.00
With This Coupon: Adults $5.00, Children $2.
Valid May 1, 1995 - April 30, 1996
Maximum 4 Persons Per Coupon

WYOMING SCENIC RAILROAD
Regular Price: Adults $32.95, Children $17.95
With This Coupon: Adults $27.97, Children $15.23
Valid May 1, 1995 - April 30, 1996
Maximum 1 Person Per Coupon

KETTLE MORAINE RAILWAY
Regular Price: Adults $7.50, Children $4.00
With This Coupon: Adults $7.00, Children $3.
Valid May 1, 1995 - April 30, 1996
Maximum 1 Person Per Coupon

WEST COAST RAILWAY HERITAGE PARK
Regular Price: Adults $3.50, Children $2.50
With This Coupon: Two for the Price of One
Valid May 1, 1995 - April 30, 1996
Maximum 1 Discount Per Coupon

BRITISH COLUMBIA FOREST MUSEUM
Regular Price: Adults $7.00, Children $4.00
With This Coupon: Free Admission with
Paid Admission of Equal or Greater Value
Valid May 1, 1995 - April 30, 1996
Maximum 1 Discount Per Coupon

HULL-CHELSEA-WAKEFIELD STEAM TRAIN
Regular Price: Adults $24.00, Children $11.00
With This Coupon: Adults $23.00, Children $10.00
Valid May 1, 1995 - April 30, 1996
Maximum 4 Persons Per Coupon

HALTON COUNTY RADIAL RAILWAY
Regular Price: Adults $6.00, Children $3.50
With This Coupon: Adults $4.75, Children $3.
Valid May 1, 1995 - April 30, 1996
Maximum 1 Person Per Coupon

DELAWARE & ULSTER RAIL RIDE
Arkville, New York
Steam Passenger Service Directory
1995 Guest Coupon

NORTHEAST RAIL/
BATTEN KILL RAILROAD
Greenwich, New York
Steam Passenger Service Directory
1995 Guest Coupon

TROLLEY MUSEUM OF NEW YORK
Kingston, New York
Steam Passenger Service Directory
1995 Guest Coupon

CATSKILL MOUNTAIN RAILROAD
Mt. Pleasant, New York
Steam Passenger Service Directory
1995 Guest Coupon

NORTH CAROLINA
TRANSPORTATION MUSEUM
AT HISTORIC SPENCER SHOPS
Spencer, North Carolina
Steam Passenger Service Directory
1995 Guest Coupon

THE DENNISON
RAILROAD DEPOT MUSEUM
Dennison, Ohio
Steam Passenger Service Directory
1995 Guest Coupon

TROLLEYVILLE, U.S.A.
Olmsted Township, Ohio
Steam Passenger Service Directory
1995 Guest Coupon

TOLEDO, LAKE ERIE
& WESTERN RAILWAY
Waterville-Grand Rapids, Ohio
Steam Passenger Service Directory
1995 Guest Coupon

HUGO HERITAGE RAILROAD
Hugo, Oklahoma
Steam Passenger Service Directory
1995 Guest Coupon

MOUNT HOOD RAILROAD
Hood River, Oregon
Steam Passenger Service Directory
1995 Guest Coupon

1995 GUEST COUPONS
Savings Available and Conditions for Use

NORTHEAST RAIL/
BATTEN KILL RAILROAD
Regular Price: Adults $8.00, Children $4.00
With This Coupon: Adults $7.00, Children $3.00
Valid May 1, 1995 - April 30, 1996
Maximum 4 Persons Per Coupon

DELAWARE & ULSTER RAIL RIDE
Regular Price: Adults $7.00, Children $4.00
With This Coupon: Adults $5.00, Children $3
Valid May 1, 1995 - April 30, 1996
Maximum 4 Persons Per Coupon

CATSKILL MOUNTAIN RAILROAD
Regular Price: Adults $5.00, Children $1.00
With This Coupon: Child Rides Free
with a Paying Adult
Valid May 1, 1995 - April 30, 1996
Maximum 1 Person Per Coupon

TROLLEY MUSEUM OF NEW YORK
Regular Price: Adults $3.00, Children 1.00
With This Coupon: Adults $2.00,
Children Admitted Free
Valid May 1, 1995 - April 30, 1996
Maximum 2 Persons Per Coupon

THE DENNISON
RAILROAD DEPOT MUSEUM
Regular Price: Adults $3.00,
Senior Citizens $2.50, Children $1.75
With This Coupon: Adults $2.00,
Senior Citizens $1.50, Children $.75
Valid May 1, 1995 - April 30, 1996
Maximum 6 Persons Per Coupon

NORTH CAROLINA
TRANSPORTATION MUSEUM
Regular Price: Adults $4.00/$3.50,
Children $3.00/$2.50
With This Coupon: Adults $3.50/$3.00,
Children $2.50/$2.00
Valid May 1, 1995 - April 30, 1996
Maximum 2 Persons Per Coupon

TOLEDO, LAKE ERIE
& WESTERN RAILWAY
Regular Price: Adults $8.00, Children $4.50
With This Coupon: Adults $7.25, Children $4.00
Valid May 1, 1995 - April 30, 1996
Unlimited Discounts Per Coupon

TROLLEYVILLE, U.S.A.
Regular Price: Adults $3.00, Children $2.25
With This Coupon: Adults $2.25, Children $1.
Valid May 1, 1995 - April 30, 1996
Unlimited Discounts Per Coupon

MOUNT HOOD RAILROAD
Regular Price: Adults $19.95, Children $11.95
With This Coupon: Child Rides Free
with a Paying Adult
Valid May 1, 1995 - April 30, 1996
Maximum 1 Discount Per Coupon

HUGO HERITAGE RAILROAD
Regular Price: Adults $15.00, Children $10.00
With This Coupon: Adults $13.50,
Children $9.00
Valid May 1, 1995 - April 30, 1996
Maximum 2 Persons Per Coupon

STEAM PASSENGER SERVICE DIRECTORY 1995 GUEST COUPONS
Savings for you and your family are shown on the back of the coupon

---

WASHINGTON PARK & ZOO RAILWAY
Portland, Oregon
Steam Passenger Service Directory
1995 Guest Coupon

RAILROADERS MEMORIAL MUSEUM
Altoona, Pennsylvania
Steam Passenger Service Directory
1995 Guest Coupon

PIONEER TUNNEL COAL MINE RAILROAD
Ashland, Pennsylvania
Steam Passenger Service Directory
1995 Guest Coupon

BELLEFONTE HISTORICAL RAILROAD
Bellefonte, Pennsylvania
Steam Passenger Service Directory
1995 Guest Coupon

GETTYSBURG RAILROAD
Gettysburg, Pennsylvania
Steam Passenger Service Directory
1995 Guest Coupon

BIG BEAR FARM
Honesdale, Pennsylvania
Steam Passenger Service Directory
1995 Guest Coupon

STOURBRIDGE LINE RAIL EXCURSIONS
Honesdale, Pennsylvania
Steam Passenger Service Directory
1995 Guest Coupon

WANAMAKER, KEMPTON & SOUTHERN, INC.
Kempton, Pennsylvania
Steam Passenger Service Directory
1995 Guest Coupon

WEST SHORE RAIL EXCURSIONS
Lewisburg, Pennsylvania
Steam Passenger Service Directory
1995 Guest Coupon

ROCKHILL TROLLEY MUSEUM
Rockhill-Orbisonia, Pennsylvania
Steam Passenger Service Directory
1995 Guest Coupon

1995 GUEST COUPONS
Savings Available and Conditions for Use

RAILROADERS MEMORIAL MUSEUM
Regular Price: Adults $2.50, Children $1.50
With This Coupon: Adults $2.00, Children $1.25
Valid May 1, 1995 - April 30, 1996
Maximum 4 Person Per Coupon

WASHINGTON PARK & ZOO RAILWAY
Regular Price: Adults $2.75,
Senior Citizens & Children $2.00
With This Coupon: Adults $2.20,
Senior Citizens & Children $1.60
Valid May 1, 1995 - April 30, 1996
Maximum 1 Person Per Coupon

BELLEFONTE HISTORICAL RAILROAD
Regular Price: Adults $5.00, Children $2.00
With This Coupon: Adults $4.00, Children $1.00
Valid May 1, 1995 - April 30, 1996
Maximum 1 Person Per Coupon

**PIONEER TUNNEL
COAL MINE RAILROAD**
Regular Price: Adults $5.00/$2.50,
Children $3.00/$1.50
With This Coupon: Adults $4.50/$2.25,
Children $2.70/$1.35
Valid May 1, 1995 - April 30, 1996
Maximum 6 Persons Per Coupon

BIG BEAR FARM
Regular Price: Adults $5.50, Children $3.50
With This Coupon: Adults $4.50, Children $2.50
Valid May 1, 1995 - April 30, 1996
Maximum 1 Person Per Coupon

GETTYSBURG RAILROAD
Regular Price: Adults $8.00, Children $3.50
With This Coupon: Adults $7.50, Children $3.
Valid May 1, 1995 - April 30, 1996
Maximum 4 Persons Per Coupon

**WANAMAKER, KEMPTON
& SOUTHERN, INC.**
Regular Price: Adults $4.00, Children $2.00
With This Coupon: Adults $3.50, Children $1.75
Valid May 1, 1995 - April 30, 1996, Except
During Special Events
Maximum 6 Persons Per Coupon

STOURBRIDGE LINE RAIL EXCURSION
Regular Price: Varies
With This Coupon: $1.00 Off
Valid May 1, 1995 - April 30, 1996
Maximum 1 Person Per Coupon

ROCKHILL TROLLEY MUSEUM
Regular Price: Adults $3.00
With This Coupon: Adults $2.75
Valid May 1, 1995 - April 30, 1996
Maximum 1 Person Per Coupon

WEST SHORE RAIL EXCURSIONS
Regular Price: Adults $9.00/$7.00,
Children $5.00/$4.00
With This Coupon: Adults $8.00/$6.00,
Children $4.00/$3.00
Valid May 1, 1995 - April 30, 1996
Maximum 1 Person Per Coupon

California, Felton
R

GEORGE A. FORERO, JR

SANTA CRUZ, BIG TREES & PACIFIC RAILWAY
Diesel, scheduled
Standard gauge

Ride/Operation: Built in 1875 as the Santa Cruz & Felton Railroad and considered one of the most scenic railroads in the West, this line offers a 14-mile, 2 1/2–hour round trip along the spectacular San Lorenzo River Canyon to the beach at Santa Cruz. The train travels across two wooden trestles, crosses the San Lorenzo River on a long steel bridge, traverses a tunnel, passes the fabled Big Trees stand of California redwoods, and rolls down quiet Santa Cruz streets lined with Victorian homes. The SCBT&P is a working 10-mile common carrier railroad that provides freight and passenger service. Plans are under way to operate a steam locomotive on the line.

Train: Three 1900-era wooden passenger coaches; two 1920s-era steel coaches; four open-air cars; restored 1895 caboose, former Lake Superior & Ishpeming.

Schedule: Daily in summer; weekends and holidays in spring and fall; 10:30 a.m. & 2:30 p.m. from Felton, 12:30 p.m. from Santa Cruz. Additional trains may operate depending on the season.
Fare: Adults $14.00, children (3-12) $10.50.
Locomotives: Nos. 2600 & 2641, CF-7 1500-horsepower diesels, former Santa Fe; No. 20, 50-ton center-cab Whitcomb. Steam locomotive to be announced.

Location: 6 miles inland from Santa Cruz, California, on Graham Hill Road.

Contact: Georgiana P. Clark
Chief Executive Officer

Mailing Address:
P.O. Box G-1
Felton, CA 95018
Telephone: (408) 335-4484
Fax: (408) 335-3509

California, Fillmore
D-R

FILLMORE & WESTERN RAILWAY
Steam, diesel, scheduled
Standard gauge

COURTESY OF FILLMORE & WESTERN RAILWAY

Ride/Operation: This railway offers a 31-mile ride through the Santa Clara Valley, the last remnant of southern California as it looked more than fifty years ago. In both Fillmore and Santa Paula, an original 1887 depot building serves as the centerpiece of a downtown district featuring museums and shopping.

Displays/Exhibits: Visitors can see the extensive Short Line Enterprises collection of historic railroad equipment, which has appeared in more than 135 Hollywood motion pictures, television series, and commercials.

Train: Heavyweight and/or streamlined passenger cars pulled by either a steam locomotive or F-7 diesels.

Schedule: Steam: Trips depart Fillmore on March 25-26, May 20-21, July 1-4, September 2-4 & December 2-3. Trips depart Santa Paula on April 22-23, July 29-30, September 30 & October 1. Diesel: Special dinner trips depart Fillmore on selected Saturday evenings. Please call or write for a current timetable.

Fare: Varies depending upon length and type of trip. Group charters available.

Locomotives: No. 1, 1891 Porter 0-4-0, former Rouge River Valley; No. 51, 1906 Baldwin 2-8-0, former Great Western; Nos. 100 & 101, 1949 EMD F-7As, former Chicago & North Western; No. 4009, 1961 Alco RS-32, former Southern Pacific.

Rolling Stock: Heavyweight passenger cars built between 1910 and 1929; lightweight cars built between 1946 and 1950; several business cars; many historic freight cars.

Special Events: Hot August Night dinner and dance, August 19. Haunted Express, October 28. Santa Claus Special, December 2-3. New Year's Eve Party Train, December 31.

Location: Approximately forty-five miles northwest of Los Angeles in rural Ventura County. Fillmore and Santa Paula are on state route 126, between I-5 and U.S. 101. Trains depart from Central Park in downtown Fillmore and from the depot on 10th Street in Santa Paula.

Oxnard

Contact: Larry Jensen
Passenger Traffic Manager

Mailing Address:
351 Santa Clara Avenue
Fillmore, CA 93015
Telephone: (805) 524-2546

22

California, Fish Camp
M-R

YOSEMITE MOUNTAIN-
SUGAR PINE RAILROAD
Steam, scheduled
36" gauge

HEIDI STAUFFER

Ride/Operation: From 1899 to 1931 the Madera Sugar Pine Lumber Company logged more than thirty thousand acres of timber, using wood-burning Shay locomotives to haul logs to the sawmill at Sugar Pine. The YM-SP operates a narrated, 4-mile, 45-minute round trip over the restored line of the Madera Sugar Pine Lumber Company. Track runs through the scenic Sierra Nevada at an elevation of 5,000 feet, winds down a 4-percent grade into Lewis Creek Canyon, passes Horseshoe Curve, crosses Cold Spring Crossing, and stops at Slab Creek Loop.

Displays/Exhibits: A museum housed in an 1856 log cabin displays railroad artifacts, antique Yosemite photos, and many relics of sawmill life. Steam donkey engine and assorted rolling stock on display.

Schedule: Railcars: Daily, April-October. Steam train: Weekends, May, June 1-11, September & October, 11:00 a.m. & 12:30 p.m.; June 17-August, 11:00 a.m., 12:30, 2:00 & 3:30 p.m. Weekdays, May 15-June 10 & September, 11:00 a.m.; June 13-August 31, 11.00 a.m. & 12:30 p.m.

Fare: Railcars: Adults $6.50, children (3-12) $3.50. Steam train: Adults $9.75, children (3-12) $4.75.

Locomotives: No. 10, 1928 Lima 3-truck Shay (largest narrow-gauge Shay built) & No. 15, 1913 Lima 3-truck Shay, both former Westside Lumber Co.; No. 5, 1934 Vulcan 10-ton gas-mechanical; three former WL Model A powered railcars.

Passenger Cars: Logging cars; covered and open converted flatcars, former Westside Lumber Co.

Rolling Stock/Equipment: Wedge snowplow, oil tankcar, refrigerator cars, parts car, Model A speeder, side dump car, crane/handcar.

Special Events: Moonlight Special with steak barbecue and music every Saturday night in summer; reservations advised.

Notes: Operating in the Sierra National Forest.

Location: Four miles south of Yosemite National Park on Highway 41.

Contact: Max Stauffer
President

Mailing Address:
56001 Yosemite Highway 41
Fish Camp, CA 93623
Telephone: (209) 683-7273

CALIFORNIA WESTERN RAILROAD
Steam, diesel, scheduled
Standard gauge

GEORGE A. FORERO, JR

Ride/Operation: Scenic, relaxing, full-day (7-hour) or half-day (3-hour) train trips through remote redwood forests in northern California.

Train: Stilwell, Harriman, Southern Pacific *Daylight,* and open observation cars. Equipment operated depends on time of year, schedule, and number of patrons.

Schedule: Full-day round trips: Daily from Fort Bragg, summer season from Willits. Half-day round trips: March-October from Fort Bragg, summer season from Willits. Closed Thanksgiving, Christmas, and New Year's Day.

Fare: Full day: Adults $26.00, children (5-11) $12.00. Half day or one way: Adults $21.00, children (5-11) $10.00. Children under 5 not occupying a seat ride free.

Locomotives: No. 45, 1924 Baldwin 2-8-2; No. 56, 1955 Baldwin RS-12 diesel; No. 62, 1957 Alco RS-11 diesel; Nos. 64 & 65, 1957 EMD GP-9s.

Note: Please call or write for free comprehensive timetable/brochure. Reservations are recommended, especially during the off-season.

Location: The Redwood Route extends from Fort Bragg on the Mendocino Coast 40 miles inland to Willits on Highway 101, 180 miles north of San Francisco.

Martinez/Willits

Contact: Lynn A. Hakin

Mailing Address:
P.O. Box 907
Fort Bragg, CA 95437
Telephone: (707) 964-6371

24

NILES CANYON RAILWAY
Steam, diesel, scheduled
Standard gauge

GEORGE A. FORERO, JR.

Ride/Operation: A 12-mile, 1-hour round trip through scenic Niles Canyon over a portion of the original transcontinental railroad, built in the 1860s.

Displays/Exhibits: Three operating trains plus steam engines, diesel engines, and cars are on display at the terminal area.

Train: Several consists: a four- or five-car train of a coach plus open excursion cars, pulled by a vintage 44-ton diesel (to be replaced or supplemented by a steam engine); a one-car train pulled by a steam engine; a 1926 diesel railbus.

Schedule: First and third Sundays of every month, 10:00 a.m.-4:00 p.m. Charters available.

Fare: Suggested donations are adults $6.00, children (3-12) $3.00.

Locomotives: Nos. 1 & 5, 3-truck Heislers, and Nos. 7 & 12, 3-truck Shays, all former Pickering Lumber; 2-6-2T No. 2, former Quincy Railroad; 0-4-0T No. 3, former Steptoe Valley; 2-6-6-2T No. 4, former Clover Valley; 2-6-2 No. 30, former Sierra Railroad; 2-6-2T No. 233, former Central Pacific; 0-6-0 No. 1269 and 4-6-2 No. 2467, both former Southern Pacific.

Passenger Cars: 1911 Harriman coach, former Southern Pacific; 1910 open excursion cars (former flatcars); homemade coach; others.

Special Events: Fourth of July Special. Spring Wildflower excursion. Fall Color excursion. Christmas Train of Lights, December.

Location: Sunol, southern Alameda County, between Pleasanton and Fremont.

Contact: Alan Ramsay
Director of Public Relations

Mailing Address:
P.O. Box 2247, Niles Station
Fremont, CA 94536-0247
Telephone: (510) 862-9063

SOCIETY FOR THE PRESERVATION OF
CARTER RAILROAD RESOURCES

Horse, scheduled
36" gauge

BRUCE MAC GREGOR

Ride/Operation: This group is dedicated to acquiring and restoring railroad cars constructed by Carter Brothers of Newark, California, in the late 1800s. The society currently has seven Carter cars and three other cars. The cars are restored using appropriate hand tools, following the techniques used in the original construction.

The 1 1/2-mile ride is powered by one of the society's two draft horses, making this the only regularly scheduled horse-drawn railroad in the United States; the line is a re-creation of the nearby Centerville Branch of the South Pacific Coast Railroad, which was horse-drawn for more than 25 years. The trip takes passengers through the Ardenwood Historic Farm, a 200-acre working farm.

Displays/Exhibits: The open-air restoration shop is open to the public and contains two boxcars, two flatcars, a combine, and a handcar. The Ardenwood Historic Farm, which consists of a historic farmhouse, a blacksmith shop, and a farmyard, demonstrates life on a farm at the turn of the century.

Schedule: Train: April-October; Thursdays & Fridays, 10:30a.m.-3:00p.m.; weekends, 10:30a.m.-4:00p.m.

Admission: Adults $6.00, senior citizens $4.00, children (4-17) $3.50. Train fare is included with park admission. Admission for special events is $1.00 extra.

Locomotives/Trolleys: "Spike," 1981 Belgian; "Robbie," 1989 Persheron; both 0-2-2-0T hay-burners.

Rolling Stock/Equipment: No. 47, 1881 caboose; No. 1010, 1882 combine, former San Joaquin & Sierra Nevada; No. 253, 1874 8-ton boxcar, former Monterey & Salinas Valley; Nos. 10 & 472, 1880 10-ton boxcars, and No. 444, 1880 10-ton combination boxcar, all former Oregonian; No. 1725, 1888 15-ton flatcar, former SPC; No. 439, 15-ton flatcar, former Diamond & Caldor; No. 8, 1885 single-truck horsecar, former Oakland.

Special Events: Washington Township Railroad Heritage Fair and Exposition, May 20-21. Harvest Festival, early October.

Location: 34600 Ardenwood Boulevard, 15 miles south of Oakland at the intersection of I-880 and highway 84.

Contact: Andrew Cary
President

Mailing Address:
SPCRR
P.O. Box 783
Newark, CA 94560
e-mail: Andrew.Cary@syntex.com
Telephone: (510) 796-0663

26

California, Goleta   **SOUTH COAST RAILROAD MUSEUM**
M-R   *Railway museum*
     Standard gauge

DAVID HIETER

Ride/Operation: The Goleta Depot, built in 1901 by the Southern Pacific Railroad, was relocated in 1981 to Lake Los Carneros County Park and restored; it now houses a museum. A 7 1/2-inch-gauge train operates over one-third of a mile of track, and handcar rides are given.

Displays/Exhibits: A central exhibit is the 300-square-foot HO-scale model railroad. Visitors can also see the refurnished depot office, operating signal and communications equipment in the building and on the grounds, and various small exhibits and displays of railroad artifacts, rare photographs, and memorabilia.

Schedule: Museum: Wednesday-Sunday, 1:00-4:00 p.m. Miniature train: Wednesdays, Fridays & Sundays, 2:00-3:30 p.m.; Saturdays, 1:00-4:00 p.m. Handcar rides: Third Saturday of every month, 1:00-4:00 p.m.

Location: 300 North Los Carneros Road (7 miles west of Santa Barbara on U.S. 101).

Fare/Admission: Museum: donation ($1 suggested for adults). Miniature train: $1.00. Handcar rides: No charge.

Rolling Stock/Equipment: 1960s Southern Pacific bay-window caboose No. 4023.

Special Events: Depot Day, September 24, 11:00 a.m. to 4:00 p.m., features rides on handcar, inspection car, and miniature steam trains; barbecue; special one-day exhibits; and silent auction. "Another Steaming Summer," June 24, July 22, and August 26, 11:00 a.m.-4:00 p.m., features miniature steam train rides, refreshments, special films, and activities.

Contact: Gary B. Coombs
Director

Mailing Address:
300 North Los Carneros Road
Goleta, CA 93117
Telephone: (805) 964-3540

RAILTOWN 1897
SIERRA RAILWAY COMPANY
Steam, diesel, scheduled
Standard gauge

Ride/Operation: Railtown 1897, a California State Historic Park, is the original office/shop/roundhouse complex of the Sierra Railway, built in 1897. Trips include a 1-hour excursion, 2-hour wine-and-cheese trains, and bar-b-que dinner trains.

Displays/Exhibits: A working steam roundhouse.

Schedule: Weekends. One-hour excursions operate from 10:30 a.m. to 3:00 p.m. Please call or write for schedules of other excursions.

Fare: $9.00-$35.00.

Locomotives: No. 28, 1922 Baldwin 2-8-0, No. 3, 1891 Rogers 4-6-0, and No. 34, 1925 Baldwin 2-8-2, all original Sierra Railroad; No. 2, 1922 Lima 3-truck Shay, former Feather River Railroad; No. 7417, 1942 45-ton General Electric; No. 546, Alco MRS-1; No. 613, Alco RSX 4.

Passenger Cars: No. 5, "shorty" coach, and No. 6, "shorty" combine, original Sierra Railroad; parlor car and four suburban coaches, all former Southern Pacific; 1868 coach and two Mountain observation coaches, former Canadian Pacific; 1910 Harriman-type coach; circa 1910 baggage car; Pullman "Dover Patrol."

Rolling Stock/Equipment: Steam crane, former Pickering Lumber; freight cars.

Special Events: Railfan Days. Early Day Gas Engine Show. Santa Trains. New Year's Eve Party Trains.

Note: Many films and television shows have been produced here; something might be "in the works" during your visit.

Location: 5th Avenue at Reservoir Road.

Riverbank (bus connection)

Contact Person: Larry Ingold
President

Mailing Address:
P.O. Box 1250
Jamestown, CA 95327
Telephone: (209) 984-3953

28

LOMITA RAILROAD MUSEUM
Railway museum
Standard gauge

COURTESY OF LOMITA RAILROAD MUSEUM

Displays/Exhibits: This museum is a replica of the Boston & Maine station at Wakefield, Massachusetts. No expense was spared to create a suitable treasury for the railroad artifacts on display, which include many live-steam models as well as a huge collection of railroadiana. The station agent's office is complete in every respect. Outside, a 1902 Southern Pacific Mogul and a 1910 Union Pacific caboose wait at the station platforms. A 1913 wooden boxcar and a 1923 oil tank car are also on display at the museum's Annex Park, a charming recreation park decorated with benches, a water fountain, lights, and brickwork of the Victorian era.

Schedule: Wednesday-Sunday, 10:00 a.m.-5:00 p.m. Closed Thanksgiving and Christmas.

Admission: Adults $1.00, children $.50.

Locomotives: No. 1765, 1902 Baldwin 2-6-0, former Southern Pacific, with a large whaleback tender.

Rolling Stock/Equipment: 1910 Union Pacific class CA-1 caboose No. 25730; 1910 wooden boxcar; 1923 oil tank car, former Union Oil Company (Alaska).

Location: 250th & Woodward avenues; just south of Los Angeles.

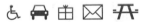

Contact: Alice Abbott
Manager

Mailing Address:
250th & Woodward Avenue
Lomita, CA 90717
Telephone: (213) 326-6255

TRAVEL TOWN
Railway museum
Standard gauge

ED SIKORA

Ride/Operation: Founded in 1952 as a last resting place for steam locomotives and other railroad and obsolete transportation equipment, Travel Town now boasts a fine collection of rare, valuable pieces that is being used to educate the public about railroad history as well as to entertain. Visitors may take a 10-minute, propane-powered ride with covered cars on 16-inch-gauge track around the perimeter of the museum. Volunteers also operate the "Caboose Train" on the first weekend of February, April, June, August, October, and December, usually using an EMD Model 40 diesel.

Displays/Exhibits: Fourteen steam locomotives; one electric; eight passenger cars; five cabooses; eight freight cars; five other major pieces; two operating diesel switchers.

Schedule: Daily except Christmas, 10:00 a.m.-4:00 p.m. Summers: Daily, 10:00 a.m.-5:00 p.m.

Fare/Admission: Park: No charge. Train Ride: Adults $1.75, children $1.25. Caboose Train: No charge. Group rates available.

Locomotives/Trolleys: No. 1, 1864 Norris-Lancaster 4-4-0, former Stockton Terminal & Eastern; No. 664, 1899 Baldwin 2-8-0, former Santa Fe; No. 3025, 1904 Alco 4-4-2, former Southern Pacific; No. 1544, 1902 steeple-cab electric, former Pacific Electric; newly acquired 1955 Baldwin Rs-12, former McCloud River No. 33, later California Western No. 56; others.

Rolling Stock/Equipment: "The Little Nugget," club-dorm No. 701 from the Union Pacific Streamliner *City of Los Angeles,* and sleeping cars "Rose Bowl" (1937) and "Hunter's Points" (1940), both originally on *City of San Francisco;* others.

Notes: Persons interested in Travel Town improvements may join the Southern California Scenic Railway Association, (213) 667-1423.

Location: Northwest corner of Griffith Park. Take Zoo Drive west or exit from the 134 freeway at Forest Lawn Drive.

Los Angeles, Glendale

Contact: Operations Manager

Mailing Address:
3900 W. Chevy Chase Drive
Los Angeles, CA 90039
Telephone: (213) 662-5874

California, Los Gatos
R

BILLY JONES WILDCAT RAILROAD
Steam, scheduled
18" gauge

Ride/Operation: A 1-mile, 8-minute loop through a park, featuring a 40-foot wooden trestle, a 2 percent grade, and a hand operated turntable. The railroad crosses Los Gatos Creek on an 86-foot-long bridge. The railroad is a 1/3-scale operation.

Displays/Exhibits: A 1910 Savage carousel is also operated.

Schedule: Train: March 15-beginning of school summer vacation and September 6-October 31, weekends, 10:30 a.m.-4:30 p.m.; beginning of school summer vacation-September 5, daily, 10:30 a.m.-4:30 p.m.; November 1-March 14, weekends, 11:00 a.m.-3:00 p.m. Carousel: March 15-beginning of school summer vacation and September 6-October 31, Tuesday-Sunday, 10:30 a.m.-4:30 p.m.; beginning of school summer vacation-September 5, daily, 10:30 a.m.-4:30 p.m.; November 1-January 1, Tuesday-Sunday, 11:00 a.m.-3:00 p.m.; January 2-March 14, weekends, 11:00 a.m.-3:00 p.m. Weather permitting.

Fare: Train and carousel: $1.00; handicapped persons and children under 2 ride free.

Locomotives: No. 2, 1905 Johnson Machine Works 2-6-2, former Venice miniature railroad.

Passenger Cars: 1915 MacDermott San Francisco Overfair Railway; wheelchair-accessible car available.

Location: Oak Meadow Park, one block west of state highway 17; entrance is on Blossom Hill Road.

Contact: Jerry Kennedy
General Manager

Mailing Address:
P.O. Box 234
Los Gatos, CA 95031
Telephone: (408) 395-RIDE

California, Napa
R

GEORGE A. FORERO, JR.

Ride/Operation: This line offers a 36-mile, 3-hour round trip through California's wine-producing region over a former Southern Pacific branch line. Passengers relax in air-conditioned cars amid mahogany paneling, brass trim, and etched glass as the Napa Valley scenery rolls by the oversized viewing windows. Three-star cuisine prepared aboard the train is served in white linen style, and complete beverage service, including more than 60 Napa Valley varietals, is available. The line, one of the oldest in California, was established in 1865 and has been in continuous operation since.

Displays/Exhibits: Art gallery; wine emporium.

Train: Four 1917 Pullman coaches converted to lounge cars, former Denver & Rio Grande Western; Pullman sleeper converted to dining car; Pullman coach converted to kitchen car, former Southern Railway.

Schedule: Monday-Friday, two trains daily. Weekends, 3 trains daily. Reduced weekday schedule in winter.

Fare: Lunch or brunch trains: $30.00. Dinner trains: $24.00. Meals additional: brunch $22.50, lunch $25.00, dinner $39.50; alcohol additional. All food and beverages are subject to service charge and sales tax.

Locomotives/Trolleys: 2 Alco FR engines, circa 1950; spare Alco F4; switcher.

Rolling Stock/Equipment: Six freight cars; 5 cabooses; flatcar; 8 other cars, awaiting restoration.

Special Events: Vintners' Luncheons, weekly. Winemaker Dinners, monthly. Murder Mystery on the Wine Train, monthly. Celebrity Chef Programs. Microbrewery Dinners. Santa Claus trains, annually.

Location: Approximately 50 miles north of San Francisco.

Contact: Erica Ercolano
Sales Director

Mailing Address:
1275 McKinstry Street
Napa, CA 94559
Telephone:
Reservations: (800) 427-4124
General: (707) 253-2111

ORLAND, NEWVILLE & PACIFIC RAILROAD
*Steam, scheduled
15" gauge*

COURTESY OF ORLAND, NEWVILLE & PACIFIC RAILROAD

Ride: The ON&P is an all-volunteer railroad operating in the Glenn County Fairgrounds. A 1-mile ride takes visitors past the original Orland Southern Pacific depot, the picnic site, and the demonstration orchard, then through a tunnel and along Heritage Trail. The train is normally pulled by a magnificent 5/12th scale live steam model of the North Pacific Coast's 1875 Baldwin narrow-gauge locomotive "Sonoma." The picnic grounds at Deadowl Station are open whenever the train is running.

Displays/Exhibits: Former Orland Southern Pacific depot, 1918 Southern Pacific 2-8-0 No. 2852, caboose, schoolhouse, blacksmith shop, print shop, 1920s gas station, miscellaneous steam machinery, old farm equipment. Livestock is also exhibited at fair time, during May and October.

Train: Fifteen-inch gauge (5 inches = 1 foot) locomotive, four open cars, caboose.

Schedule: April 15-16, 22-23 & 29-30; May 6-7 & 13-14; 12:00 p.m.-dusk. May 17-21, Glenn County Fair, fair hours. June 18; July 4; September 2-4, 9-10, 16-17, 23-24 & 30; October 7-8 & 14-15; 12:00 p.m.-dusk. October 21-22, Harvest Festival, festival hours. Private parties by appointment.

Fare/Admission: $1.00, children under 2 ride free. Admission charged for Glenn County Fair and Harvest Festival.

Locomotive: Replica of 1876 Baldwin narrow-gauge 4-4-0 "Sonoma"; gas-powered work-train engine.

Passenger Cars: Wood-sided gondolas, covered excursion car; one car is equipped to carry wheelchairs.

Rolling Stock: Caboose.

Special Events: Glenn County Fair, May 17-21; Harvest Festival, October 21-22.

Location: Glenn County Fairgrounds, Woodruff Avenue & East Yolo Street, two blocks south of highway 32. Orland is 100 miles north of Sacramento on I-5 and 20 minutes west of Chico on 32.

 (Heritage Trail, by appointment)

Contact: Frank Allen
Manager

Mailing Address:
221 East Yolo
P.O. Box 667
Orland, CA 95963
Telephone: (916) 865-1168

ORANGE EMPIRE RAILWAY MUSEUM
Electric, diesel, steam, scheduled
Standard gauge, 42" gauge

ORANGE EMPIRE RAILWAY MUSEUM

Ride/Operation: Interurbans and trains operate on a 2-mile former railroad right-of-way; streetcars operate on a half-mile route around the museum.

Displays/Exhibits: More than 150 pieces of equipment, including streetcars; interurbans; work cars; electric, steam, and diesel locomotives; and passenger and freight cars. Grizzly Flats enginehouse with three-foot-gauge equipment is on display, including the steam engine "Emma Nevada" from the Ward Kimball collection.

Train: Santa Fe and Union Pacific coaches; U.S. Navy flatcar; UP vintage flatcar; Santa Fe, Southern Pacific, and Union Pacific cabooses.

Schedule: <u>Equipment</u>: Weekends and some school holidays, 11:00 a.m.-5:00 p.m. <u>Museum grounds</u>: Daily, 9:00 a.m.-5:00 p.m. Closed Thanksgiving and Christmas.

Fare/Admission: <u>Equipment rides, all-day pass</u>: Adults $6.00, children (6-11) $4.00, children under 6 ride free when accompanied by an adult. <u>Admission</u>: No charge except for special events. Prices vary for special events. Call or write for specific information.

Locomotives/Trolleys: No. 2, 1922 Baldwin 2-6-2, former Ventura County Railroad; No. 653, 1928 General Electric, former Sacramento Northern; No. 1624, 1925 Pacific Electric Shops; Nos. 498, 418 & 717, all former PE Shops; No. 8580, 1944 General Electric, former U.S. Air Force; No. 3165, former Los Angeles Transit Lines; Nos. 665, 1160, 1201 & 3100, all former Los Angeles Railway; No. 19, former Kyoto (Japan) Street Railway; No. 167, former Key System; RPO car, former Santa Fe; first-generation diesels.

Special Events: <u>Rail Festival</u>, April. <u>Fall Festival</u>, October. <u>Spring and Fall Swap Meets</u>. <u>Santa Train</u>, December. Write for dates.

Location: One mile south of Perris at 2201 South "A" Street, about 18 miles southeast of Riverside on Interstate 215. Perris has Greyhound bus service from Los Angeles and San Diego.

Contact: Olivette Shannon
Gift Shop Manager

Mailing Address:
P.O. Box 548
2201 South A Street
Perris, CA 92572
Telephone: (909) 943-3020

SOUTHERN CALIFORNIA CHAPTER
RAILWAY & LOCOMOTIVE HISTORICAL SOCIETY
Railway display

COURTESY OF SOUTHERN CALIFORNIA CHAPTER, R&LHS

Standard gauge

Displays/Exhibits: Motor cars; berth section of business car displaying various day and night arrangements; horse car with stabling section. Former Atchison, Topeka & Santa Fe Arcadia Station has many displays.

Schedule: Second Sunday of every month, 10:00 a.m.-3:30 p.m. Daily during Los Angeles County Fair, September 8-October 1. Other times by request. Call for schedule updates.

Admission: No charge other than general admission to L.A. County Fair during September.

Locomotives: "Big Boy" 4-8-8-4 No. 4014, largest steam engine built, "Centennial" No. 6915, largest diesel engine built, and 4-12-2 No. 9000, all former Union Pacific; 4-10-2 No. 5021, former Southern Pacific; 4-6-4 No. 3450, former ATSF; 18870-6-0 No. 2, former Outer Harbor Term; No. 3, 3-truck Climax, former Fruit Growers Supply; narrow-gauge 2-8-2 No. 3, former U.S. Potash.

Passenger Cars: Pullman business car, former Nickel Plate.

Rolling Stock/Equipment: Six-bunk drover's caboose No. 1314 & 1990 horse express car (used as library), both former ATSF; GATX ice refrigerator car.

Special Events: Open daily during L.A. County Fair.

Note: Meetings are held in the basement Carillon Room of the Glendale (CA) Federal Savings, 401 North Brand Boulevard, first Tuesday of every month, September 1-June 30, 7:30 p.m.

Location: Enter through gate 12 at White Avenue on the east side of the Los Angeles County Fairgrounds.

🚗(not available during L.A. County Fair)

Contact: Ted Liddle

Mailing Address:
R&LHS
L.A. County Fairplex
P.O. Box 2250
Pomona, CA 91769
Telephone: (818) 917-8454

PORTOLA RAILROAD MUSEUM
Diesel, scheduled
Standard gauge

GEORGE A. FORERO, JR.

Ride/Operation: A 1-mile ride around a balloon turning track through pine forest.

Displays/Exhibits: More than 70 freight cars representing nearly every car type of the Western Pacific Railroad; several passenger cars; other rolling stock; railroad artifacts in the diesel shop building.

Train: Diesel locomotive; cabooses.

Schedule: Daily, year-round, 10:00 a.m.-5:00 p.m. Train operates weekends, May 27-September 10, every half-hour, 11:00 a.m.-4:00 p.m.

Fare/Admission: Train ride: Adults $2.00, family rate $5.00 (valid all day). Museum: Free admission; donations welcomed.

Locomotives: One electric locomotive and 35 diesels of all types: 14 Electro-Motive Division engines, including a former Western Pacific SW1, an NW2, a GP7, an F7, a former Union Pacific GP30, a DDA40X, a GP9, and a former Southern Pacific SD9; 9 Alcos, including a former Western Pacific S-1, a former Southern Pacific RS-32, a former VIA FPA-4 & FBB-4, and a former Kennecott Copper RS-3; 5 Baldwins, including a former Oregon & North Western AS616 and a former U.S. Steel S-12; 5 General Electrics, including a former Western Pacific U30B and a former Milwaukee Road U25B; a Fairbanks Morse, former U.S. Army H-12-44; a 1929 IR 600-horsepower engine; and a Plymouth, former U.S. Army ML8.

Location: Fifty miles northwest of Reno, Nevada, on the main line of the former Western Pacific Railroad, near the Feather River Canyon in the Sierra Nevada. The museum is in the former Western Pacific diesel service facility west of the Portola depot. From state route 70, travel one mile south on county road A-15 (Gulling) across the river and through town. Follow signs to the museum.

Radio Frequency: 161.01

Contact: Norman W. Holmes
Executive Director

Mailing Address:
P.O. Box 608
Portola, CA 96122
Telephone: (916) 832-4131

POWAY -MIDLAND RAILROAD

Ride/Operation: The Poway-Midland Railroad began operation on July 4, 1993, on a half-mile narrow-gauge loop around Old Poway Park.. The park, being developed by the city of Poway, will look like a turn-of-the-century small American town.

Displays/Exhibits: Poway Historical Society museum, operating replica nineteenth-century train barn, 1937 Southern Pacific caboose, water tower, windmills. Planned displays include a band gazebo, a train depot, and a boxcar housing a railroad equipment museum.

Train: 1950 Fairmont speeder and two 1880s mine gondolas. Beginning March 1995, the railroad's 1907 Baldwin 0-4-0 will operate with a 30-passenger coach; in May 1995, the 1894 Los Angeles Yellow Car will begin operations.

Schedule: Saturdays, 9:00 a.m.-4:00 p.m. Sundays, 11:00 a.m.-2:00 p.m. Holidays, 9:00 a.m.-5:00 p.m. Closed second Sunday of each month.

Fare/Admission: Speeder and gondolas: Adults $1.00, children $.50. Locomotive: Adults $2.00, children $.50. Trolley: Adults $1.50, children $.50.

Locomotives/Trolleys: 1907 Baldwin 0-4-0, class 4-11-C, former Cowell Portland Cement Company Railroad No. 3; 2 Fairmont speeders; 1890s narrow-gauge Los Angeles "Yellow Car" trolley.

Passenger Cars: Replica 1880s 30-passenger car.

Special Events: Farmers' Market, Saturdays. Fourth of July. Poway Days (early October).

Location: Midland Road between Temple and Aubry. Poway is 20 miles north of San Diego.

San Diego

Contact: PMRR Volunteers

Mailing Address:
P.O. Box 1244
Poway, CA 92074
Telephone: (619) 486-4063

California, Rio Vista Jct.
M-R

BAY AREA ELECTRIC RAILROAD ASSN.
WESTERN RAILWAY MUSEUM
Electric, scheduled; diesel, irregular

Standard gauge

Ride/Operation: Streetcars and interurbans carry passengers on a 3.9-mile round trip circling the museum grounds and extending south on the former Sacramento Northern Railway. The museum's line is being re-electrified 6.5 miles south towards Montezuma; diesel-powered excursion trains operate on another 6-mile portion of the line north of the museum.

Displays/Exhibits: More than 100 pieces of historic rolling stock, including former SN wooden combine No. 1005 and diner-parlor-observation "Bidwell"; Oregon Electric parlor-observation "Champoeg"; Pullman heavyweight lounge No. 653; and eight-section/diner "Circumnavigators Club."

Schedule: Streetcars and interurbans: Weekends, September-May; Wednesday-Sunday, June-August; 11:00 a.m.-5:00 p.m., at 10-to 20-minute headways. Diesels: spring and winter; coach and first-class available.

Fare: Museum (including streetcar/interurban rides): Adults $5.00, children (3-11) $2.00, families $15.00 maximum. Excursion trains: Please call or write for information.

Locomotives/Electric Cars: No. 94, 1909 Alco 4-6-0, and F-unit No. 917, former Western Pacific; freight motors Nos. 652 & 654, GP-7 No. 711, Birney No. 62, and interurbans Nos. 1005, 1019 & 1020, former SN; Nos. 178, 1003 & 1016, former San Francisco Municipal Railway; No. 4001, former Portland Traction; "Bay Bridge" articulated units Nos. 182, 186 & 187 and streetcars Nos. 271, 352 & 987, former Key System; No. 111, former CRANDIC; No. 63, former Petaluma & Santa Rosa; Nos. 52 & 61, former Peninsular Railways; express motor No. 7, former Central California Traction Co.

Rolling Stock/Equipment: Observation No. 751, former Salt Lake & Utah; Bamberger coach No. 400; "Harriman" coaches, former Southern Pacific; heavyweight Pullman lounge and sleeper-diner; large freight-car collection.

Location: About 30 miles northeast of San Francisco on state route 12, between Fairfield and Rio Vista in Solano County, twelve miles from I-80.

Suisun-Fairfield

Radio Frequency: 161.355

Contact: Chris A. Pagni
Secretary

Mailing Address:
5848 State Highway 12
Suisun City, CA 94585
Telephone:
Weekends: (707) 374-2978
Reservations: (800) 900-RAIL
Fax: (415) 567-2901

CALIFORNIA STATE RAILROAD MUSEUM
Railway museum

Displays/Exhibits: One of the finest railroad museums in the country, CSRM features more than 30 meticulously restored locomotives and cars from the beginning of railroading in the West to the present day. The museum complex, located on an 11-acre site in Old Sacramento, includes the reconstructed 1870s Central Pacific Railroad freight and passenger stations, the Big Four Building, housing the museum's extensive library and archive, and the 100,000-square-foot Museum of Railroad History.

Schedule: Daily, 10:00 a.m.-5:00 p.m. Closed Thanksgiving, Christmas & New Year's Day.

Fare/Admission: Adults $5.00, children (6-12) $2.00, children under 6 admitted free.

Locomotives: Diminutive "C.P. Huntington," 1863 Cooke 4-2-4T, former Southern Pacific No. 1; "Gov. Stanford," 1862 Norris 4-4-0, former Central Pacific No. 1; "Genoa," "Empire," and "J.W. Bowker," all former Virginia & Truckee; giant 1944 Baldwin cab-forward 4-8-8-2, former Southern Pacific No. 4294; E-9A passenger diesel; "Warbonnet" F-7's Nos. 347C & 347B, former Santa Fe; others.

Rolling Stock/Equipment: Atchison, Topeka & Santa Fe premiere "Super Chief"; diner "Cochiti"; the 1929 heavyweight sleeping car "St. Hyacinthe," which gives the illusion of speeding through the night, with simulated sound, light, and motion; a completely equipped Great Northern Railway Post Office car; "The Gold Coast," Lucius Beebe and Charles Clegg's famous private car; many others.

Special Events: California Railroad Festival, a 3-day event held every Father's Day weekend. The museum also runs steam-powered excursions.

Note: The museum is home of the U.S. National Handcar races and the annual National Railway Preservation Symposium. Museum membership and volunteer programs available.

Sacramento

Radio Frequencies: 160.335, 160.440

Contact: Nanci Kramer
Director of Public Relations

Mailing Address:
111 "I" Street
Sacramento, CA 95814
Telephone: (916) 552-5252 ext. 7245

CALIFORNIA STATE RAILROAD MUSEUM
SACRAMENTO SOUTHERN RAILROAD
Steam, diesel, scheduled
Standard gauge

CALIFORNIA STATE RAILROAD MUSEUM

Ride/Operation: The Sacramento Southern is the excursion railroad of the California State Railroad Museum. The line was built as a subsidiary of the Southern Pacific at the turn of the century; museum trains have been in regular service since 1984. A 6-mile, 40-minute round trip takes passengers along the historic Sacramento River. Extension of the line is planned to the towns of Freeport and Hood, 17 miles down the river.

Train: Open and closed excursion-type cars.

Schedule: Weekends, April 1-September 4, departures on the hour, 10:00 a.m.-5:00 p.m. First weekend of the month, October-December, departures on the hour, 12:00-3:00 p.m. Also Thanksgiving weekend.

Fare: Adults $5.00, children (6-12) $2.00, children under 6 ride free.

Locomotives: No. 4466, 1920 Lima 0-6-0, former Union Pacific; diesel locomotives from the collection of the California State Railroad Museum.

Location: Northern terminus is the reconstructed Central Pacific Railroad Freight Depot at Front and "K" Streets in Old Sacramento.

🚦 TRAIN arm ➤ Sacramento

Radio Frequencies: 160.335, 160.440

Contact: General Manager

Mailing Address:
111 "I" Street
Sacramento, CA 95814
Telephone: (916) 445-7387
Fax: (916) 327-5655
Beeline: (916) 552-5252 ext. 7245

T. J. WEGMANN

Operation: The world's largest indoor model railroad museum includes four large model railroad exhibits, toy trains, educational displays, and a railroad-themed gift shop.

Displays/Exhibits: Cabrillo Southwestern O-scale layout, San Diego & Arizona Eastern and Southern Pacific/Santa Fe Tehachapi Pass HO-scale layouts, and Pacific Desert Lines N-scale layout; the HO exhibits are of railroads that run through southern California. On the SD&AE, trains leave San Diego heading east and descend into the desert over the huge wooden trestle in spectacular Carriso Gorge. A narrow-gauge railroad connects with the standard-gauge trains on the final leg of the journey. The SP/SF layout models southern California's busiest rail artery—nearly all north-south rail traffic passes through this notch in the Tehachapi mountains northeast of Los Angeles. Leaving the yards in Bakersfield, trains roll through California's Central Valley to the Caliente Creek, where a steep, winding climb begins. The PDL, an alternative route east from San Diego, includes scale models of many downtown buildings circa 1950 and a view of Carriso Gorge modeled in 1/160 size. Also featured are G-gauge exhibits and interactive Lionel model trains in a new "Toy Train Gallery."

Schedule: Tuesday-Friday, 11:00 a.m.-4:00 p.m.;
Saturday-Sunday, 11:00 a.m.-5:00 p.m.
Admission: Adults $3.00; discounts for senior citizens, military personnel, and students; children under 15 admitted free.
Location: Off I-5 or California route 163. Take Park Boulevard to Space Theater Way; museum is located in the Casa de Balboa Building at 1649 El Prado in Balboa Park.

San Diego

Contact: John Rotsart

Mailing Address:
1649 El Prado
San Diego, CA 92101
Telephone: (619) 696-0199
Gift Shop: (800) 446-8738

GOLDEN GATE RAILROAD MUSEUM
Steam, scheduled

GEORGE A. FORERO, JR

Ride/Operation: The Golden Gate Railroad Museum, set on a 17-acre site near San Francisco, is an operating restoration facility where volunteers meet to work on projects on a regular basis; it is open to the public by appointment only. Visitors can see ongoing activities in the enginehouse, be escorted to tour rolling stock, and visit the caboose photo gallery and museum store. Steam-powered passenger excursions led by No. 2472 are occasionally offered.

Displays/Exhibits: Caboose gallery shows history of the restoration effort of 4-6-2 No. 2472. Visitors can also have escorted tours of private passenger cars and close-up tours of locomotive No. 2472.

Schedule: Weekends, by appointment only, 8:00 a.m.-5:00 p.m. Closed major holidays that fall on weekends.

Fare/Admission: Donations welcomed.

Locomotives: Former Southern Pacific class P-8 4-6-2 No. 2472; 65-ton General Electric diesel switcher, former U.S. Navy; former California State Belt Railroad 0-6-0.

Passenger Cars: Eight Harriman commuter coaches; private lounge car, circa 1930-1940, and dome lounge, both former Southern Pacific; articulated diner-lounge "Cascade Club."

Rolling Stock: Various maintenance-of-way and freight cars.

Notes: Escorted visits only, because of Navy requirements.

Location: Hunter's Point Naval Shipyard,.

San Francisco, Oakland

Contact: Ray Brown
Director of Marketing

Mailing Address:
P.O. Box 3315
Redwood City, CA 94064
Telephone: (415) 363-2472
Fax: (415) 363-0682

SAN FRANCISCO CABLE CAR MUSEUM

Displays/Exhibits: This museum, located in the historic San Francisco cable-car barn and powerhouse, allows visitors to view the actual cable-winding machinery as well as the path of the cable entering the building and leaving under the street. Included in the displays are three antique cable cars: a Sutter street dummy and trailer, and the first cable car, built in 1873. Historic information gives visitors a peek at the cable cars' glorious past. Also on display is a photo narration of the 1981-84 reconstruction effort, as well as various mechanical devices, such as grips, track, trucks, cable, and brake mechanisms, with corresponding explanations.

Schedule: Daily, April 1-September 30, 10:00 a.m.-6:00 p.m., and October 1-March 31, 10:00 a.m.-5:00 p.m. Closed Thanksgiving, Christmas, and New Year's Day.

Admission: No charge.

Location: 1201 Mason Street (corner of Mason and Washington streets). The best way to get to the museum is by cable car; automobile parking is almost nonexistent. MUNI bus lines 1 and 30 run closest to the museum.

San Francisco, Oakland

Mailing Address:
1201 Mason Street
San Francisco, CA 94108
Telephone: (415) 474-1887

SAN FRANCISCO MUNICIPAL RAILWAY
San Francisco Historic Trolley Festival
Electric, irregular
Standard gauge

Ride/Operation: When running, cars operate between the Transbay Terminal at 1st & Mission Streets and Castro & Market Streets via Market Street. Usual service includes four or five cars, two of which are usually PCCs. The open-top single-decker from Blackpool, England, is popular, as are the Peter Witt from Milan and the V6 from Hamburg.

Schedule: Occasional operation on or near major holidays, such as Thanksgiving, Christmas, July Fourth, and Labor Day. Service is funded by charter, so service at holiday times should not be presumed—please call ahead.

Fare/Admission: Regular Municipal Railway fares: adults $1.00; seniors (over 65), youths (5-17), and disabled with ID, $.35. For full Muni fare information, write to the address below.

Trolleys: Collection of electric streetcars from San Francisco and seven foreign countries: single-truck "California" configuration No. 578, built in 1895; Muni's first car, double-truck No. 1; Muni double-truck No. 130; Muni PCCs No. 1006 (double-ended) and No. 1040 (the last American PCC); former St. Louis PCC No. 1704; Hamburg, Germany, V6 No. 3557; Oryol, Russia, single-truck No. 106; Milan, Italy, Peter Witt No. 1834; Blackpool, England, boat tram No. 228; Hiroshima, Japan, former Kobe double-truck No. 578; Osaka, Japan, Hankai Railway double-truck No. 151; Porto, Portugal, single-truck No. 187; and Melbourne, Australia, W2 No. 496. Not all are operational.

Rolling Stock/Equipment: Line car No. 0304, flatcar No. C1, work cars.

Note: Volunteers work on some cars at Market at Duboce. Support group for historic vehicle maintenance can be contacted at the Market Street Railway, (415) 552-3055.

San Francisco, Oakland/Emeryville

Contact: Nicolas Finck or Alan Siegel

Mailing Address:
949 Presidio Avenue, Room 238
San Francisco, CA 94115
Telephone: (415) 923-6162

KELLEY PARK TROLLEY
Electric, scheduled
Standard gauge

KELLEY PARK TROLLEY

Ride/Operation: Since 1984 San Jose Trolley Corporation volunteers have restored six trolley cars for operation in the downtown San Jose Transit Mall, on the tracks of the new light rail system. Kelley Park trolleys operate on 1/4 mile of track through the grounds of the San Jose Historical Museum.

Displays/Exhibits: Visitors can watch volunteers restore cars and artifacts for the San Jose Historical Museum.

Schedule: Weekends, 12:00-4:00 p.m., except Thanksgiving, Christmas & New Year's Day.
Fare: Included with admission to the San Jose Historical Museum: Adults $4.00, senior citizens $3.00, children $2.00, children under 6 ride free.
Trolleys: Operational trolley No. 168, former Porto, Portugal No. 154; No. 120, former Sacramento No. 35. Horse car runs on special occasions.
Special Events: Civil War Days, May 27-29. Living History Days, June 24-25. Chinese Festival, July 30. Victorian Christmas, December 9-10.

Location: The museum is located in Kelley Park, a short distance from the intersection of highways 280, 680, and 101.

Contact: Fred Bennett
Project Manager

Mailing Address:
1600 Senter Road
San Jose, CA 95112
Telephone:
Museum: (408) 287-2290
Trolley Barn: (408) 293-2276

45

California, Sonoma
D-R

TRAIN TOWN
Steam, scheduled
15" gauge

KERMIT PARKER

Ride/Operation: Train Town is a 10-acre railroad park filled with thousands of trees, animals, lakes, bridges, tunnels, waterfalls, and historic replica structures. Fifteen-inch-gauge live-steam locomotives and diesel replicas pull long passenger trains through the park.

Displays/Exhibits: Railroad shops and a complete miniature town, built to the same 1/4-inch scale as the railroad. Full-sized rail equipment includes Santa Fe caboose No. 999648; Union Pacific caboose No. 25155; and Southern Pacific's first steel caboose, No. 11.

Train: Sixteen scale-reproduction passenger and freight cars.

Schedule: <u>Daily</u>, June 1-September 30; <u>Friday-Sunday</u>, year-round; 10:30 a.m.-5:00 p.m. Closed Christmas and Thanksgiving.

Fare: Adults $2.80, senior citizens & children (16 months-16 years) $1.90.

Locomotives/Trolleys: Replica of No. 5212, 1937 Alco J-1a 4-6-4, former New York Central; No. 1, 1960 Winton Engineering 2-6-0; SW 1200, 1992 custom locomotive; No. 401, 1975 gas-electric motor car.

Location: Sonoma is in wine country, less than an hour north of San Francisco. Train Town is on Broadway, one mile south of the Sonoma Town Square.

Contact: Robert Frank
Superintendent

Mailing Address:
P.O. Box 656
Sonoma, CA 95476
Telephone: (707) 938-3912

46

California, Woodland
R

RICHARD JONES

YOLO SHORTLINE
RAILROAD COMPANY
Steam, diesel, scheduled
Standard gauge

Ride/Operation: This common-carrier freight railroad offers a 28-mile, 2 1/2-hour round trip between Woodland and West Sacramento over the former Sacramento Northern's Woodland Branch. The trip begins in Woodland, crosses the Yolo bypass on an 8,000-foot trestle, and offers views of scenic Yolo County farmlands and wetlands and the Sacramento River.

Displays/Exhibits: Near the parking and passenger-loading area are the Hayes Truck Museum (admission separate) and the Southern Pacific Depot, which is under restoration.

Schedule: May 28-October 9; Sundays and holidays, 10:00a.m. & 2:00p.m.

Fare: Adults $10.00, senior citizens $8.00, children (4-14) $5.00, children under 4 ride free. Steam excursions have an additional $2.00 fare. Charter and special excursions have separate fares.

Locomotives/Trolleys: No. 1233, S-10 0-6-0 switcher, and Nos. 131 & 133, EMD GP-9s, all former Southern Pacific; No. 50, 1939 50-ton General Electric, former Spreckels Sugar.

Passenger Cars: No. 701, Budd coach, former Seaboard; No. 702, Pullman coach, former Santa Fe; No. 501, maintenance-of-way flatcar converted to open-air car, and No. 502, gondola converted to open-air car, both former Southern Pacific; baggage car under restoration for use as a commissary car.

Special Events: Special runs, charter trips, and Clarksburg branch excursions are scheduled from time to time; please call or write for information.

Note: Snacks and souvenirs are available on board.

Location: East Main Street and Thomas Street. The site is about 1 mile west of the East Main Street exit of I-5, about 22 miles northwest of Sacramento.

Radio Frequency: 160.260

Contact: David Magaw
President

Mailing Address:
1583 #C Enterprise Boulevard
West Sacramento, CA 95691
Telephone: (916) 372-9777
Fax: (916) 372-3545

47

California, Yreka
D-R

YREKA WESTERN RAILROAD
Steam, scheduled
Standard gauge

YREKA WESTERN RAILROAD

Ride/Operation: Constructed in 1888 as the Yreka Railroad Company, this line began operations on January 8, 1889, providing rail service between the city of Yreka and the newly constructed California & Oregon Railroad 7.4 miles to the east at the cattle town of Montague, California. Today's YWR offers a 15-mile, 3-hour round trip between Yreka and Montague, including a one-hour stopover at Montague. The train travels through local lumber mills and across the scenic Shasta Valley, where passengers see panoramic views of 14,162-foot Mount Shasta.

Displays/Exhibits: One-thousand-square-foot model railroad; historic displays.

Train: Open-air car; two 1948 former Milwaukee Hiawatha cars; two former Southern Pacific Harriman cars.

Schedule: May 27-June 11 & September 5-October 29, weekends; June 14-September 4, Wednesday-Sunday; 10:00a.m.

Fare: Not available at press time. Please call or write for information.

Locomotives: No. 19, 1915 Baldwin 2-8-2, and No. 18, 1914 Baldwin 2-8-2, both former McCloud River Railroad; Nos. 20 & 21, EMD SW-8s.

Special Events: Murder on the Blue Goose, late June, features murder mystery with barbecue dinner at Montague; sponsored by the American Lung Association. The Great Wild Goose Chase, August 26; runners race the train to Montague and return by train.

Location: On the east side of the central exit off I-5 in Yreka.

Contact: Larry G. Bacon
General Manager

Mailing Address:
P.O. Box 660
Yreka, CA 96097
Telephone: (916) 842-4146

48

FORNEY HISTORIC TRANSPORTATION MUSEUM
Railway museum
Standard gauge

Displays/Exhibits: This museum features three steam locomotives: former Union Pacific "Big Boy" No. 4005, built by Alco in 1941; former Chicago & North Western 4-6-0 No. 444; and an 0-4-0T locomotive from Germany. The collection also includes four executive and business cars, two dating from the 1890s; a dining car; a rotary snowplow; and three cabooses. The museum has a fine collection of horse-drawn vehicles and a large display of antique automobiles.

Schedule: Monday-Saturday, except Thanksgiving, Christmas, and New Year's Day, 10:00 a.m.-5:00 p.m.; Sunday, 11:00 a.m.-5:00 p.m.

Admission: Adults $4.00, children (12-18) $2.00 and (5-11) $1.00. Group rates available.

Location: Near I-25 and Speer Boulevard in Denver. From I-25 take exit 211 (23rd Avenue) and travel 5 blocks east on Water Street to 1416 Platte Street.

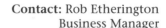Denver

Contact: Rob Etherington
Business Manager

Mailing Address:
1416 Platte Street
Denver, CO 80202
Telephone: (303) 433-3643

Colorado, Denver
R

PLATTE VALLEY TROLLEY
Electric, scheduled
Standard gauge

PLATTE VALLEY TROLLEY

Ride/Operation: A 25-minute, 2.5-mile round trip along the west bank of the South Platte River between 15th and Decatur streets. One-hour route 84 excursions are made to Lakewood at specified times.

Schedule: April, May & September-November: weekdays, 11:00-3:00 p.m.; weekends, 11:00-4:00 p.m.; every half hour. June-August: daily, 11:00 a.m.-4:00 p.m., every half hour. Route 84 excursion: April-October; weekdays, 12:00 p.m.; weekends, 2:00 p.m.

Fare: Adults $2.00, senior citizens & children $1.00. Route 84 excursion: Adults $4.00, senior citizens $3.00, children $2.00. Group and charter rates available.

Trolleys: No. 1977, built in 1986 by the Gomaco Trolley Company of Ida Grove, Iowa, is an authentic reproduction of open-air cars once produced by the J.G. Brill Company; a built-in diesel-electric generator provides power. Denver & Intermountain interurban No. 25, built in 1911 by the Woeber Carriage Company of Denver, is being restored by its owner, the Rocky Mountain Railroad Club, and is anticipated to be operational by fall 1995.

Notes: The Platte Valley Trolley is a project of the Denver Rail Heritage Society, a nonprofit, educational, volunteer organization.

Location: West of downtown Denver with stops at 15th Street & Speer Boulevard (Confluence Park near the Forney Transportation Museum), 7th Street, and the Children's Museum. Just east off exit 211 of I-25.

Denver

Contact: Mike Heirty
General Manager

Mailing Address:
2200 7th Street
Denver, CO 80211-5215
Telephone: (303) 458-6255

Colorado, Denver
R

THE SKI TRAIN

THE SKI TRAIN
Diesel, scheduled
Standard gauge

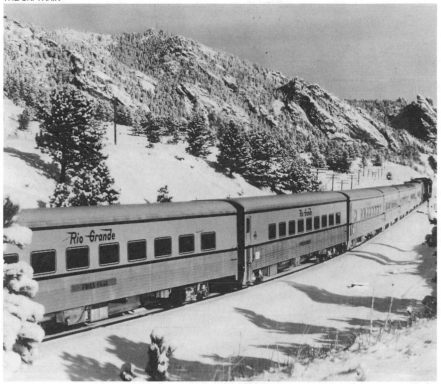

Ride/Operation: The Ski Train, a Colorado tradition since 1940, offers a 120-mile round trip from Denver's Union Station over the main line of the Rio Grande, passing through the famous Moffat Tunnel and stopping at West Portal, the location of Winter Park Resort.

Train: First-class, coach-class, and cafe-lounge cars.

Schedule: <u>Weekends</u>, mid December to early April. Lv. Denver Union Station 7:15 a.m., arr. Winter Park 9:15 a.m.; lv. Winter Park 4:15 p.m., arr. Denver 6:15 p.m.

Fare: <u>Coach</u>: $30.00; <u>first class</u>: $45.00.

Locomotives: Two SD-40 or SD-50 diesels.

Note: Nonskiers are also welcome and may take a guided tour of the ski slopes or spend the day shopping or relaxing. Snowmobiling and cross-country skiing are also available.

Location: Train departs from Denver Union Station.

TRAIN ➤➤ Denver

Contact: Jim Bain

Mailing Address:
555 17th Street, Suite 2400
Denver, CO 80202
Telephone: (303) 296-4754

51

DURANGO & SILVERTON
NARROW-GAUGE RAILROAD
Steam, scheduled
36" gauge

AMOS CORDOVA

Ride/Operation: The Durango & Silverton was established in 1881 to transport miners to and from Silverton and to haul precious metals to smelters. Today, a coal-fired, steam-powered, narrow-gauge train travels through the wilderness of the two-million-acre San Juan National Forest, following the Animas River through breathtaking Rocky Mountain scenery, where the only noises are those of the working locomotives, the river, and their echoes. The 90-mile round trip, which originates at Durango, takes approximately nine hours, including a 2 1/4-hour layover at Silverton for lunch and sightseeing. A half-day trip to Cascade Canyon is also offered.

Displays/Exhibits: Daily tours are offered of the roundhouse, car shop, and yards.

Train: Coaches; open-side observation car; coach for handicapped; parlor car; concession cars; rail camp (camping car); 1886 caboose in daily service; two private coaches.

Schedule: Daily, April 29-October 11, lv. Durango 8:30 a.m.; May 15-October 28, 9:15 a.m. train added; June 5-August 17 & September 2-October 1, 10:10 a.m. train added; June 20-August 17, 7:30 a.m. train added. Monday-Friday, July 10-August 9, 4:45 p.m. train to Cascade Canyon. Consult timetable for exact schedule on day of your visit. Spring Cascade Train: April 15-28, 10:00 a.m. Winter Holiday Train: November 22-January 1, except Christmas Day, 10:00 a.m.

Fare/Admission: Silverton: Adults $42.70, children (5-11) $21.45; parlor car $73.40; caboose $67.85. Cascade Canyon: Adults $36.15, children (5-11) $18.00. Yard Tours: Adults $5.00, children (5-11) $2.50.

Locomotives: Nos. 473, 476 & 478, 1923 Alco class K-28 2-8-2s; Nos. 480, 481 & 482, 1925 Baldwin class K-36 2-8-2s; Nos. 493, 498 & 499, 1930 Burnham Shops class K-37 2-8-2s; all former Denver & Rio Grande Western.

Location: In the southwestern part of the state on U.S. 160 & 550.

Contact: Amos Cordova
Vice President

Mailing Address:
479 Main Avenue
Durango, CO 81301
Telephone: (303) 247-2733

Colorado, Fort Collins
R

FORT COLLINS MUNICIPAL RAILWAY
Electric, scheduled
Standard gauge

AL KILMINSTER

Ride/Operation: A 3-mile ride on a restored portion of the historic Fort Collins trolley system on a painstakingly restored 1919 trolley. The tracks are in a grass median down the center of Mountain Avenue, then down the center of Roosevelt Avenue to City Park. Passengers board at the City Park terminus.

Schedule: Weekends & holidays, May 1-September 30, 12:00-5:00 p.m., weather permitting.

Fare: Adults $1.00, children (under 12) $.50. Group charters and special rates available.

Trolleys: No. 21, 1919 American single-truck Birney Safety Car, purchased new by the city of Fort Collins and in daily service until 1951.

Note: The Fort Collins Municipal Railway Society is a nonprofit group of volunteers. The streetcar and railway are the property of the city of Fort Collins.

Location: In the northern part of the state. Take exit 269-B off I-25 and proceed west on state route 14 to Mountain Avenue, then west on that street.

Contact: Robert Hutchison
President

Mailing Address:
P.O. Box 635
Fort Collins, CO 80522
Telephone: (303) 224-5372

53

GEORGETOWN LOOP RAILROAD
Steam, scheduled
36" gauge

GEORGE A. FORERO, JR.

Ride/Operation: A 6.5-mile, 70-minute round trip over the right-of-way of the former Colorado & Southern. The train travels through highly scenic, mountainous terrain and over the reconstructed Devil's Gate Viaduct, a spectacular 96-foot-high curved trestle. Located in the Old Georgetown Station are the railroad's headquarters, the Depot Express Cafe with an operating LGB model, and Baggage Cart Gifts. The Georgetown Loop Railroad is a project of the Colorado Historical Society.

Displays/Exhibits: Displayed at the Old Georgetown Station (the original Colorado & Southern depot) are 2-8-0 No. 44, a rail and tie car, former Rio Grande Southern caboose No. 0400, and a 1"-to-100'-scale diorama of the Clear Creek valley from Georgetown to Silver Plume, depicting the historic and present-day railroad. The Colorado Historical Society's 80-minute mine tour and exhibit can be reached by train.

Train: Open excursion-type cars.

Schedule: Daily, May 27-October 1; lv. Silver Plume 9:20 & 10:40 a.m., 12:00, 1:20, 2:40 & 4:00 p.m.; lv. Devil's Gate 10:00 & 11:20 a.m, 12:40, 2:00 & 3:20 p.m. Limited schedule weekdays in September. No mine tours after Labor Day.

Fare/Admission: Train: Adults $10.95, children $6.50, children under 4 ride free. Charters available year-round. Group rates available. Mine tour: Adults $4.00, children $2.00.

Locomotives: No. 40, 1920 Baldwin 2-8-0 & No. 44, 1921 Baldwin 2-8-0, both former International Railways of Central America; No. 8, 1922 Lima 3-truck Shay, No. 12, 1926 Lima 3-truck Shay & No. 14, 1916 Lima 3-truck Shay, all former West Side Lumber Co.; Nos. 130 & 140, 54-ton General Electric diesels, former U.S. Gypsum Company.

Notes: Trails and Rails Downhill Mountain Bike Tours trace the historic Argentine Central Railway. Reservations can be made with the Georgetown Loop Railroad.

Location: West of Denver. Take exit 226 off Interstate 70 for Silver Plume, exit 228 for Georgetown.

Denver   Radio Frequency: 161.115

Contact: Lindsey G. Ashby
President & General Manager

Mailing Address:
P.O. Box 217
Georgetown, CO 80444
Info & Reservations: (303) 670-1686
(303) 569-2403
Fax: (303) 569-2894

COLORADO RAILROAD MUSEUM
Railway museum
Standard gauge, 36" gauge

ROBERT W. RICHARDSON

Ride/Operation: This 35-year-old museum, oldest and largest in the Rocky Mountain area, houses an extensive collection of Colorado railroad memorabilia as well as the layout of the Denver HO Model Railroad Club. On outdoor trackage are more than 50 cars and locomotives, both narrow- and standard-gauge, including the oldest locomotives and cars in the state. No. 346, an 1881 Baldwin 2-8-0, and a Rio Grande "Galloping Goose" operate on selected weekends.

Schedule: Museum: daily; June-August, 9:00 a.m.-6:00 p.m.; September-May, 9:00 a.m.-5:00 p.m. Train: June 3-4, July 8-9, August 26-27, October 14-15, December 2-3 (Santa Claus Train). HO Model Railroad: First Thursday of every month, 7:30-9:30 p.m.

Admission: Adults $3.50, senior citizens (over 60) $3.00, children (under 16) $1.75, family rate (parents and children under 16) $7.50.

Locomotives: Include 4-6-0 No. 20 (Schenectady, 1899), former Rio Grande Southern; 2-8-0 No. 583 (Baldwin, 1890), former Denver & Rio Grande—the only surviving D&RG standard-gauge steam locomotive; and 4-8-4 No. 5629 (West Burlington, 1940), former Chicago, Burlington & Quincy.

Passenger Cars: Former Rio Grande Southern Galloping Geese Nos. 2, 6 & 7; former Colorado Midland observation car No. 111, used on wildflower trains; and former Santa Fe observation car "Navajo" (Budd, 1937), from the original streamlined *Super Chief*; others.

Location: Twelve miles west of downtown Denver. Take I-70 westbound exit 265 or eastbound exit 266 to 17155 West 44th Avenue.

Denver

Contact: Charles Albi
Executive Director

Mailing Address:
P.O. Box 10
Golden, CO 80402
Telephone: (303) 279-4591
(800) 365-6263
Fax: (303) 279-4229

Colorado, Idaho Springs NATIONAL HISTORIC ARGO GOLD MILL
D-R
Model, scheduled
Half scale

BOB BOWLAND

Ride/Operation: Visitors ride in half-scale models of 1800s mining cars behind a gas-powered model of the 0-4-0 "H.K. Porter" to the Double Eagle gold mine, then to world-famous Argo Tunnel and the Argo gold mill.

Displays/Exhibits: Mining museum, gold and gemstone panning.

Train: Models of locomotive, ore cars, passenger car, cattle car, caboose.

Schedule: <u>Year-round</u>, 10:00 a.m.-7:00 p.m.

Admission: <u>Year-round pass</u>: Adults $10.00, children (7-12) $8.00 & (1-6) $5.00. Pass includes train ride and tour of mine, mill, and museum.

Special Events: <u>Monthly themes</u> include: Horseback riding, Wild West days, gunfights (June); Gold Rush days, mining events (July); Pow-wow (August).

Location: 2350 Riverside Drive.

Contact: Darrell Chauncey
Program Director

Mailing Address:
P.O. Box 1503
Idaho Springs, CO 80452
Telephone: (303) 567-2421

LEADVILLE, COLORADO & SOUTHERN RAILROAD
Diesel, scheduled
Standard gauge

Ride/Operation: The 22 1/2-mile, 2 1/2-hour train trip follows the headwaters of the Arkansas River to an elevation of 11,120 feet, over an old narrow-gauge roadbed converted to standard gauge in the 1940s. Train leaves from the restored 1894 railroad depot (formerly Colorado & Southern, built originally for the Denver, South Park & Pacific) in Leadville, highest incorporated city in the United States.

Displays/Exhibits: No. 641, 1906 Brooks 2-8-0, former Colorado & Southern.

Train: GP-9 with open and enclosed excursion cars; boxcar with concessions.

Schedule: Daily, May 27-June 11, 1:00 p.m.; June 12-September 4, 10:00 a.m. & 2:00 p.m. September 5-October 1: weekdays, 1:00 p.m.; weekends, 10:00 a.m. & 2:00 p.m.

Fare: Adults $18.50, children $9.75. Group rates available.

Locomotives: No. 1714, 1955 EMD GP-9, former Burlington Northern.

Passenger Cars: Six excursion cars, boxcar, caboose.

Special Events: Geology Special. Flower Special.

Location: Depot at 326 East 7th Street.

Contact: Stephanie Olsen
President

Mailing Address:
P.O. Box 916
Leadville, CO 80461
Telephone: (719) 486-3936

MANITOU & PIKE'S PEAK RAILWAY
Diesel, scheduled
Standard gauge (cog)

Ride/Operation: The M&PP, the highest cog railway in the world, was established in 1889 and has been operating continuously since 1891; it celebrated its centennial of passenger operations in June 1991. A 3 1/4-hour round trip takes passengers to the summit of Pike's Peak (elevation 14,110 feet) from Manitou Springs (elevation 6,575 feet) and includes a 40-minute stop at the summit.

Train: Twin-unit diesel passenger units and single diesel units.

Schedule: Daily; May-mid June, September & October, 9:20 a.m. & 1:20 p.m.; mid June-August, every 80 minutes, 8:00 a.m.-5:20 p.m.

Fare: Adults: $21.00, children (5-11) $9.50. Group rates available.

Special Events: Occasional steam-up of former M&PP steam locomotive No. 4, built by Baldwin in 1896.

Location: Six miles west of Colorado Springs at 515 Ruxton Avenue.

Radio Frequency: 161.55

Contact: D. M. Doane
General Manager
or W. Spencer Wren
Traffic Manager

Mailing Address:
P.O. Box 351
Manitou Springs, CO 80829
Telephone:
Reservations: (719) 685-5401

TINY TOWN RAILWAY
Steam, scheduled
15" gauge

COURTESY OF TINY TOWN RAILWAY

Ride/Operation: Tiny Town Railway, a 1/4-scale live-steam railroad, takes passengers from its full-sized station on a 1-mile loop ride around Tiny Town. The railroad carried more than 75,000 riders in its 1994 season.

Displays/Exhibits: At 75 years old, Tiny Town is the oldest miniature town in the United States. It features more than 100 hand-crafted, 1/6-sized structures laid out in the configuration of a real town.

Train: Two live-steam and two gas-powered 1/4-scale locomotives.

Schedule: <u>Daily</u>, May 29-September 4; <u>weekends</u>, May, September & October; 10:00 a.m.-5:00 p.m. Train runs continuously.

Fare/Admission: <u>Train rides</u>: $1.00. <u>Tiny Town Admission</u>: Adults $2.00, children (3-12) $1.00, children under 3 admitted free.

Locomotives: 1970 standard-gauge 4-6-2 "Occasional Rose," propane-fired; 1970 narrow-gauge 2-6-0 "Cinderbell," coal-fired; 1954 F-unit "Molly," gas-powered; 1952 A- & B-unit "Betsy," gas-powered.

Passenger Cars: Open amusement-park-style cars; caboose.

Notes: Tiny Town is operated by the nonprofit Tiny Town Foundation.

Location: Twenty-five minutes southwest of downtown Denver.

Denver

Mailing Address:
6249 South Turkey Creek Road
Morrison, CO 80465
Telephone: (303) 697-6829

SHORE LINE TROLLEY MUSEUM
Electric, scheduled
Standard gauge

T. SHADE

Ride/Operation: The Shore Line Trolley Museum operates the sole remaining segment of the historic 95-year-old Branford Electric Railway. The 3-mile ride passes woods, salt marshes, and meadows along the scenic Connecticut shore. Trolley operator escorts passengers and provides interpretation for a cross section of the extensive collection.

Displays/Exhibits: Parlor car No. 500, Atlanta No. 948, work cars, and the world's first electric locomotive. The restoration shop, which is on the guided tour, houses cars undergoing restoration or maintenance. Automated sound show, "Birth of the Trolley Era"; hands-on exhibits; a slide/video theater.

Schedule: Daily, May 29-September 4; weekends and holidays, September & October; weekends, May. Sundays, April & November; 11:00 a.m.-5:00 p.m. Trolleys run every 30 minutes.

Fare: Unlimited rides and guided tour: Adults $5.00, senior citizens $4.00, children (2-11) $2.00, children under 2 ride free. Rates and program may vary on special-event weekends. Group charter rates available (203-467-7635).

Trolleys: Connecticut Co. open car No. 1414; Connecticut Co. suburban No. 193; Montreal double-truck No. 2001; Johnstown lightweights No. 356 & 357; Brooklyn (NY) convertible No. 4573; Third Avenue Railway No. 629. Other cars may be operated.

Special Events: Write for flyer.

Location: Take exit 51 east or 52 west off the Connecticut Turnpike (I-95) and follow signs to the museum.

New Haven

Contact: George T. Boucher
Director

Mailing Address:
17 River Street
East Haven, CT 06512-2519
Telephone: (203) 467-6927

Connecticut, East Windsor
M-R

CONNECTICUT TROLLEY MUSEUM
Electric, scheduled
Standard gauge

SCOTT R. BECKER

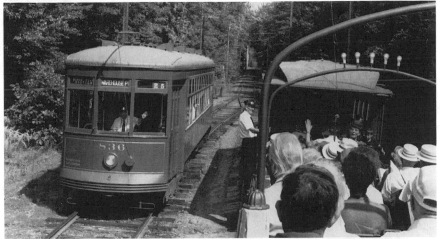

Ride/Operation: A 3-mile, 25-minute round trip through scenic woodlands over a rebuilt portion of the former Rockville branch of the Hartford & Springfield Street Railway, originally built in 1906. The ride often includes meets with other trolleys, and the line features a historic working semaphore signal system. Trolleys leave from the "Isle of Safety" trolley-stop shelter built in 1913 for downtown Hartford, Connecticut, and from the CTM North Road terminal.

Displays/Exhibits: More than 60 pieces of rolling stock, including streetcars, interurbans, rapid-transit cars, electric freight equipment, work cars, steam and diesel locomotives, wooden passenger cars from the 1890s, and freight cars. A 1910 Climax geared steam locomotive (former Middle Fork Railroad) is on display. The new exhibit building includes the "Great Trolley Exhibit Hall," with display cars from the storage barn, as well as a picture history of the trolley.

Schedule: <u>Daily</u>, May 29-September 4; weekdays, 10:00 a.m.-4:00 p.m.; Saturdays, 10:00 a.m.-6:00 p.m.; Sundays, 12:00-6:00 p.m. <u>Weekends and holidays</u> (except Thanksgiving and Christmas), September 5-May 28, 12:00-5:00 p.m.

Fare: Adults $6.00, senior citizens $5.00, children (5-12) $3.00, children under 5 ride free. <u>Group rates</u> available.

Trolleys: Nos. 65, 355, 840 & 1326, former Connecticut Co.; Nos. 4, 2056 & 2600, former Montreal Tramways; No. 1850, former Rio de Janeiro; Nos. 4436 & 4284, former Chicago Transit Authority; No. 451, former Illinois Terminal.

Passenger Cars: Two 1899 Jackson & Sharp coaches; 1890 wooden open-vestibule combine, former New Haven; 1894 coach, former Philadelphia & Reading.

Rolling Stock/Equipment: Wooden boxcars built before 1880; steel and wooden cabooses.

Special Events: <u>Halloween Festival</u>, "Rails to the Dark Side," October 20-22 & 27-29 (adults), October 21-22 & 28-29 (children, ages 3-10). <u>Winterfest</u>, November 24-January 1, a festival of Christmas lights with nightly operation.

Location: Halfway between Hartford, Connecticut, and Springfield, Massachusetts. Take exit 45 off I-91 and travel 3/4 mile east on route 140.

Windsor Locks

Contact: Business Office

Mailing Address:
P.O. Box 360
East Windsor, CT 06088-0360
Telephone:
Gift Shop: (203) 623-7417
Office: (203) 627-6540

61

RAILROAD MUSEUM OF NEW ENGLAND
Railway museum
Standard gauge

HOWARD PINCUS

Displays/Exhibits: This museum, operated by the 25-year-old Connecticut Valley Railroad Museum, owns a 60-piece collection of historic railroad equipment, the largest in New England. Some of this equipment is on display at Essex.

Schedule: <u>Weekends</u>, May-October.

Fare: No charge; donations accepted.

Locomotives/Trolleys: Diesel locomotives include RS-3 No. 529, Alco FA-1 No. 0401, and General Electric U-25B No. 2525, all former New Haven; EMC SW-1 No. 1109, former Boston & Maine; and E-33 No. 4601, former Conrail and New Haven electric freight locomotive. Steam locomotives include No. 1246, 1946 Montreal 4-6-2, former Canadian Pacific Railway, and 2-6-2 No. 103, former Sumter & Choctaw, which heads a display train of vintage freight cars.

Rolling Stock/Equipment: Numerous cars from Northeastern railroads, including passenger, head-end, and freight cars and cabooses.

Location: At the Essex yards of the Valley Railroad, just west of exit 3 off state route 9.

 Old Saybrook

Contact: Howard Pincus
President

Mailing Address:
P.O. Box 97
Essex, CT 06426
Telephone: (203) 395-0615

Connecticut, Essex
R

VALLEY RAILROAD COMPANY
Steam, scheduled
Standard gauge

HOWARD PINCUS

Ride/Operation: A 2 1/2-hour excursion along the scenic banks of the Connecticut River on restored 1920s-vintage cars. All trains except the last of the day connect with a riverboat cruise at Deep River. The first train of the day travels the entire length of the restored tracks, to Haddam.

Train: Open gondola car; restored coaches; extra-fare Pullman parlor car "The Great Republic."

Schedule: May 6-June 9: Wednesday-Friday, 2:00 & 3:30 p.m.; weekends & May 29, 12:00, 1:30, 3:00 & 4:00 p.m. June 10-September 4: weekdays, 10:00 a.m., 12:00, 1:30, 3:00 & 4:30 p.m.; weekends, July 4 & September 4, 5:45 p.m. train added (on Saturdays, 5:45 p.m. is a "Chicken Train"). September 6-October 29: Wednesday-Sunday & October 12, 10:00 a.m., 12:00, 1:30, 3:00 & 4:30 p.m.

Fare: Train and boat: adults $14.00, children (2-11) $7.00, children under 2 ride free. Train only: adults $8.50, children (2-11) $4.25, children under 2 ride free. Parlor car: extra fare. Discounts for senior citizens. Group rates for groups of 25 or more.

Locomotives: No. 97, 1926 Alco 2-8-2, former Birmingham & Southeastern; No. 40, 1920 Alco 2-8-2, former Aberdeen & Rockfish; 44-ton diesel No. 0800; 80-ton diesel No. 1000.

Special Events: Presidents' Day Special, February 18-20. Spring Special, March 18-19. Easter Eggspress, April 8-9 & 14-15. Antique Machinery and Transportation Day, May 7. May Market of Arts and Crafts, May 13-14. Hot Steam Music Festival, June 23-25. Harvest Craft Festival, September 30-October 1. Ghost Train, October 27-28. North Pole Express, November 24-December 22. Tuba Concert, December 16. Call for schedules.

Location: From shoreline, take exit 69 off I-95, then travel north on state route 9 to exit 3. From Hartford, take exit 22 off I-91, then travel south on state route 9 to exit 3. Valley Railroad is a half-mile west of route 9 on state route 154.

Old Saybrook

Contact: Staci M. Roy
General Manager

Mailing Address:
P.O. Box 452
Essex, CT 06426
Telephone: (203) 767-0103

63

Connecticut, Kent
M

CONNECTICUT ANTIQUE MACHINERY

CONNECTICUT ANTIQUE MACHINERY ASSOCIATION, INC.
Railway exhibit
36" gauge

Ride/Operation: A short stretch of three-foot-gauge track is in operation during this group's popular Fall Festival, with a locomotive shunting ore cars from their turn-of-the-century operating rock crusher to the end of the line (currently being extended; plans call for a loop around the museum grounds).

Displays/Exhibits: A wide range of exhibits showing the development of the country's agricultural and industrial technology from the mid 1800s to the present, including a collection of large stationary steam engines in the Industrial Hall; a large gas-engine display; a tractor and farm-implement display in the large tractor barn; and the reconstrucrted Cream Hill Agricultural School buildings, which housed an early agricultural school that was the forerunner of the University of Connecticut. Future plans include a large engine-pumping exhibit and a sawmill.

Train: 1921 8-ton Plymouth diesel; three Koppel tip cars.

Schedule: Museum: Saturdays and by appointment. Train: Spring Gas-Up, May 7; Fall Festival, September 23-24.

Admission: Adults $3.00, children (5-12) $1.50, children under 5 admitted free.

Locomotives: No. 4, 1908 Porter 2-8-0, former Argent Lumber Co.; No. 16, 1921 Plymouth D1, former Hutton Brick Co.; No. 18, 1917 Vulcan limited-clearance 0-4-0T, former American Steel & Wire Co.

Rolling Stock: No. 111, caboose, former Tionesta Valley Railway; miscellaneous ore cars.

Special Events: During Spring Gas-Up and Fall Festival, grounds are filled with restored, operating antique machinery, including gas engines, steam engines, cars, trucks, tractors, hot-air engines, steam launches, and more.

Location: One mile north of the village on route 7; adjacent to the Housatonic Railroad.

Contact: Bob Hungerford
President

Mailing Address:
P.O. Box 1467
New Milford, CT 06776
Telephone: (203) 927-0050

AVONDALE RAILROAD CENTER, DELAWARE PROJECT
Railway museum
Standard gauge

Displays/Exhibits: This display, a component of the Avondale Railroad Center of Avondale, Pennsylvania, features a Pennsylvania Railroad class B-6sa 0-6-0, the only surviving locomotive of its class, which is being cosmetically restored; a Union Pacific caboose; a PRR baggage car; and two Reading Railroad passenger cars. The equipment is located on the siding of the Minker Construction Company's Stone Mill Business Center, and Minker's offices are housed in a newly built replica of a turn-of-the-century railroad station. The facility is on the main line of the Wilmington & Western Railroad.

Schedule: Year-round.

Admission: Free.

Special Events: Art shows, seasonal celebrations. Please call or write for information.

Location: Route 41, in the center of town.

Mailing Address:
State & Pomeroy Streets
P.O. Box 809
Avondale, PA 19311
Telephone: (215) 268-2397

Delaware, Lewes
R

COURTESY OF QUEEN ANNE'S RAILROAD

QUEEN ANNE'S RAILROAD
ROYAL ZEPHYR DINNER TRAIN
Steam, scheduled
Standard gauge

COURTESY OF QUEEN ANNE'S RAILROAD

Ride/Operation: The Queen Anne Railroad's excursion train takes passengers on a 1 3/4-hour ride in open-window coaches through southern Delaware countryside on the former Pennsylvania Railroad Lewes-Georgetown line. Brunch trains with coach and dining-car seating operate on selected dates. The *Royal Zephyr* travels a 2 1/2-hour course, during which passengers enjoy a full dinner with linen and silver service and live musical entertainment. A murder-mystery dinner theater is featured on selected trains. A cash bar is available on all dinner trains.

Train: Excursion: open-window heavyweight coaches. Brunch: open-window coaches, climate-controlled dining cars. *Royal Zephyr:* climate-controlled dining cars.

Schedule: Excursion train: May 17, 24 & 31, 12:00 p.m.; June, Wednesdays & Saturdays; 12:00 p.m. July-August, Wednesdays, 12:00 & 3:30 p.m.; Fridays & Saturdays, 12:00 p.m. September, Saturdays, 12:00 p.m. Brunch train: April 16; May 14; October 8, 15 & 22; December 3; 1:30 p.m. *Royal Zephyr:* May 28; June 10, 17, 24; July-August, Saturdays; September 3, 9, 16, 23, 30; 6:00 p.m. October 29; November 11 & 18; December 16; 5:00 p.m.

Fare: Excursion train: adults $7.00, children (3-12) $5.00; groups of 35 or more please call for availability. Brunch train: dining car with meal, adults $24.95, children (under 13) $19.95; coach seats without meal, adults $7.00, children (3-12) $5.00. *Royal Zephyr:*: adults $39.95, children (under 13) $32.95. Paid, nonrefundable reservations required 24 hours before departure for all food-service trains. Group rates and charters available upon request.

Locomotives: No. 3, 1943 Vulcan Locomotive Works 0-6-0T, former U.S. Navy.

Passenger Cars: 1947 Pullman Standard Osgood Bradley coaches, former New Haven; MP-54 coach, former PRR; coach, former New York Central; heavy combine, former Norfolk & Western; baggage car, former Amtrak/U.S. Army.

Special Events: Easter Bunny, April 16. Mother's Day, May 14. Father's Day, June 17. Civil War Weekend, August 19-20. Santa Express, December 3.

Note: The railroad reserves the right to make equipment and schedule changes without notice. Full refunds are given if train is canceled.

Wilmington

Contact: Mark Jordan, General Manager or Keith Cranor, Assistant Manager

Mailing Address:
730 King's Highway
Lewes, DE 19958
Telephone: (302) 644-1720

WILMINGTON & WESTERN RAILROAD
Steam, scheduled
Standard gauge

EDWARD J. FEATHERS

Ride/Operation: A 10-mile, 1 1/4-hour round trip over a portion of the former Baltimore & Ohio Landenberg Branch, from Greenbank Station to the Mt. Cuba Picnic Grove. Also offered are occasional trips past Mt. Cuba along the Red Clay Creek Valley to either Yorklyn or Hockessin.

Displays/Exhibits: Original W&W Yorklyn station serves as the Greenbanks Gift Shop.

Train: Steel open-platform combine and coaches, former Delaware, Lackawanna & Western; closed-platform coaches, former Pennsylvania Railroad and DL&W; wood-sided cabooses, former B&O.

Schedule: Mt. Cuba: diesels run Saturdays, July 1-September 2, 12:30 & 2:00 p.m.; steam engines run Sundays, May 7-October 29, 12:30, 2:00 & 3:30 p.m., and Sundays, November 5-19, 12:30 & 2:00 p.m. Yorklyn or Hockessin: May 29, June 25, July 8 & 30, August 12 & 27, September 4 & 10, October 8. Yorklyn/Hockessin dates are subject to change; please call or write for latest timetable.

Fare: Mt. Cuba: Adults $7.00, senior citizens (60+) $6.00, children (2-12) $4.00. Yorklyn or Hockessin: call for fares. Group rates and charters available.

Locomotives: No. 98, 1909 Alco 4-4-0, former Mississippi Central; No. 37, 1924 Alco 2-8-2T, former Sugar Pine Lumber Co.; No. 8408, 1942 EMD SW-1, former B&O; No. 114, EMD SW-1, former Lehigh Valley; No. 4662, 1929 Pullman Standard Doodlebug, former PRR.

Special Events: Wild West Robberies, June 27, July 30, August 27. Autumn Leaf Specials, October 7, 14 & 21. Santa Claus Specials, November 25-26, December 2-3, 9-10 & 16-17. Tuesday School Trains and Epicurean Express Dinner Trains: please call.

Location: Trains leave from Greenbank Station, on route 41 just north of route 2, four miles southwest of Wilmington. Take exit 5 off I-95, follow route 141 north to route 2 west, then follow route 41 north.

Wilmington

Radio Frequency: 160.755

Contact: Edward J. Feathers
Director of Operations

Mailing Address:
P.O. Box 5787
Wilmington, DE 19808
Telephone: (302) 998-1930

COURTESY OF SMITHSONIAN INSTITUTION

Displays/Exhibits: The Smithsonian's Railroad Hall symbolizes the achievements of railroads and rail transit in the United States from the 1820s to about 1965. On display are original pieces of the "Stourbridge Lion" and the "DeWitt Clinton," a complete Winton 201-A engine from the *Pioneer Zephyr*, a series of 1/2-inch-scale models showing locomotive development from the earliest steam engine to present-day diesels, and many other exhibits.

Schedule: Daily (except Christmas Day), 10:00 a.m.-5:30p.m.

Admission: Free.

Locomotives/Trolleys: No. 1401, 1926 Alco 4-6-2, former Southern Railway; "John Bull," 1831 Stephenson 4-2-0, former Camden & Amboy Railroad; "Pioneer," 1851 Wilmarth 2-2-2, former Cumberland Valley Railroad; "Olomana," 1883 Baldwin 0-4-2T, former plantation locomotive; "Jupiter," 1876 Baldwin narrow-gauge 4-4-0 (in Arts & Industries Building).

Note: Information leaflet No. 455, available on request, describes the railroad exhibits. (Extensive research inquiries cannot be answered.)

Location: National Museum of American History, 14th Street & Constitution Avenue.

Washington

Contact: William L. Withuhn
Supervising Curator
Division of Transportation

Mailing Address:
National Museum
of American History
Washington, D.C. 20560

Florida, Fort Myers
D-R

THE RAILROAD MUSEUM
OF SOUTH FLORIDA
Steam, diesel, scheduled
7 1/2" gauge

Ride/Operation: This museum, which is located in the Metro Mall, sponsors a 12- to 15-minute, 1 1/8-mile ride at Train Village in Lakes Park.

Displays/Exhibits: Historical exhibits featuring railroads that operated in South Florida, steam locomotives, artifacts, and people who worked on the railroads.

Train: Three 7 1/2-inch-gauge FP7A diesels with four cars each.

Schedule: Weekends and holidays, 10:00 a.m.-4:00 p.m. Closed Christmas Day. Charters and groups at other times by special arrangement.

Fare/Admission: Train: $2.00. Lakes Park: $3.00 per car.

Locomotives: Nos 1994, 1995 & 1996, FP7A diesels; No. 143, 1905 Baldwin 0-6-0, former Atlantic Coast Line, awaiting restoration.

Special Events: Holiday Express, December, at Train Village; features lighted miniature villages along the tracks, with nighttime operation from 5:00 to 9:00 (fare is $2.50). Others, to be announced. Please call or write for information.

Note: Lakes Park is wheelchair-accessible; train will be accessible in the near future. Steam is operated occasionally.

Location: Museum: Metro Mall, 2855 Colonial Boulevard No. 405. Train Village: Lakes Park, Gladiolus Drive.

Contact: Kent E. Schneider
President

Mailing Address:
P.O. Box 7372
Fort Myers, FL 33911
Telephone: (813) 275-3000
(813) 275-3331

Florida, Fort Myers
R

COURTESY OF SEMINOLE GULF RAILWAY

Ride/Operation: The *Excursion Train* leaves Metro Mall Station for a 2-hour round trip on the railway's original overland route between Fort Myers and Bonita Springs; environmental and historical programs are featured. The *Dinner Train,* which consists of three vintage dining cars named after Sanibel, Marco Island, and Gasparilla, leaves from Fort Myers for a 60-mile, 3 1/2-hour round trip including a five-course meal with a choice of wine or other beverages. The Sunday *Brunch Train* leaves the Metro Mall Station in Fort Myers and crosses the Caloosahatchee River over the railroad's lift bridge towards Punta Gorda for a 3-hour daytime round trip with meal.

Train: *Excursion Train*: GP-9 locomotive with 2 or 3 former Boston & Maine non-propelled RDC Budd cars. *Dinner Train* and *Brunch Train*: GP-10 with "Sanibel," former Canadian National coach; "Marco," former Southern Railroad diner built by Budd; "Gasparilla," former Richmond, Fredericsburg & Potomac King William Pullman; and "Bay Colony" coach with bar, former CN.

Schedule: *Excursion Train*: Please call or write for information. *Dinner Train*: Wednesday, Friday & Saturday, 6:30 p.m. *Brunch Train*: Sunday, 10:30 a.m.

Fare: *Excursion Train*: Adults $12.50, children $7.50, plus tax. *Dinner Train*: $39.75 plus tax. Murder Mystery: $49.75 plus tax. Additional fare of $5.00 on Saturdays.

Locomotives: No. 571-577, GP-9, former Baltimore & Ohio or Chesapeake & Ohio; No. 578, GP-10, former Illinois Central Gulf.

Passenger Cars: Nos. 6120, 6122 & 6155, non-propelled former Boston & Maine RDC Budd cars; kitchen & dining cars.

Special Events: Fort Myers-to-Arcadia Rodeo Special, March and July. Holiday dinner trains. Murder Mystery dining trips. Christmas Lights Canal Trips, special combined train and boat trips to Punta Gorda.

Location: Metro Mall Passenger Station, 2805 Colonial Boulevard between I-75 exit 22 and U.S. 41.

   ♿ ☐ 🚻 🎬 🚗 🚌

   ⊞ ✉ 📷 ⚑ 🏕

Express Bus: Tampa-Fort Myers
Radio Frequency: 160.710

Contact: Carl J. Appelberg

Mailing Address:
4110 Centerpointe Drive
Suite 207
Fort Myers, FL 33916
Telephone: (813) 275-8487

Florida, HighSprings
M

HIGH SPRINGS STATION MUSEUM
Railway museum

LARRY BENKE

Displays/Exhibits: This privately funded museum, dedicated to the preservation of American railroad heritage, is an ever-changing showcase of railroad history. Housed in a restored turn-of-the-century Atlantic Coast Line depot, it includes rail artifacts from the Atlantic Coast Line and the Pennsylvania Railroad, as well as other lines across the country. Exhibits feature tools, communication equipment, china, silver, photos, and railroad motor cars.

Schedule: Wednesdays, Thursdays & Sundays, 12:00-5:00 p.m. Fridays, 10:00 a.m.-7:00 p.m. Saturdays, 10:00 a.m.-6:00 p.m. Other times by appointment.

Admission: Adults $3.00, children $2.00. Discounts for families, senior citizens, and groups.

Rolling Stock: Motor cars include Fairmont M-9, M-19s, M-1, S-2, A-4, MT-14; Kalamazoo W-27; Fairbanks-Morse 40-Bs; Buda handcar; Buda and Sheffield velocipedes.

Location: In the center of town on Railroad Avenue. Take exit 79 off I-75 and travel five miles southwest.

Contact: Barbara Tritsch
Tour and Publicity Coordinator

Mailing Address:
P.O. Box 2008
20 NW Railroad Avenue
High Springs, FL 32643-2008
Telephone: (904) I LIKE RR
(454-5377)

71

GOLD COAST RAILROAD MUSEUM
Steam, diesel, scheduled
Standard gauge

COURTESY OF GOLD COAST RAILROAD MUSEUM

Ride/Operation: A 2 1/2-mile, 25-minute ride around the site.

Displays/Exhibits: Model-train exhibits.

Schedule: Weekends, 11:00 a.m.-4:00 p.m.; train departs on the hour.

Admission: Adults $4.00, children (under 12) $2.00.

Locomotives: Steam engines Nos. 7, 113 & 153; diesels Nos. 1, 106, 167 & 1555.

Passenger Cars: "Ferdinand Magellan"; "California Zephyr"; "Silver Stag"; private car "Castleblaney"; "Silver Valle"; café car.

Rolling Stock: Burrow crane; 150-tin crane; side-dump hopper; four boxcars.

Special Events: Group trips. School trips. Private birthday parties. Photo, film, and video shoots. All are scheduled upon request; please call or write for information.

Location: At the Metro Zoo.

Contact: Connie Greer
President

Mailing Address:
12450 SW 152nd Street
Miami, FL 33177
Telephone: (305) 253-0063

HENRY M. FLAGLER MUSEUM
Railway display

COURTESY OF HENRY M. FLAGLER MUSEUM

Display/Exhibits: The restored historic home of Henry Morrison Flagler, founder of the Florida East Coast Railroad and developer of much of Florida's east coast from Jacksonville to Key West. Featured are period rooms, many with original furnishings; special exhibits are in the museum's exhibit gallery.

Schedule: Tuesday-Saturday, 10:00 a.m.-5:00 p.m.; Sunday, 12:00-5:00 p.m. Closed Christmas and New Year's Day.

Admission: Adults $5.00, children (6-12) $2.00, children under 6 admitted free.

Passenger Cars: Private car No. 91, built circa 1886 for Henry M. Flagler by Jackson & Sharp of Wilmington, Delaware, contains its original woodwork and interior fittings and is located on the museum's south lawn. Flagler traveled in this car on his trips to Florida and on inspection trips during the construction of the FEC Key West extension.

Special Events: Anniversary Day Celebration, first Saturday in February. Free admission, entertainment, refreshments (punch & cookies), and special exhibits.

Location: Cocoanut Row at Whitehall Way.

Contact: Kay Graham
Publicity

Mailing Address:
P.O. Box 969
Palm Beach, FL 33480
Telephone: (407) 655-2833

SOUTHEASTERN RAILWAY MUSEUM
Steam, diesel, irregular
Standard gauge

MICHAEL DZIADIK

Ride/Operation: At the museum, locomotives No. 2 and No. 5 pull cabooses around a half-mile loop, and the North Georgia Live Steamers operate a 1 1/2-inch-scale live-steam train over 4,000 feet of track.

Displays/Exhibits: Twelve-acre museum site at Duluth features steam and diesel locomotives and passenger and freight cars. The museum library, housed in former Southern RPO No. 153, is open by appointment.

Train: Cabooses Nos. X-92, former Central of Georgia; No. 1064, former Clinchfield Railroad; and No. 2866, former Georgia.

Schedule: Museum: Saturdays (except on excursion dates), 9:00 a.m.-5:00 p.m. Loop: April-November, third Saturday and Sunday of each month; please call or write for more information. North Georgia Live Steamers: Please call or write for specific dates.

Fare: Nonoperating days: donations welcomed. Operating days: please call or write for fare information.

Locomotives: No. 97, Porter 0-6-0T, former Georgia Power; No. 9, 1924 Heisler, former Campbell Limestone Co.; No. 1100, 1950 EMD SW-7 diesel, former Southern Railway; Nos. 2 & 5, 44-ton General Electric center-cab diesels.

Location: At 3966 Buford Highway, Duluth, about 10 miles north of Atlanta.

  Atlanta

Contact: Gary V. Singleton
Director

Mailing Address:
Southeastern Railway Museum
or Atlanta Chapter, N.R.H.S.
P.O. Box 1267
Duluth, GA 30136-1267
Telephone:(404) 476-2013

74

Georgia, Kennesaw
M

BIG SHANTY MUSEUM
Railway museum
Standard gauge

Operation: The Andrews Raid and the Great Locomotive Chase, one of the unusual episodes of the Civil War, has been much publicized over the years. The "General," now one of the most famous locomotives in American history, is enshrined in a museum within 100 yards of the spot where it was stolen on April 12, 1862. The old engine, still operable, last ran in 1962. The Big Shanty Museum was officially opened on April 12, 1972, 110 years after the historic seizure of the "General."

Displays/Exhibits: Locomotive "General" and tender; train and Civil War memorabilia; video show about the Great Locomotive Chase.

Schedule: March 1-November 30: Monday-Saturday, 9:30 a.m.-5:30 p.m.; Sunday, 12:00-5:30 p.m. December 1-February 28: Monday-Friday, 10:00 a.m.-4:00 p.m.; Saturday, 9:30 a.m.-5:30 p.m.; Sunday, 12:00-5:30 p.m.

Admission: Adults $3.00, senior citizens & AAA service $2.50, children $1.50, children (under 7) admitted free.

Locomotives: The "General," No. 3, 1855 Rogers, Ketchum & Grosvenor 4-4-0, former Western & Atlantic Railroad.

Location: Off highways 41 & 75 about 25 miles north of Atlanta. Take exit 118 off I-75 north, turn left, and travel 2 1/2 miles.

Contact: Catherine L. Fletcher
Director

Mailing Address:
2829 Cherokee Street
Kennesaw, GA 30144
Telephone: (404) 427-2117
(800) 742-6897

HAWAIIAN RAILWAY SOCIETY
Diesel, scheduled
36" gauge

COURTESY OF HAWAIIAN RAILWAY SOCIETY

Ride/Operation: This site offers a 90-minute, 6 1/2-mile ride from the historic plantation town of Ewa to the water's edge, where passengers can witness the surf crashing against the rocks. The train travels along the fence and main gate of Barbers Point Naval Air Station and through cane fields, the old town sites of Gilberts and Sisal, and the Ko Olina Resort and golf course. Passengers also get a view of pre-World War II Fort Barrette not normally available to the public. Narration on the ride provides the history of the area and railroading in Hawaii.

Displays/Exhibits: Nos. 6 and 12, former Oahu Railway & Land Co.; No. 6, former Waialua Agricultural Co.; No. 1, former Ewa Plantation Co.; No. 65-00174, former U.S. Navy; Hawaii's 40 & 8 "Merci" boxcar.

Train: No. 65-00302, former U.S. Navy; Whitcomb 0-4-4-0; converted U.S. Army flatcars, three covered and two open.

Schedule: Sundays (except major holidays), 1:00 & 3:00 p.m. Group charters available.
Fare: Adults $8.00, senior citizens (62+) and children (2-12) $5.00.

Location: Take exit 5A off freeway H-1; travel south on Fort Weaver Road to the fourth stoplight (Renton Road); turn right onto Renton Road and travel all the way to the end; the site is on the left.

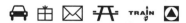

Contact: Jan Lorimer
Administrator

Mailing Address:
P.O. Box 1208, Ewa Station
Ewa Beach, HI 96706
Telephone: (808) 681-5461
Fax: (808) 681-4860

LAHAINA, KAANAPALI & PACIFIC RAILROAD
Steam, scheduled
36" gauge

COURTESY OF LAHAINA, KAANAPALI & PACIFIC RAILROAD

Ride/Operation: The LK&P offers an old-fashioned passenger-train ride behind steam locomotives. Passengers are entertained by a singing conductor as the train passes through fields of sugar cane and the Kaanapali Golf Courses. The 12-mile, 1-hour round trip takes passengers between the historic old town of Lahaina and the resort of Kaanapali Beach. During busy periods, trains pass each other at Hahakea siding, the midpoint of the ride. The train crosses a 400-foot-long trestle, and the trip features spectacular views of the West Maui Mountains and the neighboring islands of Molokai and Lanai. Locomotives are turned on a turntable at Lahaina station at the end of each trip.

Train: Six open-window coaches are patterned after 1880 Kalakaua-style coaches that ran on the Hawaiian Railroad. Nos. 101, 102, and 103 were built in 1969, No. 104 in 1983, and Nos. 105 and 106 in 1991.

Schedule: Daily except Thanksgiving and Christmas. Twenty-four one-way trips per day between 8:55 a.m. and 5:30 p.m.

Fare: Round trip: adults $13.00, children $6.50. One way: adults $9.00, children $4.50.

Locomotives: No. 1, "Anaka," 1943 Porter 2-4-0 & No. 3, "Myrtle," 1943 Porter 2-4-0, both former Carbon Limestone Co.; No. 45, "Oahu," 1959 Plymouth diesel, former Oahu Railway; No. 5, "Waikakalaua," 1908 Baldwin, former Oahu Sugar Company; No. 85, "Iniki," 1910 Alco Cooke Works, former Oahu Railway.

Special Events: Chartered trains run in the evenings to catered parties at Kaanapali station.

Notes: The Lahaina, Kaanapali & Pacific Railroad is operated by Railroads of Hawaii, Inc., a subsidiary of Kyle Railways, Inc.

Location: Kaanapali Beach Resort, Maui.

 ♿ ☐ 🚗 🚌 ⊞
✉ **TRAIN**

Radio Frequency: 154.540

Contact: Gary Getman
General Manager

Mailing Address:
P.O. Box 816
Lahaina, HI 96767-0816
Telephone: (808) 667-6851

SILVERWOOD CENTRAL RAILWAY
Steam, scheduled
36" gauge

COURTESY OF SILVERWOOD CENTRAL RAILWAY

Ride/Operation: A 3.2-mile, 20-minute ride around the perimeter of Silverwood Theme Park, crossing a trestle and passing through wooded areas.

Displays/Exhibits: Silverwood Theme Park, an upscale Victorian mining town, includes several gift shops, a full-service restaurant, an old-time theater, professional entertainment, a daily air show, and the Country Carnival, which includes the corkscrew rollercoaster, the whitewater raft ride "Thunder Canyon," and an indoor ice show. The park is also beginning construction of its new "Woodie Rollercoaster."

Train: Typical train consists of an engine, two roofed cars, and one open car.

Schedule: Daily, middle of June to Labor Day.

Fare: Included in park admission. Call for rates.

Locomotives: No. 7, 1915 Porter 2-6-2, former Eureka & Palisades Railroad; No. 12, 1928 Baldwin 2-6-2, former Kahului Railroad.

Passenger Cars: Enclosed car; two roof cars; three open cars.

Rolling Stock/Equipment: Flatcar; three boxcars, former Southern Pacific; coal car, former East Broad Top.

Location: In northern Idaho, 15 miles north of Coeur d'Alene on highway 95.

Contact: Jane A. Thompson
Administrative Assistant

Mailing Address:
North 26225 Highway 95
Athol, ID 83801
Telephone: (208) 683-3400

NORTHERN PACIFIC DEPOT
RAILROAD MUSEUM
Railway museum

MIKE GREEN

Operation: The Northern Pacific Depot at Wallace was built in 1901 in the elegant chateau style; it served the Coeur d'Alene Branch of the Northern Pacific Railway and later the Burlington Northern until 1981. As part of a freeway project, the depot was moved two hundred feet to its present location in 1986. It opened to the public as a railroad museum in 1987.

Displays/Exhibits: The first story of the depot is set up like a turn-of-the-century railroad station. On the second floor, displays interpret the history of railroading in the Coeur d'Alene mining district.

Schedule: Summer: daily, 9:00 a.m.-7:00 p.m. Spring & fall: daily, 9:00 a.m.-5:00 p.m. Winter: Monday-Saturday, 10:00 a.m.-5:00 p.m.

Admission: Adults $1.50, senior citizens $1.00, children (6-16) $.50, children under 6 admitted free.

Special Events: Depot Days, May 7, is a festival celebrating the anniversary of the depot's move in 1986.

Location: Corner of 6th & Pine Streets, 219 6th Street.

Contact: Linda Brunette
Director

Mailing Address:
P.O. Box 469
Wallace, ID 83873
Telephone: (208) 752-0111
or (208) 752-1131

HISTORIC PULLMAN FOUNDATION
Railway displays

COURTESY OF HISTORIC PULLMAN FOUNDATION

Displays/Exhibits: This organization offers guided tours of the historic Pullman district. The tour begins with an introductory video and a view of the interior of the HPF Visitor Center and the Greenstone Church; it then continues with the visitor's choice of a walk or a bus trip through the area, taking in the Pullman Suite at the Hotel Florence (once reserved for George M. Pullman), a Victorian furniture display room, and a "wood display" room containing actual pieces from Pullman's home on Prairie Avenue. Tour/luncheon packages are available, with lunch at the Hotel Florence restaurant; also, Sunday tours from May through October are scheduled to coincide with brunch hours at the Hotel Florence.

Schedule: Year-round. Tour only: 9:30 a.m.-3:00 p.m. Tour/Luncheon: usually 10:30 a.m., although other times can be scheduled. Tour/Brunch: Sundays, May-October, 12:30 & 1:30 p.m. Call or write to schedule tour and for additional information.
Admission: Tour only: Adults $4.00, senior citizens $3.00, students $2.50. Tour/Luncheon and Tour/Brunch: Adults & seniors $12.00-$22.00, students $6.00-$16.00. Rates subject to change.

Location: 11111 South Forrestville Avenue.

 (limited)

Chicago

Contact: Deborah Bellamy
Office Manager

Mailing Address:
11111 South Forrestville Avenue
Chicago, IL 60628-4649
Telephone: (312) 785-8181
Fax: (312) 785-8182

MUSEUM OF SCIENCE AND INDUSTRY
Science museum
Railway displays

MUSEUM OF SCIENCE & INDUSTRY

Displays/Exhibits: One of the largest and finest museums in the country, the Museum of Science and Industry devotes a great deal of its attention to transportation on land, sea, and air. Notable exhibits include the German submarine U-505, a World War II British Spitfire aircraft, the Apollo 8 and Aurora spacecraft on loan from the National Air and Space Museum of the Smithsonian Institution, and many historic automobiles and carriages. The Santa Fe Miniature Railroad operates model trains over 1,000 feet of track, and there are many scale models of locomotives and trains.

Schedule: Daily, May 28-September 3, 9:30 a.m.-5:00 p.m. Daily, September 4-May 27; Monday-Friday, 9:00 a.m.-4:00 p.m.; weekends, 9:30 a.m.-5:30 p.m.

Admission: Adults $6.00, senior citizens $5.00, children $2.50.

Locomotives: No. 999, 1893 West Albany Shops 4-4-0, former New York Central—the famous No. 999 reached a speed of 112.5 miles per hour west of Batavia, New York, in 1893, making it the first steam locomotive to exceed 100 miles per hour; No. 9900, the *Pioneer Zephyr*, former Chicago, Burlington & Quincy—built in 1934, the first streamlined diesel-powered passenger train in the country; the "Mississippi," 1834, oldest locomotive from the south.

Location: At 57th Street and Lake Shore Drive.

Contact: Michael Sarna
Collections Manager & Registrar

Mailing Address:
57th Street & Lake Shore Drive
Chicago, IL 60637
Telephone: (312) 684-1414, X-2296

Illinois, Freeport
R

SILVER CREEK & STEPHENSON RAILROAD
Steam, scheduled
Standard gauge

GEORGE A. FORERO, JR

Ride/Operation: The train departs from the replica Silver Creek Depot, then travels on a 4-mile round trip through Illinois farmland and stands of virgin timber known as "Indian Gardens." From there, the train journeys across the Yellow Creek on a 30-foot-high cement and stone pier bridge.

Displays/Exhibits: The "turn-of-the-century" Silver Creek Depot is a tribute to an important part of our country's transportation history. Displayed inside are lanterns, locks and keys, whistles, sounders, tickets, advertising, couplers, and much more, representing railroads from across the country. Visitors taking in the exhibits can hear the clicking of the telegraph as the telegrapher taps out messages.

Train: 1912 36-ton Heisler; 1941 bay-window caboose, former Chicago, Milwaukee, St. Paul & Pacific; 1889 wooden caboose with cupola, former Hannibal & St. Joseph, reported to be the oldest caboose running in the state; 1948 caboose, former Illinois Central Gulf; covered flatcar.

Schedule: May 28-29; June 17-18; July 4 & 28-30; August 5; September 4 & 23-24; October 7-8 & 21-22; 11:00a.m.-5:00p.m.

Location: Half-mile south of the Stephenson County Fairgrounds, at Walnut & Lamm Roads.

Fare: Adults $3.00, children (under 10) $1.50.

Locomotives: 1912 36-ton Heisler; 14-ton Brookville switch engine; 12-ton Plymouth switch engine.

Rolling Stock/Equipment: Work cars, zapper.

Notes: The Silver Creek & Stephenson Railroad and the Silver Creek Depot are projects of the Stephenson County Antique Engine Club. Information about the railroad can also be obtained from the Stephenson County Convention & Visitor Bureau, 26 South Galena Avenue, Freeport, IL 61032.

Contact: Peggy S. Althoff
Secretary

Mailing Address:
SCAEC
P.O. Box 255
Freeport, IL 61032
Telephone: (800) 369-2955
(815) 233-1357
Operating Days: (815) 235-2198

82

MONTICELLO RAILWAY MUSEUM
Diesel, scheduled
Standard gauge

PAUL YOOS

Ride/Operation: This museum, incorporated in 1966, offers a 50-minute round trip over former Illinois Central and Illinois Terminal trackage. Passengers board at the Illinois Central Depot at the museum or at the 1899 Wabash Depot in downtown Monticello.

Displays/Exhibits: 1907 Baldwin 2-8-0, former Southern Railway No. 401; Shedd Aquarium's "Nautilus" (fish car); Nickel Plate RPO; Santa Fe Pullman "Pleasant Valley"; 1931 Alco 0-4-0 tank engine No. 1; 1944 Industrial Brownhoist; freight equipment; cabooses.

Train: No. 1189, former Wabash F-7A, or No. 301, former Long Island RS-3; commuter coach, former Rock Island No. 2541, and/or baggage/coach combine, former IC No. 892, and/or vista gon, former Nickel Plate Road No. 1907; caboose No. 500836, former Norfolk & Western.

Schedule: Weekends & holidays, May 6-October 31; 1:00, 2:00, 3:00 & 4:00 p.m. at museum site; 1:30, 2:30 & 3:30 p.m. in town. Charters/private cars/birthday caboose on request.

Admission: Adults $5.00, senior citizens & children (4-12) $3.00, children under 3 accompanied by an adult ride free.

Locomotives: No. 1, 1930 Alco 0-4-0, former Montezuma Gravel Co.; No. 191, 1916 Alco 0-6-0, former Republic Steel Corp.; No. 301, 1955 Alco RS-3, former Long Island Railroad; No. 401, 1907 Baldwin 2-8-0, former Southern Railway; No. 44, 1940 Davenport 44-ton diesel; No. 1189, 1953 GMD F-7A, former Wabash No. 725; No. 6789, 1959 Alco FPA-4, former Canadian National/VIA; CTA "Skokie Swift," one of four articulated car sets.

Passenger Cars: Pullman No. 2910 & dormitory car No. 1906, both former IC; passenger coach No. 1238 & parlor car "City of Decatur," both former Wabash; others.

Rolling Stock/Equipment: Wooden vinegar tank car No. 1655, former Standard Brands; wedge snowplow No. 40065, former Canadian Pacific; 4-wheel caboose, former Baltimore & Ohio; Alco slug No. 9838, former N&W; others undergoing restoration.

Special Events: Throw Momma on the Train, May 13-14. Father's Day Bluegrass & More, June 18. Caboose Trains, August 19-20. Railroad Days, September 16-17. Depot Day, October 7. Ghost Trains, October 27-29 & 31. Please call for more information.

Notes: Monticello Railway Museum is a nonprofit volunteer organization.

Location: 20 miles southwest of Champaign; 20 miles northeast of Decatur. Take exit 63 off I-72.

Champaign

Radio Frequency: 160.635

Contact: Barbara A. Mann

Mailing Address:
P.O. Box 401
Monticello, IL 61856-0401
Telephone: (217) 762-9011

FOX RIVER TROLLEY MUSEUM
Electric, scheduled
Standard gauge

FRED LONNES

Ride/Operation: The Aurora, Elgin & Fox River country trolley line has been operating since 1896, first as a passenger interurban, later with electric freight, then as a diesel freight line. Chicago-area interurban and rapid-transit cars currently demonstrate the trolley era by operating from Castlemuir (South Elgin) to Coleman and Coleman Grove (Kane County Blackhawk Park). The nostalgic, 3-mile, 25-minute round trip takes passengers along the scenic Fox River.

Displays/Exhibits: 1926 Chicago, South Shore & South Bend coach No. 14; 1908 Chicago Transit Authority electric locomotive No. L-202; 1957 Illinois Central-built caboose No. 9648; 1895 Chicago Street Railway Post Office car No. 6 (used on special occasions).

Schedule: Sundays, May 14-November 5, plus May 29, July 4 & September 4, 11:00 a.m.-5:00 p.m. Saturdays, June 24-September 2, 11:00-5:00 p.m.

Fare: All-day pass: $6.00. Single ride: Adults $2.50, seniors (65+) $2.00, children (3-11) $1.50. Children must be accompanied by an adult. Charter and group rates available.

Locomotives/Trolleys: No. 20, 1902 Niles interurban, former Chicago, Aurora & Elgin—oldest operating interurban in America; No. 4451, 1924 Cincinnati, former Chicago Transit Authority; No. 5001, 1947 Pullman all-electric rapid-transit, former Chicago Rapid Transit; No. 715, 1926 Cincinnati, former Chicago North Shore & Milwaukee; Nos. 6101 & 6012, 1950 rapid transit cars, former St. Louis, former CTA.

Rolling Stock/Equipment: Diesel locomotive and additional interurban, rapid transit, and streetcar rolling stock on site or undergoing restoration.

Special Events: Mother's Day, May 14—free rides for Mom with paid child's fare. Spring Caboose Day, June 14. Father's Day, June 18—free rides for Dad with paid child's fare. Fox River Trolley Fest 1995, June 24-25. Red, White & Blue Dollar Day, July 4, all rides $1.00. Trolley Folk Music Fest, August 5-6. Fall Caboose Sundays, September 17 & 24. Haunted Trolley, October 29.

Notes: The museum is operated by the volunteer, nonprofit Fox River Trolley Association, Inc. Vendors and displayers: contact museum concerning Trolley Fest 1995.

Location: 375 LaFox Street (Illinois route 31), 6 miles south of I-90, 3 miles south of U.S. 20. South Elgin is about 35 miles northwest of Chicago.

Chicago

Contact: Ticket Agent
Mailing Address:
P.O. Box 315
South Elgin, IL 60177-0315
Telephone: (708) 697-4676

Illinois, Union (McHenry County)
M-R

ILLINOIS RAILWAY MUSEUM
Steam, electric, diesel, scheduled
Standard gauge

BOB BUNKE

Ride/Operation: A 5-mile, 25-minute round trip over the reconstructed right-of-way of the former Elgin & Belvedere, featuring steam and/or diesel trains and electric interurbans on weekends and streetcars on weekdays.

Displays/Exhibits: This extensive museum displays more than 300 pieces of rail equipment of all types. The museum also has a depot built in 1851, a signal tower, and an "el" station that have been moved to the site and restored.

Schedule: Daily, May 29-September 4. Weekends, May 1-28, September 5-30 & October.

Admission: Weekends when steam or diesel trains are operated: Adults $7.00, children (5-11) $5.00. All other times: Adults $5.00, senior citizens (65+) and children (5-11) $3.00. Maximum family admission: $25.00.

Locomotives/Trolleys: Midwestern interurbans and streetcars; Chicago elevated cars; North Shore, South Shore, Chicago, Aurora & Elgin, and Illinois Terminal interurbans. No. 1630, 1918 Baldwin 2-10-0, former Frisco Lines; No. 101, 1926 Baldwin 2-6-2, former Tuskegee Railroad; No. 5, 1929 Lima 3-truck Shay, former St. Regis Paper Co.; No. 8380, 1929 Baldwin 0-8-0, former Grand Trunk Western; No. 265, 1944 Alco 4-8-4, former Milwaukee Road; No. 16, 1915 Baldwin 4-4-0, former Detroit, Toledo & Ironton; No. 2050, 1922 Alco 2-8-8-2, former Norfolk & Western; No. 3719, 1900 Brooks 2-6-0, former Illinois Central; No. 2707, 1943 Alco 2-8-4, former Chesapeake & Ohio; No. 3001, 1926 Ingersoll Rand boxcab, former Delaware, Lackawanna & Western; No. 760, 1944 Fairbanks-Morse H-10-44 diesel, former Milwaukee Road; No. 9001, 1937 Electro-Motive Corporation SC-600, former Missouri Pacific; 1892 Rogers 4-6-0, 1923 Baldwin 2-8-2, and No. 9911-A, 1940 Electro-Motive Division E-5, all former Chicago, Burlington & Quincy.

Passenger Cars: Commuter cars from the Rock Island, the Chicago & North Western, and the

Lackawanna; a train of heavyweight equipment; private cars; and 1936 Budd articulated stainless-steel Burlington *Nebraska Zephyr*.

Rolling Stock/Equipment: Large collection, including refrigerator cars, cabooses, two milk cars, and steam and electric work equipment.

Special Events: Scout Day, May 20. Railroad Day, May 29. Chicago Day, June 18. Trolley Pageant, July 4. Diesel Weekend, July 15-16. Vintage Transport Extravaganza, August 6. Railfan Weekend, September 2-4. Members' Weekend, September 30-October 1.

Location: 7000 Olson Road, 1 mile east of town.

Contact: Nick Kallas
General Manager

Mailing Address:
P.O. Box 427
Union, IL 60180
Telephone:
Recorded message: (815) 923-4000
Business office: (815) 923-4391

Illinois, Union (McHenry County)   **VALLEY VIEW MODEL RAILROAD**
D   *Model railroad*

Displays/Exhibits: This display is modeled after the Chicago & North Western's Northwest line, with accurate track layouts of some of the towns modeled. Three to four trains operate simultaneously over the railroad, which has eight scale miles of track, 16 ever-changing trains, 250 buildings, 64 turnouts, 250 vehicles, 450 people, 84 operating signal lights, 250 pieces of rolling stock, and operating grade crossings with flashers and gates. Extra equipment is on static display in the gift shop.

Schedule: Wednesdays and weekends, May 29-September 4, 1:00-6:00 p.m.
Admission: Adults $3.50, children (5-12) $1.75, children under 5 admitted free.

Location: Valley View Farm, 17108 Highbridge Road.

Contact: Ted Voss

Mailing Address:
17108 Highbridge Road
Union, IL 60180
Telephone: (815) 923-4135

Indiana, Connersville
D-R

WHITEWATER VALLEY RAILROAD
Diesel, scheduled
Standard gauge

WHITEWATER VALLEY RAILROAD

Ride/Operation: This line offers a 32-mile, 5 1/2-hour round trip to Metamora, Indiana, a restored canal town that features one hundred shops and a working grist mill. A 2-hour stopover at Metamora gives passengers a chance to tour the town.

Displays/Exhibits: A small museum is located in the gift shop.

Train: No. 25, 1951 Lima; 1930s open-window coaches.

Schedule: Weekends and holidays, 12:01 p.m.

Fare: Adults $11.00, children (2-12) $5.00.

Locomotives: No. 6, 1907 Baldwin 0-6-0, former East Broad Top; No. 11, 1924 Vulcan 0-4-0T; No. 100, 1919 Baldwin 2-6-2; No. 9, 1948 Alco S1; No. 25, 1951 Lima SW7.5; No. 210, 1946 General Electric 70-ton; No. 709, 1950 Lima SW10; No. 2561, 1931 Plymouth 32-ton gas engine; No. 9339, 1948 Alco S1; No. 9376, 1950 Lima SW12, former Baltimore & Ohio.

Special Events: Christmas Trains, November 25-26, December 2-3, 9-10 & 16-17.

Location: 300 South Eastern Avenue.

Radio Frequency: 160.650

87

CORYDON SCENIC RAILROAD
Diesel, scheduled
Standard gauge

COURTESY OF CORYDON SCENIC RAILROAD

Ride/Operation: A 1 1/2-hour, 16-mile ride over part of the 112-year-old Louisville, New Albany & Corydon Railroad from Corydon (the state's first capital) to Corydon Junction. Guides are aboard to answer passengers' questions as the train travels along Big Indiana Creek into the southern Indiana woods and hills, crossing two major bridges and passing many sink holes.

Train: Erie and RDC coaches.

Schedule: <u>May 7-May 28 & September 5-October 30</u>: Fridays, 1:00 p.m.; weekends, 1:00 & 3:00 p.m. <u>June-August</u>: Wednesdays-Fridays, 1:00 p.m.; weekends, 1:00 & 3:00 p.m. <u>May 29, July 4 & September 4</u>: 11:00 a.m., 1:00 & 3:00 p.m.

Fare: Adults $8.00, children $5.00. <u>Group rates available</u> for groups of 20 or more.

Locomotives: Two 44-ton General Electric center-cab diesels; 2 Alco 1000-horsepower RS-1s.

Passenger Cars: 1952 & 1953 RDCs; 1920 & 1930 Erie Lackawanna coaches.

Notes: Schedule and equipment subject to change.

Location: Walnut and Water streets. One mile south of I-64, in downtown Corydon.

Contact: Richard P. Pearson
Public Relations

Mailing Address:
P.O. Box 10
Corydon, IN 47112
Telephone: (812) 738-8000

FORT WAYNE RAILROAD
HISTORICAL SOCIETY
Steam, irregular
Standard gauge

Ride/Operation: This group operates day-long, main-line, steam-powered passenger excursions with its former Nickel Plate class S-2 Berkshire locomotive for various clients throughout the Midwest.

Train: Air-conditioned and open-window coaches; Pullman, dome, and/or lounge car may be added to the train.

Schedule: Varies, depending on client. For further information, please send a stamped, self-addressed envelope.

Fare: $55.00 and up, depending on route.

Locomotives: No. 765, 1944 Lima 2-8-4, former Nickel Plate; maintained and operated by the society.

  Fort Wayne

FRENCH LICK, WEST BADEN & SOUTHERN RAILWAY
Diesel, electric, scheduled
Standard gauge

Ride/Operation: A 20-mile, 1 3/4-hour round trip between the resort town of French Lick and Cuzco, site of Patoka Lake. The train traverses wooded Indiana limestone country and passes through one of the state's longest railroad tunnels. The trolley makes a 2-mile round trip from French Lick to West Baden.

Displays/Exhibits: The French Lick, West Baden & Southern Railway is operated by the Indiana Railway Museum, which owns 57 pieces of railway equipment.

Train: Erie and Rock Island coaches.

Schedule: Train: weekends, April 1-November 26, plus May 29, July 4 & September 4, 10:00 a.m., 1:00 & 4:00 p.m.; Tuesdays, June 6-October 31, 1:00 p.m. Trolley: daily, June-October; weekends, April, May & November; every half hour, 10:00 a.m.-4:00 p.m. Times are Eastern Standard Time.

Fare: Train: Adults $8.00, children (3-11) $4.00, children under 3 ride free. Trolley: $1.00, children under 3 ride free.

Locomotives/Trolleys: No. 3, 1947 General Electric 80-ton diesel; No. 208, 1912 Baldwin 2-6-0, former Angelina & Neches River Railroad; No. 97, 1925 Baldwin 2-6-0, former Mobile & Gulf Railroad; No. 1, Alco S-4 diesel, former Algers, Winslow & Western Railway; No. 313, 1930 former Porto, Portugal.

Location: Trains depart from the old Monon Railroad passenger station in French Lick, located on state route 56 in southwestern Indiana, about an hour's drive from Louisville.

Radio Frequency: 160.635

Contact: G. Alan Barnett
General Manager

Mailing Address:
P.O. Box 150
French Lick, IN 47432
Telephone: (812) 936-2405

HESSTON STEAM MUSEUM
Steam, scheduled
Various gauges

COURTESY OF HESSTON STEAM MUSEUM

Ride/Operation: A 2 1/4-mile, 15-minute trip over unique dual-gauge (24-inch and 36-inch) trackage through the scenic 155-acre grounds in LaPorte County; a 1 1/2-inch-scale train that travels over a figure-eight layout and passes over and under a trestle bridge; a 14-inch-gauge train that runs over a 5,000-foot loop of track. All trains are live steam.

Displays/Exhibits: A large collection of steam-powered equipment, including a 92-ton railroad steam crane, a 350-horsepower Allis-Chalmers Corliss steam engine, steam traction engines, water pumps, sawmill, electric light plant, and antique gas engines and tractors.

Train: Open excursion-type cars.

Schedule: Weekends, May 27-September 4; Sundays, September 11-October 30; 12:00-5:00 p.m.

Fare: Train: $3.00 or $2.00, depending on choice of gauge. Steam Show: $3.00 (visitors over 12 years old).

Locomotives: No. 2, 1911 Porter 36-inch 2-6-0, former United Fruit, Guatemala; No. 1, 1935 Henschel (Germany) 24-inch 0-4-0T; No. 7, 1929 Lima 36-inch 3-truck Shay, former New Mexico Lumber Co.; No. 19-B, 1889 Sharp & Stewart (Glasgow, Scotland) 24-inch 0-4-0T, former Darjeeling & Himalayan Railway; 1940 Czechoslovakia CSK 0-4-0; Henschel (Germany) 0-4-0T. Two German-built locomotives are being restored for 24-inch-gauge use.

Special Events: Annual Steam Show, four-day Labor Day weekend show.

Location: Take exit 49 off the Indiana Toll Road, travel north on state route 39 approximately 6 1/2 miles to county road 1000N, turn right and travel 2 1/2 miles to the grounds. Alternate route: Take exit 1 (New Buffalo, Michigan) off I-94, travel south 2 miles to county road 1000N, turn left and travel 2 1/2 miles to grounds.

Contact: John P. Edris
General Manager

Mailing Address:
2946 Mt. Claire Way, Long Beach
Michigan City, IN 46360
Telephone: (219) 872-7405

THE CHILDREN'S MUSEUM
OF INDIANAPOLIS
Railway museum
Toy trains

Displays/Exhibits: In 1868 the "Reuben Wells" (named after its designer) was the most powerful engine in the world. Its job was to push freight and passenger cars to the top of Indiana's Madison Hill, which had a grade of 5.9 percent. The 35-foot-long, 55-ton steam engine reduced to fifteen minutes what would have taken a team of horses half a day to complete. The "Reuben Wells" was retired in 1905. The Children's Museum acquired the Reuben Wells in 1968, and in 1975 workers built the new museum around it. The museum also contains an 1890s train station complete with blacksmith shop and offers a view of the Ohio River and the One Spot Repair shed, where a tool car awaits.

The Toy Train Treasures exhibit at the Children's Museum is the nation's largest public display of pre-World War II toy trains. Visitors can see more than 5,000 cars, engines, and accessories in a collection of more than 1,500 train sets. Toy Train Treasures traces the rise and fall of the toy train industry, with special emphasis on trains made by Lionel, Ives, and American Flyer.

Schedule: Memorial Day-Labor Day: Monday-Wednesday & Friday-Sunday, 10:00 a.m.-5:00 p.m.; Thursday, 10:00 a.m.-8:00 p.m. Labor Day-Memorial Day: Tuesday-Wednesday & Friday-Sunday, 10:00 a.m.-5:00 p.m.; Thursday, 10:00 a.m.-8:00 p.m.

Admission: Adults $6.00, senior citizens $5.00, children (2-17) $3.00, children under 2 admitted free.

Location: 3000 North Meridian Street.

Contact: Tonya Woodard
Media Coordinator

Mailing Address:
P.O. Box 3000
Indianapolis, IN 46206
Telephone: (317) 924-5431

CARTHAGE, KNIGHTSTOWN & SHIRLEY RAILROAD
Diesel, scheduled
Standard gauge

COURTESY OF CARTHAGE, KNIGHTSTOWN & SHIRLEY RAILROAD

Ride/Operation: A 10-mile, 1 1/4-hour round trip over the former Cleveland, Cincinnati, Chicago & St. Louis Michigan Division through scenic country, crossing the Big Blue River into Carthage, Indiana. Trains leave from the former New York Central freight house in Knightstown.

Train: Open-window coaches; open-platform transfer and cupola cabooses.

Schedule: May-October; weekends & holidays, 11:00a.m., 1:00 & 3:00p.m.; Fridays, 11:00a.m.

Admission: Adults $6.00, children (3-11) $4.00, children under 3 ride free. Group rates available.

Locomotives: No. 215, 45-ton General Electric, former Air Force No. 1215.

Location: Thirty-three miles east of Indianapolis on U.S. 40; 3 miles south of I-70 on state route 109.

Contact: Marion J. Allison
President

Mailing Address:
112 West Carey Street
Knightstown, IN 46148
Telephone: (317) 345-5561

LINDEN RAILROAD MUSEUM
Railway museum

COURTESY OF LINDEN RAILROAD MUSEUM

Displays/Exhibits: Operated by the Linden-Madison Township Historical Society, this museum is housed in the former Linden depot built by the Chicago, Indianapolis & Louisville Railway and the Toledo, St. Louis & Western Railroad in 1908. Restored to its 1950s appearance, the depot houses a collection of railroadiana from the Nickel Plate and Monon railroads. The Monon agent's room houses the E. E. Kauffman Monon collection, including a 3/4-inch-scale model of the Louisville, New Albany & Chicago "Admiral" locomotive and cars and a 3/4-inch-scale live-steam model of Monon Pacific No. 440 and the observation car "Babe." An operating HO layout of Linden and vicinity is featured in the Monon baggage room. Outside, railway equipment is on display. The depot sits adjacent to the present-day Indianapolis-Chicago CSX main line (former Monon).

Schedule: April-October, Friday-Sunday, 1:00-5:00 p.m. Group tours by appointment.

Admission: Adults $2.00, teens (13-17) $1.00, children (6-12) $.50.

Rolling Stock/Equipment: Caboose No. 497, former Nickel Plate; Fairmont A-3 motor car.

Location: Linden is in west-central Indiana, about 15 miles south of Lafayette on U.S. 231 and north of the Crawfordsville exit of I-74. The depot is across from Jane Stoddard Park, at 514 North Main Street.

INDIANA TRANSPORTATION MUSEUM
Steam, electric, diesel, scheduled
Standard gauge

JIM VAWTER

Ride/Operation: This 37 1/2-mile tourist railroad offers passengers a trip through Indianapolis and rural Hamilton and Tipton counties; excursions vary in length. Visitors can also enjoy a 20-minute electric trolley ride through Forest Park aboard vintage trolleys/interurbans.

Displays/Exhibits: Many railroad cars are on display, including Henry M. Flagler's business car No. 90 from the Florida East Coast Railway (on special occasions), cabooses, boxcars, and passenger equipment.

Train: Main-line excursions with restored Budd coaches, former Santa Fe combine, former Louisville & Nashville heavyweight dining car, Pullman heavyweight coaches and Chesapeake & Ohio/Nickel Plate cabooses.

Schedule: Weekends, April 29-May 29 and September 6-October 31, 10:00 a.m.-5:00 p.m. Tuesday-Sunday, May 30-September 5, 10:00 a.m.-5:00 p.m. Call or write for excursion schedule.

Fare/Admission: Steam excursion: adults $12.00, children (3-12) $6.00. Diesel excursion: adults $7.00, children (3-12) $5.00. Excursion fares include trolley ride and admittance to museum. Museum only: adults $3.00, children (3-12) $2.00.

Locomotives/Trolleys: No. 587, 1918 Baldwin 2-8-2; former Nickel Plate Road; FP-7 No. 96C & F-7 No. 83A, former Milwaukee Road; interurban No. 172, former Chicago, North Shore & Milwaukee; Nos. 4293 & 4454, former Chicago Rapid Transit; electric locomotive No. 4, former Twin Branch Railroad; No. 1, 1898 Singer electric locomotive.

Passenger Cars: Budd coaches, former Santa Fe; 1937 Pullman heavyweight coaches.

Special Events: "I've Been Working on the Railroad" Weekend, June. Indiana State Fairtrain, August. New Earth Festival, September. Ghost

Train, October. Campaign Train, November. Christmas Train, December.

Location: On state route 19 at Forest Park, 20 miles north of Indianapolis.

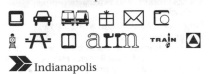

➤➤➤ Indianapolis

Contact: Michael Lennox
CEO & Chief Operating Officer

Mailing Address:
P.O. Box 83
Noblesville, IN 46060-0083
Telephone: (317) 773-6000
(800) 234-TRAIN (8724)

95

Indiana, North Judson
D

HOOSIER VALLEY RAILROAD MUSEUM
Railway display
Standard gauge

Displays/Exhibits: Miami Steam, which sponsors this site, was established in 1961, when it received 2-8-4 No. 2789 from the Chesapeake & Ohio Railroad Company. Several other pieces of railroad equipment are also on display.

Schedule: Saturday: 8:00 a.m.-5:00 p.m. Sunday-Friday: Call or write for information.

Admission: No charge.

Locomotives/Trolleys: No. 108, former Chicago, South Shore & South Bend electric; 44-ton Whitcomb diesel; 2-8-4 No. 2789, former Chesapeake & Ohio; No. 11, 95-ton General Electric, former Acme Steel.

Passenger Cars: Parlor car, former Gulf, Mobile & Ohio; baggage car, former Nickel Plate; coach, former New York Central; two coaches, former South Shore.

Rolling Stock/Equipment: 85-foot flatcar trailer train; 50-foot flat trailer train; World War II troop sleeper; transfer caboose, former Elgin, Joliet & Eastern; caboose, former Bessemer & Lake Erie; caboose, former Illinois Central; two steel boxcars, former NKP and Wabash; boxcar, former Pennsylvania Railroad; 1937 wood boxcar, former NKP; bunk car, former Norfolk & Western; weed burner, former EJ&E; 100-foot turntable, former Michigan Central; 20-ton Orton rail crane; 40-foot wood boxcar, former Wabash; tank car.

Special Events: Membership Day & Annual Dinner Party, date to be announced.

Location: East Main Street.

Contact: Bruce Emmons
Treasurer

Mailing Address:
P.O. Box 75
North Judson, IN 46366
Telephone: (219) 223-3834

Indiana, Wakarusa
M-R

OLD WAKARUSA RAILROAD
Steam, scheduled
15" gauge

DELTON SCHROCK

Ride/Operation: This railroad opened in 1989 on the grounds of the famous "Come and Dine" restaurant and gift shop. The train takes passengers on a 25-minute, 1 1/2-mile ride, traveling across two bridges, through a 100-foot curved tunnel, crossing City Street, and making a 10-minute stop at a miniature farm.

Displays/Exhibits: On display are 30 to 40 antique farm tractors (fully restored), along with other antiques and collectibles. The gift shop is located within a one-third-scale depot.

Schedule: April 1-October 31, Monday-Saturday, 11:00 a.m.-dark; train leaves the station every 30 minutes.

Fare/Admission: $3.00; children under 4 ride free.

Locomotives: One-third-scale, 15"-gauge 4-4-0 built in 1957 by Elmer and Norman Sandly; GP38 diesel-hydraulic.

Passenger Cars: Three 1/3-scale, 8-passenger coaches, built in Old Wakarusa Shop.

Rolling Stock/Equipment: Two 1/3-scale stock cars, caboose, gondola, and hopper, all built in Old Wakarusa Shop.

Special Events: Pumpkin Trains, mid-September to October. Train makes a stop at a pumpkin patch. Winter Wonderland Train, December, train rides from 6:00 to 9:00 p.m. through 100,000 Christmas lights.

Location: On the grounds of "Come and Dine" restaurant on highway 19.

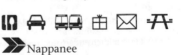
Nappanee

Contact: Tim Bainter
General Manager

Mailing Address:
P.O. Box 591
Wakarusa, IN 46573
Telephone: (219) 862-2714

97

Iowa, Boone
D-R

BOONE & SCENIC VALLEY RAILROAD
Steam, diesel, scheduled
Standard gauge

DICK WEBB

Ride/Operation: This railroad offers a 15-mile, 1 1/2-hour round trip over the former Fort Dodge, Des Moines & Southern Railroad, once Iowa's longest electric interurban; the route passes over a 156-foot-high bridge in the scenic Des Moines River valley.

Displays/Exhibits: The depot houses the Iowa Railway Museum; two railroad cars are full of photos and tool displays; and there are static displays of equipment. Boone is the home of the Kate Shelley High Bridge (longest and highest double-track railroad bridge in the world) and is Mamie Eisenhower's birthplace.

Schedule: Memorial Day weekend-October 31: weekdays (diesel operation), 1:30 p.m.; weekends (steam operation), 11:00 a.m., 1:30 & 4:00 p.m.

Fare: Diesel: adults $8.00, children (5-12) $4.00, children under 5 ride free. Steam: adults $10.00, children (5-12) $4.00, children under 5 ride free.

Locomotives/Trolleys: No. 8419, class JS steam locomotive built in Datong, China; No. 1003-1103, former Chicago & North Western diesel; No. 2554, former U.S. Government diesel; No. 106, former Chicago, South Shore & South Bend trolley.

Passenger Cars: Five passenger cars, former Erie Lackawanna; commuter coach, former Rock Island; cabooses.

Rolling Stock/Equipment: Snowplow, electric trolleys, electric locomotives, side-dump cars, flatcars.

Special Events: Train robberies. Civil War encampments. Antique tractor show and events. Carshow.

Location: In central Iowa, about 50 miles north of Des Moines, at 11th and Division streets in Boone.

Contact: George Eckstein

Mailing Address:
Box 603
Boone, IA 50036
Telephone: (515) 432-4249

98

RAILSWEST RAILROAD MUSEUM
Railway museum
Model railroad

COURTESY OF RAILSWEST RAILROAD MUSEUM

Displays/Exhibits: The Railswest Railroad Museum and HO model railroad are housed in an 1899 former Rock Island depot. The museum contains displays of historic photos, dining-car memorabilia, uniforms, and many other interesting items used during the steam era. The 22-foot by 33-foot model railroad depicts scenery of the Council Bluffs/Omaha area, featuring train lines that served the heartland: Union Pacific; Missouri Pacific; Chicago & North Western; Wabash; Norfolk & Western; Chicago & Great Western; Rock Island; Milwaukee Road; and Chicago, Burlington & Quincy.

Schedule: May 29-September 4: Monday-Tuesday & Thursday-Saturday, 10:00 a.m.-4:00 p.m.; Sunday, 1:00-5:00 p.m.

Admission: Adults $2.50, senior citizens (60+) $2.00, children (6-12) $1.25, children under 6 admitted free.

Rolling Stock/Equipment: Burlington route handcar (velocipede); No. 903690, 1963 Budd RPO car, former Union Pacific No. 5908; No. 24548, 1967 Union Pacific caboose, former Rock Island No. 17112; No. 462536, 1969 UP boxcar.

Special Events: Depot Days, September 23-24; Christmas at the Depot, November 26, December 3, 11 & 17, 1:00-5:00 p.m.

Location: 1512 South Main Street. Take exit 3 off I-80.

Omaha, Nebraska

Contact: Marcia Hastings

Mailing Address:
72 Bellevue Avenue
Council Bluffs, IA 51503
Telephone: Depot: (712) 323-5182
M. Hastings: (712) 322-0612

FORT MADISON, FARMINGTON & WESTERN RAILROAD
Diesel, scheduled

COURTESY OF FORT MADISON, FARMINGTON & WESTERN RAILROAD

Ride/Operation: The FMF&W is an old-time country railroad with tracks relaid on an abandoned Chicago, Burlington & Quincy branch chartered under its present name in 1869. A 2-mile ride takes passengers through the woods, up a 1.3-percent grade, and over a newly built trestle.

Displays/Exhibits: Exhibits include an extensive collection of memorabilia, a hand-pump cars that visitors can operate, work equipment, and rolling stock. An authentic, re-created depot and enginehouse are open for viewing, and visitors can also see a display of rare velocipedes and very early section cars in the section house. A 1920s-era filling station showcases the Model T depot hack and other antique cars and is part of the growing, re-created, early-1900s town on the grounds.

Train: 1926 Edwards Railway Motor Car Company "doodlebug" or open-air cars and caboose.

Schedule: Weekends and holidays, May 29-October 31, 12:00-5:00; trains depart hourly on the halfhour.

Fare/Admission: Adults $4.00, students (5-18) $3.00, children (under 5) admitted free with paying adult. Price includes ride and museum admission.

Locomotives: 1913 Baldwin 0-4-0 tender locomotive; 1927 Vulcan 8-ton gas-mechanical; 1945 Whitcomb 45-ton diesel-electric.

Rolling Stock/Equipment: 1917 wood caboose, former Chicago, Burlington & Quincy; 1890s wood truss-rod boxcar; various speeders; work equipment.

Special Events: Santa Train, December 3 & 10.

Notes: A 115-acre park and lake are just across the road from the railroad. Camping, with all hookups, is available at the park.

Location: Five and one-half miles east of Donnellson and 3 miles west of U.S. Route 61/Iowa Route 2 junction off Iowa Highway 2. Follow signs.

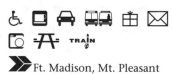

Ft. Madison, Mt. Pleasant

Contact: Dave Miner
President

Mailing Address:
2208 220th Street
Donnellson, IA 52625
(319) 837-6689

TRANS-MISSISSIPPI TROLLEY
Electric, scheduled
Standard gauge

TERRY WOODWORTH

Ride: A 9-mile, 1-hour round trip from Keokuk to "Nowhere," Illinois. Trolleys depart from the restored 1891 Union Depot, designed by Daniel Burnham, and follow part of the original Keokuk & Illinois Railway interurban route, sharing tracks of the Keokuk Junction Railway. The ride features a scenic crossing of the Mississippi River on the 2,200-foot-long Keokuk-Hamilton Bridge, built by Andrew Carnegie in 1867 and rebuilt by Ralph Modjeski in 1916. Special 57-mile round-trip Interurban Excursions between Keokuk and LaHarpe, Illinois, which operate on selected dates, replicate Midwestern interurban rides of the 1930s and 1940s.

Schedule: Send SASE or call for complete details.

Fare: Adults $7.50, children $6.00. Interurban excursion fares are based on options offered; write or call for details.

Trolleys: Nos. 161 & 168, 1927 Brill 52-seat interurbans, former Philadelphia & Western, former SEPTA. Cars are propelled by a 160-kilowatt diesel generator mounted on a single PCC truck coupled to the interurban.

Note: The Keokuk River Museum, housed aboard the *Str. George M. Verity*, a 1927 steam-powered towboat, is one block from the depot.

Location: 200 South Water Street, at the foot of Johnson Street on the riverfront.

Contact: Greg Nichols
General Manager

Mailing Address:
200 South Water Street
Keokuk, IA 52632
Telephone: (319) 524-2085

IOWA TROLLEY PARK
Electric, scheduled
Standard gauge

COURTESY OF IOWA TROLLEY PARK

Ride/Operation: A 20-mile, 90-minute round trip over the former Mason City & Clear Lake Electric Railway, built in 1896 and now known as the Iowa Traction Railroad, operating freight service between Mason City and Clear Lake. Passengers can board and disembark at either city for a ride on No. 1976, a Brill open trolley, or No. 727, a former North Shore interurban.

Displays/Exhibits: Iowa Trolley Park houses various pieces of railroad memorabilia.

Train: Open and enclosed electric trolleys.

Schedule: Weekends and holidays; departures from Clear Lake at 12:30, 2:30 & 4:30 p.m.; departures from Mason City at 1:30 & 3:30 p.m. Special tours are offered during the week.

Fare: Adults $6.00, children (under 13) $3.50.

Trolleys: No. 1976, Brill open trolley; No. 727, former Chicago North Shore interurban, former Mason City & Clear Lake Electric Railroad; No. 102, sweeper car; No. 1146, PCC car, former San Francisco; 1929 Whitcomb gas switcher.

Passenger Cars: Trailer car No. 28, former New York & New Haven (to be restored).

Location: 3500 East Main Avenue, Clear Lake.

Contact: Jim Sundberg
Vice President of Marketing

Mailing Address:
P.O. Box 956
Mason City, IA 50401
Telephone: (515) 357-RIDE (7433)
J. Sundberg: (515) 423-3313

Iowa, Mt. Pleasant
D-R

MIDWEST CENTRAL RAILROAD
Steam, irregular
36" gauge

PAUL A. KNOWLES

Ride/Operation: A 1-mile steam train ride with two station stops, through the grounds of the Midwest Old Settlers & Threshers Reunion. The reunion, held August 31 to September 4, features a large display of steam-powered farm equipment, antique cars, and an old Midwest farm village. This year is the 35th anniversary of the MCRR, a nonprofit educational organization.

Displays/Exhibits: The world's largest steam show, featuring more than one hundred operating steam traction engines, dozens of models, antique tractors, cars, trucks, and all kinds of powerhouse and farm equipment.

Train: Three vintage locomotives; six wooden coaches; two cabooses.

Schedule: <u>August 31–September</u>, 8:30 a.m.-9:30 p.m.; during the reunion, rides operate on 10-minute schedules.

Fare: Adults $1.50, children $1.00. <u>Admission to grounds</u>: $7.00 one day; $10.00 for all five days.

Locomotives: No. 6, 1891 Baldwin 2-6-0, former Surry, Sussex & Southampton Railway, Dendron, Virginia; No. 9, 1923 Lima 3-truck Shay, former West Side Lumber Company; No. 16, 1951 Henschel 0-4-0ST, Kassel, West Germany.

Location: Southeast Iowa.

Mt. Pleasant

Mailing Address:
Box 102
Mt. Pleasant, IA 52641
Telephone: (319) 385-2912

103

MIDWEST ELECTRIC RAILWAY
Electric, irregular
Standard gauge

JIM ADAMS

Ride/Operation: Trolleys provide transportation to a 60-acre campground during the Midwest Old Settlers and Threshers Annual Reunion, held this year from August 31 to September 4. Noncamping visitors can ride from the exhibition grounds to Log Village and back on a 1 1/2-mile loop track. The MER, whose volunteers come from all over the nation, hauls more than 43,000 passengers during the reunion.

Displays/Exhibits: The annual reunion of the Midwest Old Settlers and Threshers Association includes more than 100 operating steam engines, tractors, gas engines, stationary steam engines, a large working craft show, early-day villages, and antiques on 160 acres of show ground. It is held for five days each year, ending on Labor Day.

Schedule: <u>Daily</u>, August 31-September 4, 7:00 a.m.-midnight, on a 3-minute headway. <u>Sundays</u>, May 22-August 28, 11:00 a.m.-4:00 p.m. <u>Group tours</u> can be arranged during the rest of the year.

Fare: <u>During reunion</u>: $1.00 round trip; multiride discount available. <u>Admission to the Old Threshers Reunion</u>: $7.00 for one day, $10.00 for five days; children (under 10) admitted free. <u>Multiple rides</u> for $1.00 on Sundays during the summer.

Locomotives/Trolleys: No. 1718, 1920 72-passenger open bench car & No. 1779, 1911 65-passenger open bench car, both former Rio de Janeiro; No. 9, 1915 combination car, former Southern Iowa; No. 320, 1914 Jewett Car Co. wooden interurban, former Chicago, Aurora & Elgin; No. 381, 1930 Waterloo, Cedar Falls & Northern Master Unit—the last streetcar to operate in regular service in Iowa; No. 4476, 1949 St. Louis Car Co.; Canadian Car Co. PCC, former Toronto Transit Commission; and Boston Transit Authority cars Nos. 3093 & 3226 (operated in multiple-unit service).

Special Events: <u>Fourth of July Celebration</u>.

Note: The railway is a volunteer subsidiary organization of the Midwest Old Settlers and Threshers Association, Inc.

Location: Intersection of U.S. highways 218 and 34, south on Walnut or Locust Streets to Threshers Road.

Mt. Pleasant

Contact: Lennis Moore

Mailing Address:
1887 Threshers Road
Mt. Pleasant, IA 52641
Telephone: (319) 385-8937

Iowa, Waverly
D-R

IOWA STAR CLIPPER DINNER TRAIN
Diesel, scheduled
Standard gauge

COURTESY OF *IOWA STAR CLIPPER* DINNER TRAIN

Ride/Operation: The *Iowa Star Clipper* Dinner Train has the distinction of being the first dinner train in the United States. The *Star Clipper* began operation in May 1985 and has been running year-round ever since. The train, which departs from the historic depot in Waverly, a quaint Midwestern town of 8,000, runs leisurely through the Iowa countryside along rolling hills, plains, and valleys. Each 3-hour dinner excursion includes elegant 4-course cuisine served by candlelight on fine china and linen. A variety of entertainment is featured throughout the year, such as musical reviews, murder mysteries, and piano playing.

Displays/Exhibits: Depot designated Waverly Visitor and Information Center. Brochure displays for Iowa attractions; decorative railroad paraphernalia.

Schedule: Year-round, 11:30 a.m. & 7:00 p.m.
Fare: $42.50 per person, plus state tax. Group rates available; call for information.
Locomotives: Nos. 407 & 416, F7 diesel-electrics.
Passenger Cars: Two 1950s Pullman passenger cars converted to 1950s-style dining cars; 1950s Pullman passenger car converted to full-service kitchen.
Special Events: Murder mysteries. Musical reviews. Events for children. Please call or write for more information.

Location: One mile east of Highway 218 and Highway 3 intersection, on Bremer Avenue (Main Street) and 4th Street.

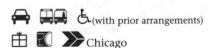 (with prior arrangements)

Chicago

Contact: Donna Saint Wendt
Sales Director

Mailing Address:
311 East Bremer Avenue
Waverly, IA 50677
(800) 525-4773
(319) 352-5467

105

ABILENE & SMOKY VALLEY RAILROAD
Diesel, scheduled
Standard gauge

COURTESY OF ABILENE & SMOKY VALLEY RAILROAD

Ride/Operation: A 10-mile, 1 1/2-hour round trip over former Chicago, Rock Island & Pacific track. Passengers can ride the train from Abilene, the premier "Cow Town," where longhorns first boarded Kansas Pacific cattle cars. The A&SV is located next to the Eisenhower Presidential Library, Museum, and Home and is adjacent to the Dickinson County Heritage Center, which includes the Museum of Independent Telephony, the operating 1900 C. W. Parker steam carousel, the Greyhound Hall of Fame, plus shops, art galleries, mansions, and restaurants.

Displays/Exhibits: No. 3415, 1921 Baldwin 4-6-2, and business car No. 5, 1891 Barney & Smith, both former Atchison, Topeka & Santa Fe; 1944 caboose, former Union Pacific; other interpretive material and equipment.

Train: No. 4, Alco S-1, former Hutchinson & Northern; No. 2002, 1903 wooden coach/ diner, former Missouri-Kansas-Texas; No. 381, 1942 Whitcomb 45-ton side-rod, former Ideal Cement; No. 6004, arch-windowed combine, former Rock Island; No. 466, caboose, former Union Pacific.

Schedule: Weekends, May and October; daily, June-August. Dinner train, weekends. Charter trips available. Please call or write for more information.

Fare/Admission: Adults $7.00, children $4.00.

Special Events: Chisholm Trail and Dickinson County Heritage Day, October 1.

Location: Off I-70 on South Buckeye Street (highway K15).

Contact: F. W. Schmidt
Vice President

Mailing Address:
P.O. Box 744
Abilene, KS 67410

Kansas, Baldwin City
D-R

MIDLAND RAILWAY
Diesel, scheduled
Standard gauge

E. N. GRIFFIN

Ride/Operation: This line was constructed in 1867 as the Leavenworth, Lawrence & Galveston, the first railroad south of the Kansas River. The Midland Railway, which began service in 1987 as Kansas's first excursion railway, is an intrastate common-carrier railroad. The 7-mile round trip to "Nowhere" passes through scenic eastern Kansas rolling farmland and woods and crosses a 250-foot wooden trestle.

Displays/Exhibits: Railroad equipment, photos, and memorabilia, including photographs of two U.S. presidents arriving in Baldwin.

Schedule: Weekends, May 20-October 29, 11:30 a.m., 2:00 & 3:00 p.m. (subject to change).

Fare: Adults $5.50, children (4-12) $2.50, children under 4 ride free. All-day fare, $8.00 (4 and older). Discounts for groups of 25 or more.

Locomotives: No. 524, 1946 EMD NW-2, former Chicago, Burlington & Quincy; No. 142, 1950/59 Alco/EMD RS-3, former Missouri-Kansas-Texas; No. 652, 1952 EMD E-8, former Chicago, Rock Island & Pacific; No. 460, 1942 44-ton General Electric, former Atchison, Topeka & Santa Fe; No. 8255, Alco RS-3, former New York Central.

Passenger Cars: Heavyweight coach No. 3106 & commuter coach No. 2507, former CRI&P; combine No. 441, former Chicago, St. Paul, Minneapolis & Omaha; steel caboose No. 32, former Northern Pacific; transfer caboose No. 55, former MKT.

Rolling Stock/Equipment: GE 20-ton boxcab diesel-electric; 2-8-2T No. 10, former Coos Bay; RPO No. 30, former Kansas City Railway; wood caboose, former CRI&P; others.

Special Events: Hobo Days, August 19-20. Maple Leaf Festival, October 21-22. Halloween Train, October 27-29.

Notes: The Midland Railway is a project of the Midland Railway Historical Association and the Santa Fe Trail Historical Society.

Location: About 30 miles southwest of Kansas City on U.S. 56 at the 1906 former AT&SF depot, 1515 High Street, 7 blocks west of downtown.

Lawrence

Radio Frequency: 161.055

Contact: Allen D. Maty
Manager of Passenger Traffic

Mailing Address:
P.O. Box 412
Baldwin City, KS 66006
Telephone:
Depot: (913) 594-6982
Kansas City area: (913) 371-3410

107

THE ELLIS RAILROAD MUSEUM
Railway museum

Ride/Operation: Opened in 1993 with two rooms of railroad memorabilia housed in a former Union Pacific depot, this museum has grown significantly. More display area has been added, and during the summer, a 1/3-scale replica of General Motors' *Aerotrain* streamliner provides rides on a 1-mile loop of track through the former railroad grounds.

Displays/Exhibits: Railroad memorabilia; replica depot office and waiting room; model-railroad display. Outside the museum is a restored former UP caboose.

Schedule: <u>Museum</u>: Monday-Saturday, 10:30 a.m.-5:00 p.m.; Sunday, 1:00-5:00 p.m. <u>Train</u>: May 1-September 4; Monday-Saturday, 10:30 a.m.-5:00 p.m.; Sunday, 1:00-5:00 p.m.

Fare/Admission: <u>Museum</u>: Adults $1.00, children (under 13) admitted free. <u>Train</u>: Adults $2.00, children (5-12) $1.00, children under 5 ride free if accompanied by an adult.

Special Events: <u>Railroad Day</u>, June 21.

Location: Eight blocks south of I-70 at 911 Washington Street.

Contact: Glen Keller
President

Mailing Address:
Box 82
Ellis, KS 67637
Telephone: (913) 726-4493
Fax: (913) 726-3294

Kentucky, Bardstown
D-R

MY OLD KENTUCKY DINNER TRAIN
Diesel, scheduled
Standard gauge

COURTESY OF MY OLD KENTUCKY DINNER TRAIN

Ride/Operation: A 2-hour, 35-mile round trip from Bardstown to Limestone Springs (near Clermont). The train travels over the historic Bardstown branch, which dates from 1854, making it one of the earliest branch lines of the Louisville & Nashville Railroad. Passengers board at the 1860 Bardstown depot, and the excursion takes them past two other original depots and across a historic wooden trestle.

Displays/Exhibits: The Bardstown depot, which has been refurbished to preserve its historical character, is the only known dry-laid limestone railroad station in Kentucky and is listed on the National Register of Historic Places.

Train: Steel-skirted Budd cars built in the late 1940s. Included in the consist is a former Pennsylvania Railroad sleeper car and a Chesapeake & Ohio private car that served the Eisenhower family on the president's funeral train. The kitchen car was used on the Santa Fe's *El Capitan*. In 1992, a day coach built for the PRR in 1946 was converted to a dining car and added to the train, bringing the total seating capacity to 176. All cars have been faithfully restored to their 1940s appearance.

Schedule: April-October: Tuesday-Sunday, lunch and dinner. November-March: Friday-Sunday. No trains on Thanksgiving or Christmas Day.

Fare: $51.95-$59.95; includes 4-course meal, fare, and tax. Charter, group, and youth rates available.

Locomotive: FP-7, former Norfolk Southern.

Special Events: New Year's Eve Excursion and Depot Party.

Note: Advance reservations suggested.

Location: On 31E (3rd Street). Accessible by I-65 via highway 245 or by the Bluegrass Parkway.

Contact: Ronald E. Boling
General Manager

Mailing Address:
P.O. Box 279
602 North Third Street
Bardstown, KY 40004
Telephone: (502) 348-7300

109

Kentucky, Covington
M-R

RAILWAY EXPOSITION COMPANY
Railway museum
Standard gauge

Ride/Operation: The Railway Exposition Company, a nonprofit organization founded in 1975, is dedicated to the preservation, restoration, and operation of historic rail equipment. Occasional motor-car rides are offered, as is an annual Christmas Train.

Displays/Exhibits: Four locomotives and fifty cars from various railroads and time periods. Included are a 1906 open-platform business car; a 1920s-era Pullman; a Railway Post Office; a dining car; a sleeper; a lounge car; the cab of a diesel locomotive; a mock-up of a steam locomotive cab; a Railway Express Agency truck; and many other items. A half-hour conducted tour takes visitors through ten cars and two locomotives.

Schedule: Weekends, May 1-October 31, 1:00-4:30 p.m. Tour lasts about 30 minutes.

Admission: Adults $3.00, children $2.00.

Locomotives: No. 332, 1947 Baldwin VO-1000 diesel, former Patapsco & Back River Railroad; an E-8A passenger diesel and an SW-1 diesel switcher, both former Pennsylvania Railroad; a 15-ton Brookville industrial locomotive.

Location: South of Cincinnati. Take I-75 south to exit 189A and travel east on route 1072 to Kentucky route 17. Travel north (left) on route 17 to the first traffic light; turn right onto Latonia Avenue; at the first stop sign, turn left onto West Southern Avenue and travel to the end of the street.

Contact: Bill Sprague
Vice President, Museum Operations

Mailing Address:
P.O. Box 15065
Covington, KY 41015-0065
Telephone: (606) 491-RAIL
(606) 655-5200

110

HARDIN SOUTHERN RAILROAD
Diesel, scheduled

HARDIN SOUTHERN RAILROAD

Ride/Operation: This line is a working common-carrier railroad offering seasonal *Nostalgia Train* passenger service for a 2-hour, 18-mile journey to the past. Built in 1890, the railroad was once a portion of the Nashville, Chattanooga & St. Louis Railway's Paducah main line through the Jackson Purchase in western Kentucky. Today's trip features the rural farms and lush forests of the Clarks River Valley.

Train: Historic first-generation diesel; open-window coaches.

Schedule: Weekends, May 1-October 31, midday & late afternoon.
Fare: Adults $9.75, children (3-12) $6.00. Tour, group, and charter rates available.
Locomotives: No. 863, 1940 Electro-Motive Corporation SW1, former Milwaukee Road; one of the oldest examples of this model still in common-carrier service.
Passenger Cars: Former main-line transcontinental equipment.
Special Events: Easter. Mother's Day. Halloween. Christmas.

Location: In western Kentucky, southeast of Paducah via I-24 and state route 641; six miles from the Tennessee Valley Authority's Land Between the Lakes national recreation area. Hardin is just east of the junction of state routes 641 and 80. The depot is in the center of town.

Fulton, Indiana

Contact: Karl R. Koenig
Vice-President & General Manager

Mailing Address:
P.O. Box 20
Hardin, KY 42048
Telephone: (502) 437-4555

KENTUCKY RAILWAY MUSEUM
Railway museum
Standard gauge

ELMER KAPPELL

Ride/Operation: Steam alternates weekends with diesel on a 20-mile, 1 1/2-hour round trip through scenic Rolling Fork River Valley, from nostalgic New Haven to Boston, Kentucky, over former Louisville & Nashville trackage initially constructed in 1857. Official Railway Museum of the Commonwealth of Kentucky, near Lincoln's birthplace and boyhood home in historic Nelson County.

Displays/Exhibits: More than 4,000 square feet of artifacts and memorabilia depicting Kentucky railroad history. Special programs for students. More than 60 pieces of equipment displayed, stored, or under restoration. The new museum building, under construction, will replicate the original New Haven depot.

Schedule: <u>Museum</u>: Daily, with special holiday hours (call for schedule). <u>Train</u>: Weekends, April, May & September-November; Tuesday-Sunday, June-August. <u>Groups and tours</u> by appointment. Call for complete schedule.

Fare/Admission: Please call or write for information.

Locomotives: No. 152, 1905 Rogers 4-6-2 No. 152, EMD E-3 No. 770 (first diesel for the *Pan-American*), and 1925 Alco 0-8-0 No. 2152, all former L&N; No. 32, 1948 EMD BL-2, former Monon; CF-7 No. 2546, former Santa Fe; 1952 Fairbanks-Morse, former USA No. 1846; No. 11, 1923 Vulcan 0-4-0T, former Louisville Cement; No. 2716, 1943 Alco 2-8-4, former C&O (stored off-site).

Passenger Cars: Former L&N and other open and closed window cars; diner "Kentucky Colonel," former Southern Pacific; Pullman solarium-lounge "Mt. Broderick"; 1910 Jackson & Sharp, "Itsuitsme," former Bangor & Aroostook No. 100.

Special Events: <u>Kentucky Homecoming Festival</u>, June 29-July 3. <u>Murder Mystery Weekend</u>, fall. <u>Rolling Fork Iron Horse Festival</u>, September 9. <u>Kentucky Bourbon Festival</u>, September 16.

<u>Halloween Trains</u>. <u>Christmas Trains</u>. <u>Civil War Train Robberies</u>, to be announced. Please call or write for specific information.

Location: Less than one hour south of Louisville on U.S. 31E; 20 minutes from I-65. Take exit 112 off I-65 to Bardstown, then U.S. 31E south.

Radio Frequency 160.545

Contact: Karl Lusk, Jr.

Mailing Address:
P.O. Box 240
New Haven, KY 40051-0240
Telephone: (502) 549-5470
(800) 272-0152

KENTUCKY CENTRAL RAILWAY
*Steam, scheduled
Standard gauge*

RUTH ANN COMBS

Ride/Operation: The Kentucky Central Railway is operated by the Kentucky Central Chapter of the National Railway Historical Society. Trips typically originate in Paris and run to Carlisle, Ewing, or Maysville. The 50-mile "Bluegrass Route," now operated by the Transkentucky Transportation Railroad, was part of the original Kentucky Central Railway, which later became part of the Louisville & Nashville Railroad. It passes through some of Kentucky's most beautiful horse farms and through two tunnels.

Schedule: Train: To be announced; please call for information. Museum: Most Sunday afternoons and by appointment.

Fare: Please call for information.

Locomotives: 1925 Baldwin 2-6-2, former Reader No. 11; No. 9, VO 100 Baldwin diesel, former LaSalle & Bureau County Railroad, former TransKentucky Transportation Railroad; 1951 SW-8, former U.S. Army.

Passenger Cars: Three coaches, former Erie Lackawanna; KCR No. 1, former Southern Railway concession/observation car.

Rolling Stock/Equipment: Bay-window caboose No. 225, former Southern Railway; caboose No. 904055, former Baltimore & Ohio.

Special Events: To be announced.

Location: U.S. 456 East (North Middletown Road).

Cincinnati, Ohio

Contact: Shirley Ross
Public Relations

Mailing Address:
1749 Bahama Road
Lexington, KY 40509
Telephone: (606) 293-0807

Kentucky, Stearns
R

BIG SOUTH FORK SCENIC RAILWAY
Diesel, scheduled

COURTESY OF BIG SOUTH FORK SCENIC RAILWAY

Ride/Operation: Passengers enjoy a narrated trip reminiscent of rail travel in the early 1900s as the Big South Fork Scenic takes them through the gorge area near Roaring Paunch Creek. The 3-hour trip features a 1 1/2-hour stop at the restored mining community of Blue Heron, where oral interpretations are offered.

Displays/Exhibits: Interpretive exhibits at the Blue Heron Mining Community tell the stories of miners and their families living and working in the mining camp.

Schedule: April, May & September; Wednesday-Friday, 11:00 a.m.; weekends, 11:00 a.m. & 3:00 p.m. June-August & October; Monday-Friday, 11:00 a.m.; weekends, 11:00 a.m. & 3:00 p.m.

Fare: Adults $9.50, senior citizens $9.00, children (3-12) $4.95, children under 3 ride free.

Locomotives: 1942 Alco.

Passenger Cars: Covered flatcars.

Contact: Vicki Kidd

Mailing Address:
P.O. Box 368
Stearns, KY 42647
Telephone: (800) 462-5664

114

BLUEGRASS RAILROAD MUSEUM
Diesel, scheduled
Standard gauge

COURTESY OF BLUEGRASS RAILROAD MUSEUM

Ride/Operation: This museum, founded in 1976, offers a 1 1/2 hour, 11 1/2-mile round trip through Kentucky's famed horse country, including a stop to view the Kentucky River Palisades and the 104-year-old Louisville Southern Railroad "Young's High Bridge," 281 feet high and 1,659 feet long.

Displays/Exhibits: Limestone sills from the Lexington & Ohio Railroad, built 1831-35; air-conditioned display car with railroad artifacts; diner "Duncan Tavern," baggage express car and caboose, all former Louisville & Nashville; baggage car, former Southern Railway.

Train: 1931 Pullman Standard commuter coaches, former New Jersey Central.

Schedule: Weekends, early May-late October; Saturdays, 10:30a.m., 1:30 & 3:30p.m.; Sundays, 1:30 & 3:30p.m.

Fare: Adults $7.00, senior citizens (62+) $6.00, children (2-12) $4.00; children under 2 not occupying a seat ride free. Additional fare possible for some special events.

Locomotives: Nos. 2042 & 2086, 1953 Alco MRS-1s, and No. 1849, Fairbanks-Morse H12-44, all former U.S. Army.

Special Events: Halloween Ghost Train. Santa Express. Train robberies. Hobo Days. Clown Days. Please send SASE for complete listing.

Location: Woodford County Park, U.S. 62 (Tyrone Pike).

(nearby)

Radio Frequency: 160.275

Contact: Don Scalf

Mailing Address:
P.O. Box 27
Versailles, KY 40383
Telephone: (606) 873-2476

DEQUINCY RAILROAD MUSEUM
Railway museum

DEQUINCY RAILROAD MUEUM

Ride/Operation: Nestled among tall pines at the beginning of Louisiana's foothills in north Calcasieu County, the city of DeQuincy was at the intersection of two major railroads in 1895. Its turn-of-the-century beginnings have been preserved, including two major historical landmarks—the All Saints Episcopal Church and the Kansas City Southern Railroad Depot. Both structures are on the National Register of Historic Places, and the depot now houses the railroad museum.

Displays/Exhibits: 1913 steam locomotive; vintage caboose; passenger coach; a host of railroad artifacts.

Schedule: Monday-Friday, 8:00 a.m.-4:00 p.m.; weekends, 1:00-4:00 p.m.
Admission: No charge; donations welcomed.
Special Events: State-approved Railroad Days Festival, second weekend in April.

Location: At the intersection of state routes 12 and 27; 20 miles north of Lake Charles, Louisiana, 47 miles east of Beaumont, Texas, and 130 miles west of Baton Rouge, Louisiana.

Lake Charles

Contact: Mrs. Fred B. Fluitt, Jr.
Treasurer

Mailing Address:
P.O. Box 997
DeQuincy, LA 70633
Telephone: (318) 786-2823
(318) 786-7113

BOOTHBAY RAILWAY VILLAGE
Steam, scheduled
24" gauge

GEORGE A. FORERO, JR

Ride/Operation: A 1.5-mile, 15-minute trip through woods and a covered bridge and past many railroad structures. The railroad is reminiscent of the many 2-foot-gauge lines that formerly ran in Maine.

Displays/Exhibits: The 8-acre village complex includes two restored railroad stations, an 1847 town hall, an exceptional display of more than 55 antique vehicles, a schoolhouse, and 26 other buildings.

Train: Closed coach; open coach; caboose.

Schedule: Daily, June 10-October 8, 9:30 a.m.-5:00 p.m., every half hour. Also May 27-29.

Fare: Adults $6.00, children $3.00, children under 2 ride free. Group rates available.

Locomotives: No. 12313, 1913 Henschel 0-4-0T, former city of Hamburg; No. 22486, 1934 Henschel 0-4-0T; No. 24022, 1938 Henschel 0-4-0T; No. 24023, 1938 Henschel 0-4-0T; No. 14283, Baldwin 0-4-0ST; No. 14522, Baldwin 0-4-0ST; Plymouth 0-4-0; Ford Model T inspection car.

Rolling Stock/Equipment: Two-foot-gauge equipment includes 1908 Sandy River & Rangeley Lakes combination car No. 11 (former Franklin & Megantic No. 1); SR&RL boxcar No. 147; Wiscasset & Quebec boxcar No. 312; Wiscasset, Waterville & Farmington handcar; dump cars; and flatcars. Standard-gauge equipment includes cabooses Nos. 563 & 653, both former Maine Central; a circa 1920 Fairmont railcar; a "40 & 8" car, built in 1885; and a velocipede.

Special Events: Father's Day Special, June 18. Antique Engine Meet, July 1-2. 30th Annual Antique Auto Days, July 15-16. Annual Rotary Club

Auction & Lobster Bake, August 5. Children's Day, August 20. Maine Narrow-Gauge Railroad Day, September 17. Fall Foliage Festival, October 7-8. Ghost Train, October 27-28 (5:00-8:00 p.m.).

Location: On state route 27, eight miles from U.S. route 1.

Contact: Robert Ryan
Director

Mailing Address:
P.O. Box 123
Boothbay, ME 04537
Telephone: (207) 633-4727

SEASHORE TROLLEY MUSEUM
Electric, scheduled
Standard gauge

CHARLES WOOLNOUGH

Ride/Operation: A 3 3/4-mile round trip takes passengers over the former Atlantic Shore Line interurban right-of-way, where they can experience the trolley era through the "National Collection" spanning a century of mass-transit vehicles. Visitors can also learn to operate a trolley in the museum's "Be a Motorman" program; please call or write for details.

Displays/Exhibits: Visitors can tour the huge exhibit barn, filled with restored trolleys from Boston to Budapest, New York to Nagasaki, and Sydney to San Francisco. A fascinating part of the visit is the world-famous Town House Restoration Shop, where "junk" is turned into gems. Also, visitors can see the trolley station that traveled by sea—the Victorian copper-clad Northampton Station from Boston's elevated railway—and many other artifacts of our history.

Schedule: Times indicated are: opening time/time of last ride. May 1-26: weekdays, 12:00/1:30 p.m.; weekends, 11:00 a.m./3:30 p.m. May 30-June 30: weekdays, 11:00 a.m./3:30 p.m.; weekends, 11:00 a.m./4:30 p.m. July 1-September 4: daily, 10:00 a.m./5:30 p.m. September 5-October 15: weekdays, 10:00 a.m./3:30 p.m.; weekends, 10:00 a.m./4:30 p.m. October 16-November 12: weekends, 11:00 a.m./3:00 p.m. Other times by appointment.

Admission: July 1-September 4: Adults $8.00, senior citizens $5.00, children (6-16) $4.00, family pass $25.00. September 5-June 30: Adults $7.00, senior citizens $6.00, children (6-16) $4.50, family pass $22.00.

Locomotives/Trolleys: More than 200 pieces from the United States, Canada, Australia, Japan, Germany, Hungary, Italy, England, and New Zealand: horse cars, city cars, buses, interurbans, rapid-transit cars, work equipment, trackless trolleys, locomotives, and freight cars.

Special Events: Kids' Days, May 6 & 20, June 3 & 11. Mother's Day Special, May 14. Annual Meeting, May 27. Father's Day Special, June 18. Trolley Parades, July 1, August 5, September 2 & October 7. Moxie Day, July 9. Maine Antique

Power Days, July 15-16. Cajun Fest, August 5. Old Tyme Family Circus, mid August. Open House, October 7-8. Ghost Trolley, October 20-21 & 27-28. Christmas Prelude, December 2-3 & 9-10.

Location: 195 Log Cabin Road; 1.5 miles off U.S. Route 1, 3 miles north of Kennebunkport, and 20 miles south of Portland. Short distance from exits 3 and 4 of the Maine Turnpike.

Contact: Donald Curry
Director

Mailing Address:
P.O. Box A
Kennebunkport, ME 04046-1690
Telephone: (207) 967-2800

MAINE NARROW GAUGE RAILROAD COMPANY AND MUSEUM

Steam, diesel, scheduled
24" gauge

ANDY BAKER

Ride/Operation: A two-foot-gauge train takes passengers on a 1-mile round trip along Casco Bay.

Displays/Exhibits: Former Sandy River & Rangeley Lakes parlor car No. 9; former Wiscasset & Quebec No. 3, built in 1884; former SR&RL combine and caboose; historic coaches, former B&SR; other rolling stock; antique freight-hauling trucks; railroad artifacts and photos.

Train: Steam- or diesel-powered passenger trains.

Schedule: <u>Daily</u> beginning May 15.

Fare/Admission: <u>Train</u>: Adults $3.00, children $2.00. <u>Museum</u>: Adults $2.00, children $1.00. <u>Fares subject to change</u> as .8-mile track extension is placed in service.

Locomotives: No. 3, 1913 Vulcan 0-4-4T, and No. 4, 1918 Vulcan 0-4-4T, former Monson; No. 8, 1924 Baldwin 2-4-4RT; No. 1, 1949 General Electric B-B diesel, former B&SR.

Passenger Cars: Circa 1890 coaches Nos. 4, 19 & 20 and combine No. 14, former SR&RL; coaches Nos. 15, 16 & 18, former B&SR; replica coaches, former Edaville; excursion cars.

Rolling Stock/Equipment: Railbus No. 4 and cabooses Nos. 551, 553 & 557, former SR&RL; Model T track car, former B&SR; tank cars Nos. 21 & 22; flanger No. 40; snowplow No. 2; boxcars.

Special Events: <u>Railfair 95</u>, Father's Day weekend.

Note: The museum offers special limited-edition Maine narrow-gauge prints by renowned artist C. W. "Gus" Swanberg.

Location: 58 Fore Street.

Contact: J. Emmons Lancaster
Superintendent

Mailing Address:
58 Fore Street
Portland, ME 04101
Telephone: (207) 828-0814

MAINE COAST RAILROAD
Diesel, scheduled
Standard gauge

COURTESY OF MAINE COAST RAILROAD

Ride/Operation: Passengers board at the historic Wiscasset waterfront for a 14-mile, 1 1/2-hour round trip along scenic trackage over wildlife marshes and tidal rivers. The line also offers "Rail & Sail," a combination train ride and 1 1/4-hour boat trip (weather permitting), where passengers board the *Henrietta* to learn how lobster traps are hauled and watch the seals and shore birds along the beautiful Sheepscot River. Lunch and beverages are available on board.

Train: Open-window coaches, former Delaware & Lackawanna and Central New Jersey.

Schedule: May 27-June 25 and September 9-October 21: Weekends and holidays. June 26-September 4: Daily. Train leaves at 11:00 a.m. & 1:00 p.m from Wiscasset and at 11:40 a.m. from Newcastle; boat leaves at 11:30 a.m., 1:30 & 3:00 p.m.

Fare: Rail & Sail: Adults $16.00, senior citizens $14.00, children $8.00, family fare (2 adults and up to 4 children) $40.00, children under 5 ride free if not occupying a seat. Train or boat only: Adults $10.00, senior citizens $9.00, children $5.00, family fare (2 adults and up to 4 children) $25.00, children under 5 ride free if not occupying a seat.

Locomotives: Alco S-1 No. 958, former Maine Central; Alco RS-11 No. 367, former Norfolk & Western, former Central Vermont; Alco RS-1 No. 46, former Washington Terminal.

Special Events: Railfans' Day, June. Bath Heritage Days, Schooner Days, BNAS Air Show, Richmond Days, July. Rockland Lobster Festival, August. Fall Foliage Tours, September & October. Halloween Phantom Express, October. Santa Train, November. Reindeer Express, December.

Note: The railroad's 1921 Rockland turntable and enginehouse (former Maine Central), used for freight operations, is on the National Register of Historic Places.

Location: U.S. Route 1, Wiscasset, 45 miles north of Portland.

Contact: Debbie Hays
Office Manager

Mailing Address:
P.O. Box 614
Wiscasset, ME 04578
Telephone: (800) 795-5404
(207) 882-8000

THE B&O RAILROAD MUSEUM
Railway museum
Standard gauge

COURTESY OF THE B&O RAILROAD MUSEUM

Ride/Operation: The B&O Railroad Museum's collection of locomotives, cars, artifacts, and archives originated as an exhibit at the 1893 Columbian Exposition in Chicago. With additional pieces, the collection was opened to the public in 1953 at Mt. Clare, the site from which the nation's first main-line railroad began building west in 1828. The museum underwent a substantial renovation in the 1970s and now operates as a tax-exempt educational foundation. Excursion trains depart Mt. Clare Station each Saturday and Sunday for a 2-mile round trip over the first main line in America.

Displays/Exhibits: A variety of equipment and interpretive exhibits, model railroads, toy-train exhibits, and railroad artifacts. Buildings include the 1851 Mt. Clare Station, the 1884 Annex Building, the 1884 covered passenger-car roundhouse, and a large 1870 car shop currently used for equipment storage.

Schedule: Daily, 10:00 a.m.-5:00 p.m. Open all holidays except Thanksgiving and Christmas.

Fare/Admission: Museum: adults $6.00, senior citizens $5.00, students (5-12) $3.00, children under 5 admitted free. Train: additional $2.00 (children under 4 ride free). Group rates available; call 752-2463.

Locomotives: Two replicas of early nineteenth-century locomotives; 9 original nineteenth-century locomotives; 12 twentieth-century steam locomotives; 14 diesel-electric locomotives; 3 electric locomotives; 2 electric m-u cars; RDC; locomotive crane; diesel tractor switcher; Vanderbilt tender.

Passenger Cars: The oldest passenger car in North America; 5 nineteenth-century cars; 15 additional passenger cars representing all significant twentieth-century types.

Rolling Stock/Equipment: Cabooses; wide variety of historic freight cars; work equipment; giant Pennsylvania Railroad 200-ton steam wreck crane; special cars such as a molten steel car and dynamometer car.

Special Events: Four all-day excursions. Membership program. Volunteer program. Museum rentals. Dining car rentals.

Location: Pratt and Poppleton Streets, 10 blocks west of the Inner Harbor.

Baltimore

Contact: Nancy Fields
Marketing Director

Mailing Address:
901 West Pratt Street
Baltimore, MD 21223-2699
Telephone: (410) 752-2464
Main Line: (410) 752-2490

BALTIMORE STREETCAR MUSEUM
Electric, scheduled
5' 4 1/2" gauge

ANDREW S. BLUMBERG

Ride/Operation: A streetcar leaves the visitors' center every fifteen minutes for a 1 1/4-mile round trip alongside Falls Road.

Displays/Exhibits: In a modern carhouse are 13 cars (11 electric and 2 horse-drawn) tracing street-rail transit in the city of Baltimore from 1859 to 1963; tours are available. The visitors' center contains displays and a video presentation.

Schedule: Weekends, June 1-October 31; Sundays, November 1-May 31; also May 29, July 4 & September 4; 12:00-5:00 p.m. Groups at these and other times by prior arrangement.

Admission: Adults $4.00, senior citizens (65+) and children (4-11) $2.00, maximum family charge $12.00.

Trolleys: No. 554, 1896 single-truck summer car, No. 1050, 1898 single-truck closed car & No. 264, 1900 convertible car, all Brownell Car Co.; No. 1164, 1902 double-truck summer car, No. 3828, 1902 double-truck closed car & No. 6119, 1930 Peter Witt car, all J.G. Brill Co.; No. 7407, 1944 Pullman-Standard PCC car.

Special Events: Mother's Day. Father's Day. Grandparents' Day. Museum Birthday Celebration, usually first Sunday in July. Antique Auto Meets, three times a year. Dixieland Concert, July or August. Phantom Trolley, Halloween. Holly Trolley, Christmas. Please call or write for a complete listing.

Location: Former Maryland & Pennsylvania Railroad terminal at 1901 Falls Road, three to four blocks from Amtrak station (Penn Station).

Baltimore

Contact: Andrew S. Blumberg
Director of Public Affairs

Mailing Address:
P.O. Box 4881
Baltimore, MD 21211
Telephone: (410) 547-0264

Maryland, Chesapeake Beach
M

CHESAPEAKE BEACH
RAILWAY MUSEUM
Railway museum
Standard gauge

COURTESY OF CHESAPEAKE BEACH RAILWAY MUSEUM

Displays/Exhibits: This museum preserves and interprets the history of the Chesapeake Beach Railroad. The CBR, which was built by a group of Colorado financiers and railroad builders that included Otto Mears and David Moffat, brought people from Washington, D.C., to the resorts of Chesapeake Beach and North Beach from 1900 until 1935. Housed in an 1898 CBR station, the museum contains photographs and artifacts from the days of the railroad and the resort, including photos of the steamships that brought visitors by water and the early amusements on the boardwalk.

Schedule: Daily, May 1-September 30, 1:00-4:00 p.m. Weekends, April & October, 1:00-4:00 p.m. By appointment at all other times.

Admission: No charge.

Passenger Cars: The Chesapeake Beach Railroad car "Dolores," the last known surviving piece of CBR rolling stock, is under restoration by museum staff and volunteers.

Special Events: Antique Car Show & Founders Day, May 21. Concerts, second Thursday evening of June, July & August; please call or write for details. Children's Railroad History Program, Thursdays, 10:00 a.m., mid-June to mid-August.

Location: Chesapeake Beach (Calvert County).

Contact: Harriet M. Stout
Curator
or Bernard Loveless

Mailing Address:
P.O. Box 783
Chesapeake Beach, MD 20732
Telephone: (301) 257-3892

123

TIM WILSON

WESTERN MARYLAND
SCENIC RAILROAD
Diesel, scheduled
Standard gauge

Ride/Operation: A 32-mile, 3-hour round trip over tracks of the former Western Maryland Railway and Cumberland & Pennsylvania Railroad, including a 1 1/2-hour layover at Frostburg, the site of The Old Depot restaurant, the Depot Center Shops, a carriage museum, and an active turntable. The route passes through the Cumberland Narrows, traverses the famous Helmstetter's Horseshoe Curve, includes a tunnel, climbs 1,300 feet, and has spectacular mountain scenery. Trains depart from downtown Cumberland's Western Maryland Station Center, which houses the Transportation and Industrial Museum, the Allegany Arts Council Gallery, the Western Maryland gift shop, the Allegany County Tourism Information Office, the Western Maryland Chapter of the National Railway Historical Society, and a National Park Service Chesapeake & Ohio Canal Visitors Center. The western terminus of the C&O Canal is adjacent to the station.

Schedule: May-September, Tuesday-Sunday, 11:30 a.m. October, Tuesday-Sunday, 10:45 a.m. & 3:30 p.m. November-December, weekends, 11:30 a.m.

Fare: May-September & November: Adults $13.75, senior citizens (60+) $12.25, children (2-12) $8.50. October: Adults $15.75, senior citizens (60+) $15.25, children $9.50. Children under 2 not occupying a seat ride free. Call for reservations, group rates, and charters.

Special Events: Mother's Day, May 14. Murder Mysteries, May 27, July 15, September 9 & October 28. Train Raid, June 10-11. Father's Day, June 19. Halloween Trains, October 28 (adults) & 29 (children). Santa's Express, November 25-26 and December 2-3 & 9-10.

Location: Take exit 43-C off I-68 (downtown Cumberland); follow signs to Tourist Information.

Cumberland

Contact: Ed Kemmet
General Manager

Mailing Address:
13 Canal Street
Cumberland, MD 21502
Telephone: 1-800-TRAIN-50
Local: (301) 759-4400

THE ELLICOTT CITY B&O RAILROAD STATION MUSEUM
Railway museum

COURTESY OF THE ELLICOTT CITY B&O RAILROAD STATION MUSEUM

Displays/Exhibits: Built in 1831, this stone station is the oldest surviving railroad station in America and is a registered National Historic Landmark. Visitors may tour the restored building and see many railroad displays. An HO-gauge model-railroad layout of the 13 miles from Baltimore to Ellicott City is housed in the restored 1885 freight house.

Schedule: Changes seasonally. Please call or write for current information.

Admission: Adults $3.00, senior citizens $2.00, children (5-12) $1.00, children under 5 admitted free. Group rates available.

Special Events: Please call or write for schedule.

Location: At Maryland Avenue and Main Street in Ellicott City. Take exit 13 via Catonsville off the Baltimore Beltway (I-695) and travel west 4 1/2 miles.

Contact: Ed Williams
Director

Mailing Address:
2711 Maryland Avenue
Ellicott City, MD 21043
Telephone: (410) 461-1944

GAITHERSBURG RAILWAY MUSEUM
Railway museum

GERALD A. HOTT

Displays/Exhibits: The city of Gaithersburg purchased and renovated its former Baltimore & Ohio Railroad brick passenger station and freight house, and the Potomac Chapter of the National Railway Historical Society and other volunteers have helped to gather and renovate a steam locomotive and various pieces of rolling stock. Displays include a highly detailed, operating HO-gauge model-railroad display originally constructed for the National Geographic Society in 1989 by the Gaithersburg Model Railroad Society; large photographs of Buffalo Creek & Gauley steam locomotive No. 14 in service in West Virginia; and many color photographs of scenes along the Baltimore & Ohio Railroad and Western Maryland Railway.

Schedule: January-October, second and fourth Saturdays of each month, 10:00 a.m.-2:00 p.m. Special hours in November and December.

Admission: Free. Outside exhibits available at all times.

Locomotives: Buffalo Creek & Gauley 2-8-0 No. 14, built by Alco (Schenectady) in 1918. Cosmetically restored.

Passenger Cars: Southern Railway Post Office No. 36, 1920s Pullman; Defense Transportation Corps. troop kitchen car, 1940s American Car & Foundry (under restoration).

Rolling Stock/Equipment: Steel bay-window wagon-top caboose, built by the B&O at Keyser, West Virginia, in 1942; Norfolk & Western type C-31 steel cupola caboose, built in 1968 (being restored to its original blue paint scheme).

Special Events: Gaithersburg Olde Towne Day, third Sunday in September. Retired Railway Post Office employees and special postal cancellations in the RPO car. Miniature live-steam train rides for children. Other special railroad displays and equipment.

Location: Summit and Diamond Avenues in Olde Towne, Gaithersburg, three blocks from Maryland route 355.

Rockville

Contact: Gerald A. Hott
Volunteer Coordinator

Mailing Address:
Gaithersburg Dept. of
Parks & Recreation
502 South Frederick Avenue
Gaithersburg, MD 20877
City of Gaithersburg: (301) 258-6355
Museum Volunteers: (301) 926-4660

THE ENTER*TRAIN*MENT LINE
Diesel, scheduled
Standard gauge

STEWART RHINE

Ride/Operation: The Enter*train*ment Line is a year-round casual luncheon- and dinner-buffet train that operates over the former main line of the Western Maryland Railway. The Catoctin Mountain Limited, a 50-mile, 3-hour round trip from Union Bridge, Maryland, to Blue Ridge Summit, Pennsylvania, offers three classes of service: traditional excursion; lunch or dinner buffet, an all-you-can-eat buffet with dessert bar and open bar; and luxury, in which meals and beverages are served in the opulent splendor of a private railroad car (minimum party of eight). Romance on the Rails, a 50-mile, 3-hour round trip from Westminster to Thurmont, Maryland, is a romantic train ride restricted to adults over 21 years old, featuring a casual dinner buffet, complimentary beverages, dancing, and a disc jockey playing requests in the dance car. Each scenic trip features mountain grades and panoramas, rushing streams, high bridges, pastoral vistas, historic farms, and a horseshoe curve.

Schedule: Advance reservations required. Catoctin Mountain Limited: Sundays and selected Saturdays & weekdays, 1:00 p.m. Romance on the Rails: Fridays, 8:00 p.m.; Saturdays, 7:00 p.m.

Fare: Coach: adults $19.20, children (under 12) $11.00. Romance on the Rails: adults $41.00-$45.00. Scenic rides: Adults $41.00-$45.00, children $16.75. Luxury class: $52.00. 1 1/2-hour round trips: adults $13.75. Children's specials: $7.15. Tour bus and special charter rates available. Senior citizens' and group discounts available.

Special Events: Murder Mystery specials operate several times each month; adults only, $49.95-$54.95. Matinee Mystery: adults $45.95, children $20.95.

Notes: Call for current fares, schedules, and departure locations.

Locations: North Main Street Station, Union Bridge; Railroad Avenue near Main Street in downtown Westminster.

Contact: Jerry Pilcher
Vice President, Marketing

Mailing Address:
P.O. Box 478
Union Bridge, MD 21791
Telephone: (800) 553-3115
Baltimore area: (410) 775-8724

NATIONAL CAPITAL TROLLEY MUSEUM
Electric, scheduled
Standard gauge

PAM MCCOMB

Ride/Operation: A 1 3/4-mile, 20-minute round trip in Northwest Branch Park on cars selected from the museum's collection of 15 streetcars. Passengers board the trolleys at the Visitors' Center Station.

Displays/Exhibits: *Washington Trolleys: Rediscovered,* a 10-minute slide show; an operating O-gauge streetcar layout; *Radio Theatre,* recalling Glen Echo Amusement Park; displays interpreting streetcar and interurban systems of the national capital region; architecture reminiscent of the turn of the century.

Schedule: Weekends, January 2-November 30, plus Memorial Day, July 4 & Labor Day, 12:00-5:00 p.m. Wednesdays, July 1-August 31, 11:00 a.m.-3:00 p.m. Also December 2-3, 9-10, 16-17, 23 & 30, 5:00-9:00 p.m. Selected school days; please call or write.

Fare: Adults $2.00, children (2-17) $1.50, children under 2 and those presenting valid membership cards from the Association of Railway Museums, the National Railway Historical Society, or the Railroaders' Enthusiasts ride free.

Trolleys: No. 678, New York City; No. 352, Johnstown; No. 120, Graz, Austria; No. 955, Dusseldorf, Germany; No. 5954, Berlin, Germany; No. 6062 with trailer No. 7802, Vienna, Austria; Nos. 766, 1053, 1101 & 1540, Washington, D.C.

Rolling Stock/Equipment: Sweepers Nos. 07 & 51 and work cars Nos. 0509 & 0522, former Washington, D.C.

Special Events: Cabin Fever Day, February. Snow Sweeper Day, March. Trolley Car Spectacular, April 23. Antique Auto Gathering, July 9. Fall Open House, October 15. Holly Trolleyfest, December.

Notes: Bus service on route C-8 from Twinbrook Station is available Saturdays from 12:00 to 5:00 p.m.

Location: On Bonifant Road between Layhill Road (Maryland route 182) and New Hampshire Avenue (Maryland route 650), north of Wheaton.

Washington

Contact: Kenneth Rucker
Curator

Mailing Address:
P.O. Box 4007
Silver Spring, MD 20914
Telephone: (301) 384-6088

WALKER TRANSPORTATION COLLECTION
BEVERLY HISTORICAL SOCIETY
& MUSEUM

WALKER TRANSPORTATION COLLECTION

Railway museum

Displays/Exhibits: The Walker Transportation Collection has been preserving items of New England railroading since 1969. Thousands of photographs and color slides, as well as a complete library, motion pictures, videotapes, and recordings, are available to researchers; copies of photos can be obtained at a reasonable charge. The collection also contains material on street railways, coastal and lake shipping, aviation, industrial and firefighting equipment, and the great hotels and resorts where travelers of yesteryear spent their vacations. Rotating displays of transportation artifacts and models are featured, as are periodic exhibits of various transportation modes relating to New England.

Schedule: Wednesdays, 7:00-10:00 p.m. Other times by appointment.

Admission: Adults $2.00, children (under 16) $1.00.

Location: 117 Cabot Street.

    (partially)

Contact: Richard W. Symmes
Curator

Mailing Address:
117 Cabot Street
Beverly, MA 01915
Telephone: (508) 922-1186

OLD COLONY & FALL RIVER RAILROAD MUSEUM

Railway museum
Standard gauge

DAVID SOUZA

Displays/Exhibits: The museum, located in railroad cars that include a renovated former Pennsylvania Railroad coach, features artifacts of the Old Colony, New Haven, and Penn Central railroads, Conrail, and other New England lines. Also on display is New Haven rail diesel car No. 42, "Firestone"; New Haven boxcar No. 33401, which houses a video theater and displays; and caboose No. 21052.

Schedule: Weekends, April 22-June 18 & September 9-December 2, 9:00 a.m.-4:00 p.m. Daily, June 24-September 4; Sunday-Friday, 12:00-5:00 p.m.; Saturday, 10:00 a.m.-5:00 p.m.

Admission: Adults $1.50, children (5-12) $.75, children under 5 admitted free.

Special Events: Annual Railroad Show, third weekend in January. Fall River Celebrates America, mid-August waterfront celebration with craft fair, exhibits, Tall Ships, Conrail exhibit, fireworks, and more.

Notes: Battleship Cove, which houses the *U.S.S. Massachusetts* and other warships, is directly across the street from the railroad museum. Also within walking distance is Heritage State Park (with picnic area and boat rides), the Marine Museum at Fall River with a large *Titanic* display, the Fall River carousel, and the Tall Ship *H.M.S. Bounty*.

Location: The museum is located in a railroad yard at the corner of Central and Water streets, across from the entrance to Battleship Cove.

♿ (ramp to car but small door clearance)

🚶 (walking distance)

📱 🚗 🚌 🎁 ✉ 🚂 🔺

Contact: Jay K. Chatterton
Curator

Mailing Address:
P.O. Box 3455
Fall River, MA 02722
Telephone: (508) 674-9340

BERKSHIRE SCENIC RAILWAY
Diesel, scheduled
Standard gauge

JOHN STABER

Ride/Operation: Fifteen-minute Short Shuttle train ride within Lenox station yard, with narrative of Berkshire railroading and Lenox station history. Locomotive cab tours for youngsters. The museum is in the restored Lenox station.

Displays/Exhibits: Restored former New York, New Haven & Hartford NE-5 caboose; Fairmont speeder and track-gang train; displays about Berkshire railroading history; railroad videos; two model railroads.

Train: Fifty-ton General Electric; one former Erie-Lackawanna coach.

Schedule: Weekends & holidays, May 27-October 29; every half hour, 10:00a.m.-4:00p.m.

Fare/Admission: Train ride: adults $1.50, children $1.00. Museum admission: no charge.

Locomotives: No. 67, 1957 50-ton General Electric, former United Illuminating; No. 8619, 1953 EMD SW-8, former New York Central; No. 954, Alco S-1, former Maine Central.

Special Events: Santa runs, December 9-10 & 16-17.

Location: At the foot of Housatonic Street, east off U.S. route 20; five miles north of exit 2 (Lee) of Massachusetts Turnpike.

 TRAIN

Pittsfield

Mailing Address:
P.O. Box 2195
Lenox, MA 01240
Telephone: (413) 637-2210

LOWELL NATIONAL HISTORICAL PARK
Electric, scheduled
Standard gauge

GEORGE A. FORERO, JR.

Ride/Operation: Lowell National Historical Park, established in 1978 as part of the National Park Service, U.S. Department of the Interior, encompasses a canal system, restored mill buildings, and nineteenth-century commercial buildings. Two circa 1901 open-air trolleys, Nos. 1601 and 1602, and one circa 1919 closed car, No. 4131, provide transportation through this historic mill town.

Displays/Exhibits: A display in former Boston & Maine combine/tool car No. M3031, staffed by the Boston & Maine Railroad Historical Society, will be open periodically in 1995. Former B&M 0-6-0 No. 410, a restored 1911 Manchester Locomotive Works G-11, is displayed next to the tool car.

Schedule: Changes seasonally. The trolley operates daily, March through November; the combine exhibit has infrequent hours.

Fare/Admission: No charge for these items, although a fee is charged for other tours and museums affiliated with the National Park Service.

Locomotives/Trolleys: Two circa 1901 open-air trolleys; one circa 1919 closed trolley; 1911 0-6-0, former Boston & Maine.

Rolling Stock/Equipment: Combine/tool car, built in 1907 by Pullman as a 72-passenger open-platform coach, remodeled in 1946.

Special Events: The combine is usually staffed by the B&M Railroad Historical Society during the Lowell Folk Festival (last full weekend in July). Trolleys are used for special events.

Boston

Mailing Address:
169 Merrimack Street
Lowell, MA 01852
Telephone: (508) 970-5000

ADRIAN & BLISSFIELD RAILROAD
Diesel, scheduled
Standard gauge

COURTESY OF ADRIAN & BLISSFIELD RAIL ROAD

Ride/Operation: This working, common-carrier freight and passenger railroad offers 14-mile, 1 1/2-hour round trips from Blissfield to Lenawee Junction over a former New York Central line—the first railroad built west of the Allegheny Mountains and the oldest in the former Northwest Territory. The train travels through the village of Blissfield, crosses the River Raisin, and runs through Lenawee County farmland to Lenawee Junction. The "Old Road Dinner Train" is a 2- to 3-hour round trip featuring traditional, impeccable dining-car service including an elegant four-course dinner. Murder mystery dinner train service is also available.

Train: Open-window coaches and dining cars built in the 1930s, 1940s, and 1950s.

Schedule: Excursion train: May-June & September-October, weekends; July & August, Tuesday, Thursday & weekends; 2:00 p.m. Dinner train: Schedule varies; call for information.

Fare: Adults $7.50, senior citizens $6.50, children (3-12) $4.50, children under 3 ride free. Group rates and charters available. Additional fare for dinner train.

Locomotives: Nos. 1751 & 1752, 1957 EMD GP-9s, former Grand Trunk Western/Central Vermont. No. 1752, painted as a "Lionel Lines" prototype, is the world's only full-sized Lionel locomotive.

Passenger Cars: No. 5197, 1937 *Canadian Flyer* coach, former Canadian National; No. 721; No. 3370, 1949 diner, former Union Pacific.

Special Events: School field trips. Fall color tours. Ghost Train. Santa Train. Winter Snow Train. Occasional mixed-train service as freight requirements dictate throughout the year.

Notes: Cars may be chartered on scheduled runs; special trains may be chartered.

Location: U.S. 223 and Depot Street. Ten miles west of exit 5 of U.S. 23 and 20 miles northwest of Toledo.

Toledo-Ann Arbor

Contact: Dale Pape
General Manager

Mailing Address:
708 East Michigan Street
Adrian, MI 49221
Telephone: (517) 486-5979

JUNCTION VALLEY RAILROAD
Diesel, scheduled
14 1/8" gauge

JUNCTION VALLEY RAILROAD

Ride/Operation: This line, more than 2 miles long, travels 22 feet down into a valley around a lake, over several bridges and trestles, and through a 100-foot tunnel and a park area. The Junction Valley is the "Largest Quarter-Size Railroad in the World."

Displays/Exhibits: Railroad shops; 10-stall roundhouse with turntable; seventeen railroad and six highway bridges; thirty buildings and stations; more than 830 feet of bridges and trestles; the only diamond-crossing trestle in the world; four miles of track; and a five-track switch yard.

Train: Fifty-five freight cars, thirty converted to haul passengers; four cabooses.

Schedule: Daily, mid May-Labor Day; Monday-Saturday, 10:00 a.m.-6:00 p.m.; Sunday, 1:00-6:00 p.m. Weekends, September-October 15, 1:00-5:00 p.m.

Fare: Adults $4.00, senior citizens $3.75, children $3.25. Group rates available. Railroad Days, Halloween Spook Ride, and Christmas Fantasyland Train: $5.00, no discounts. Rates subject to change.

Locomotives: No. 555, MP-15; No. 1177, GP-45; No. 333, SW-1500; No. 4, Plymouth; No. 300, SW-1500 booster; No. 5000, WS-4A; No. 6000, WS-4B; No. 7000, WS-4A.

Special Events: Opening Day, featuring a 2,000-balloon launch. Railroad Days, June 24-25, July 15-16 & August 19-20. Valley of Flags, July 4. Halloween Spook Ride, October. Christmas Fantasyland Train Ride, December. Others.

Note: The entire railroad, including engines, cars, bridges, trestles, tunnel, and buildings, was designed, engineered, and built by William A. Stenger.

Location: Two miles south of the Bridgeport exit of I-75; five miles west of historic Frankenmuth.

Flint

Contact: Lillian M. Stenger

Mailing Address:
7065 Dixie Highway
Bridgeport, MI 48722
Telephone: (517) 777-3480

Michigan, Clinton
R

SOUTHERN MICHIGAN RAILROAD SOCIETY
Diesel, motor cars, scheduled
Standard gauge

COURTESY OF SOUTHERN MICHIGAN RAILROAD SOCIETY

Ride/Operation: Rides are offered over two portions of the former Clinton Branch of the New York Central. Regular summer service is a 4 1/2-mile, 2-hour round trip from Clinton to Tecumseh, featuring travel across the 116-foot-long timber trestle over the River Raisin in a scenic wildlife area and across the steel bridge over Evans Creek. Fall Color Tours are 6-mile, 2-hour round trips between Tecumseh and Raisin Center, featuring an overlook of the River Raisin Valley and a spectacular crossing high above the river on a steel truss bridge.

Displays/Exhibits: An indoor museum is open during train operation.

Train: Plymouth diesel, former South Shore commuter car, gondola, cabooses.

Schedule: Summer service: June-September; lv. Clinton 11:00a.m., 1:00 & 3:00p.m.; lv. Tecumseh 12:00 & 2:00p.m. Clinton Fall Festival: September 23-24; lv. Clinton 10:00a.m., 12:00, 2:00 & 4:00p.m.; lv. Tecumseh 11:00a.m., 1:00, 3:00 & 5:00p.m. Fall Color Tours: Weekends, October; lv. Tecumseh 11:00 a.m., 1:30 & 4:00p.m.

Fare: Summer service and Clinton Fall Festival: Adults $6.00, senior citizens (65+) $5.00, children (2-12) $4.00, children under 2 ride free. Fall Color Tours: Adults $10.00, senior citizens (65+) $8.00, children (2-12) $6.00, children under 2 ride free.

Locomotives: No. 1, 1938 Plymouth, former Hayes Albion Corp.; Alco RS-1 diesel, former Ann Arbor (stored at Lenawee Jct.).

Passenger Cars: No. 1, commuter car, former Chicago, South Shore & South Bend.

Rolling Stock/Equipment: 1950 caboose No. 21692, former New York Central; 1944 caboose No. 19882, former New Haven; 1949 gondola No. 726456, former New York Central.

Special Events: Call or write for schedule.

Location: On U.S. 12 about 25 miles southwest of Ann Arbor and 45 miles northwest of Toledo, Ohio. The museum is at the corner of Clark and Division Streets. In Tecumseh, passengers board at the corner of Evans and Chicago.

Ann Arbor

Contact: Orcelia Davison
Publicity & Promotion

Mailing Address:
P.O. Box K
Clinton, MI 49236-0009
Business Office: (517) 456-7677
Ticket Office: (517) 423-7230

135

LITTLE RIVER RAILROAD
Steam, scheduled
Standard gauge

COURTESY OF LITTLE RIVER RAILROAD

Ride/Operation: The Little River Railroad offers two round trips: a 10-mile, 80-minute ride from Coldwater to Batavia, and a 24-mile, 2 1/2-hour ride from White Pigeon to Sturgis. Both trips run over tracks of the Michigan Southern Railroad.

Train: Combination car No. 2594, former Chicago & Alton; *Hiawatha* coaches, former Milwaukee Road; open-air cars; World War II troop car; cabooses, former Baltimore & Ohio.

Schedule: Coldwater: Sundays, August & September, plus September 4, 1:00 & 3:00 p.m. White Pigeon: May 28-29 and Sundays, June, July & October, 1:30 p.m.

Fare: Coldwater: adults $7.00, children (3-11) $4.00. White Pigeon: adults $15.00, children (3-11) $8.00. Fares vary for special events. Charters available.

Locomotives: No. 110, 1911 Baldwin 4-6-2, former Little River Railroad—the smallest standard-gauge Pacific locomotive ever built.

Special Events: Spring Train Robbery, June 4. Father's Day, June 18. White Pigeon Days, July 7-9. Fall Train Robbery, September 10. Fall Color Run, October 8. Ghost Train, October 29.

Contact: Terry Bloom
President

Mailing Address:
13187 SR 120
Middlebury, IN 46540
Telephone: (219) 825-9182

THE COOPERSVILLE & MARNE RAILWAY COMPANY

Diesel, scheduled
Standard gauge

COOPERSVILLE & MARNE RAILWAY COMPANY

Ride/Operation: A 13-mile, 1 1/2-hour trip through western Michigan farmland, pastures, and woods on a former Grand Trunk Western route to Muskegon and Grand Haven car-ferry boats. Tracks parallel busy interstate 96 for several miles.

Train: No. 7014, former Grand Trunk Western EMD SW-9, two "el" commuter coaches, three former Canadian National heavy coaches, former GTW steel caboose, 1895-era former GTW wood caboose.

Schedule: Saturdays, June-September. Weekends, October & December.

Fare: June-September: Adults $7.00, children $4.00. October & December: Adults $9.00, children $6.00.

Locomotives: SW-9 No. 7014, former Grand Trunk Western; 4-6-0 No. 1395 and 0-6-0 No. 7456, both former Canadian National; Alco RS-1.

Rolling Stock/Equipment: 250-ton wreck crane, former Chesapeake & Ohio; several 1900-era wooden cabooses

Special Events: Murder Mystery Trains, spring and fall. Great Train Robbery, September. Pumpkin Trains, October. Santa Trains, December.

Location: Western Michigan near Grand Rapids. Take exit 16 or 19 off I-96 and follow signs to downtown Coopersville.

Grand Rapids

(Murder Mystery trains only)

Contact: Thomas Chubinski
Co-Manager

Mailing Address:
P.O. Box 55
Coopersville, MI 49404
Telephone: (616) 949-4778

HENRY FORD MUSEUM &
GREENFIELD VILLAGE RAILROAD
Steam, scheduled
Standard gauge

Ride/Operation: A 2 1/2-mile, 20-minute ride around the grounds of the world-famous Greenfield Village.

Displays/Exhibits: The Henry Ford Museum, a general museum of American history occupying about twelve acres under one roof, contains a huge transportation collection, including the widely acclaimed "Automobile in American Life" exhibit. Greenfield Village is an eighty-one-acre outdoor museum comprising more than eighty historic structures. Also at the site are 1941 Lima 2-6-6-6 No. 1601; a 1902 Schenectady 4-4-2; an 1858 Rogers 4-4-0; an 1893 replica of the "DeWitt Clinton"; 1909 Baldwin 2-8-0, former Bessemer & Lake Erie No. 154; a 1923 Canadian Pacific snowplow; a 1924 F.G.E. reefer; and a 1925 Detroit, Toledo & Ironton caboose.

Train: Specially constructed open excursion-type; two circa 1890 wooden coaches.

Schedule: Museum and village: Daily, 9:00 a.m.-5:00 p.m. Closed Thanksgiving & Christmas. Train: Daily, April 14-October 15.

Fare/Admission: Museum and village: Adults $12.50, senior citizens (62+) $11.50, children (5-12) $6.25, children under 5 admitted free; does not include train fare. Train: All-day pass, $2.00. Prices subject to change.

Locomotives: No. 1, 1876 Ford Motor Co. 4-4-0 (rebuilt 1920s); No. 3, 1873 Mason-Fairlie 0-6-4T, former Calumet & Hecla Mining; No. 8, 1914 Baldwin 0-6-0, former Michigan Alkali Co.

Special Events: Railroad Days, September 24-25.

Location: One-half mile south of U.S. 12 (Michigan Avenue) between Southfield Road and Oakwood Boulevard.

Dearborn

Contact: Robert Casey
Transportation Curator

Mailing Address:
P.O. Box 1970
Dearborn, MI 48121
Telephone: (313) 271-1620

DOWNTOWN TROLLEY
Electric, scheduled
Meter gauge

CITY OF DETROIT

Ride/Operation: A 1-mile, 12-minute ride between the Renaissance Center, Cobo Center, and Grand Circus Park. The line is single-track, primarily curbside, and in median, with a passing siding at Cobo Hall and along the route. The line is operated by the Detroit Department of Transportation; all motormen are also qualified bus drivers.

Displays/Exhibits: Nonoperating cars can be viewed through the glass walls of the carbarn at the north end of the line.

Schedule: <u>Daily;</u> Monday-Friday, 8:00 a.m.-6:00 p.m.; weekends, 10:00 a.m.-6:00 p.m.; at 10-minute intervals. <u>Weekend hours extended</u> during some special events.

Fare: $.50 each direction. Senior citizens (65+) and children not occupying a seat ride free.

Locomotives/Trolleys: Seven closed cars and 2 open-air cars, one of which is a double-decker. Eight of the cars were built in the U.S., Portugal, or England between 1899 and the 1920s; the ninth is an 1895 Berlin-built car that operated in Vevey, Switzerland.

Location: On Washington Boulevard and Jefferson Avenue.

Detroit

SOCIETY FOR THE PRESERVATION
OF THE S.S. *CITY OF MILWAUKEE*
Railway display

SOCIETY FOR THE PRESERVATION OF THE S.S. CITY OF MILWAUKEE

Displays/Exhibits: This society was founded to preserve the last remaining railroad-car ferry in Betsie Bay. These ferries were an integral part of the community between 1892 and 1982, hauling railroad cars and passengers across Lake Michigan. The S.S. *City of Milwaukee* represents the classic design created by the Manitowoc Shipbuilding Company; ships of the same class served the Ann Arbor, Pere Marquette/Chesapeake & Ohio, and Grand Trunk Western railroads.

Today, the ship, coal tower, turntable, roundhouse, and marine terminal buildings remain at the site. The property adjacent to the ferry is an active lumberyard, so visitors who have not arranged a tour are asked to view the ship and artifacts from the route M-168 overlook or the Frankfort library and marina public access.

Schedule: Tours of the ship are available by special arrangement to society members. Please call or write for more information. Former railyard buildings are not currently accessible.

Admission: Society membership is $10.00 for adults and $25.00 for a family; includes tour of car ferry and newsletter.

Car Ferry: 1931 triple-expansion steamer, capacity twenty-two 50-foot railroad cars/50 passengers & crew, former Ann Arbor, former Grand Trunk Western.

Rolling Stock: Five steel boxcars and one idler flatcar, former AA.

Note: The future of the former railyard is under discussion between the Michigan Department of Transportation and the village of Elberta. Also, the former C&O railroad-car ferry S.S. *Badger*, the last steam passenger-car ferry operating on Lake Michigan, operates seasonally between Ludington, Michigan, and Manitowoc, Wisconsin. Ludington is approximately one hour south of Frankfort on U.S. 31.

Location: Elberta is across Lake Betsie from Frankfort. From Manistee, take M-22 north, and continue west on M-168 to the scenic overlook.

HUCKLEBERRY RAILROAD
Steam, scheduled
36" gauge

GEORGE A. FORERO, JR.

Ride/Operation: This railroad is operated in conjunction with Crossroads Village, a historic community of twenty-nine late-nineteenth-century buildings including homes, a church, a school, a business district, and three operating mills. The *Genesee Belle*, a paddle-wheel riverboat, is new for 1995. The 8-mile, 35-minute excursion runs over a section of an original Flint and Pere Marquette branch line.

Train: Restored open- and closed-platform coaches from the Denver & Rio Grande Western, the Rio Grande Southern, and several Mexican narrow-gauge railroads.

Schedule: <u>Daily</u>, May 13-September 4, hourly. <u>Weekends</u>, September.

Admission: Adults $8.25, senior citizens $7.25, children (4-12) $5.50, children under 4 admitted free.

Locomotives: No. 2, 1920 Baldwin 4-6-0, former Alaska Railroad No. 152; No. 464, 1903 Baldwin 2-8-2, former Denver & Rio Grande Western.

Special Events: <u>Railfan Weekend</u>, September 16-17, includes shop tours, photo runs, and model train exhibits. <u>Halloween Trains</u>, October 6-30. <u>Christmas Trains</u>, November 24-December 30.

Location: Take exit 13 (Saginaw Street) off I-475. Travel north on Saginaw to Stanley Road, east on Stanley to Bray Road, then south on Bray to the entrance.

Contact: Janet S. Weaver
Public Information Officer

Mailing Address:
5045 Stanley Road
Flint, MI 48506
Telephone: (810) 736-1700
(800) 648-PARK

IRON MOUNTAIN IRON MINE
Electric, scheduled
24" gauge

COURTESY OF IRON MOUNTAIN IRON MINE

Ride/Operation: Designated a Michigan Historical Site, the Iron Mountain Iron Mine offers guided underground tours by mine train. Visitors travel 2,600 feet into the mine to see mining demonstrations and the history of iron mining in Michigan's Upper Peninsula. Mining equipment dating from the 1870s is shown and explained.

Train: Electric locomotive, 5 cars.

Schedule: <u>Daily</u>, June 1-October 15, 9:00 a.m.-5:00 p.m.

Admission: Adults $5.50, children (6-12) $4.50, children under 6 admitted free. <u>Group rates</u> available.

Location: Nine miles east of Iron Mountain on U.S. 2.

Contact: Albert or Dennis Carollo

Mailing Address:
P.O. Box 177
Iron Mountain, MI 49801
Telephone: (906) 563-8077

MICHIGAN TRANSIT MUSEUM
Electric, diesel, scheduled
Standard gauge

WILLIAM H. HENNING

Ride/Operation: This unique train ride is an 8-mile, 45-minute trip through farmlands and a park on trackage of the Selfridge Air National Guard Base. Eastbound, the train is controlled from "el" cars, with a diesel locomotive providing electricity. Westbound, the locomotive powers the train. Located on the route is the Selfridge Military Air Museum, with more than twenty military aircraft, plus photos, models, and memorabilia. A small donation for the museum is collected with the train fare.

Displays/Exhibits: The group leases the Mt. Clemens Grand Trunk Railroad station, built in 1859, and operates it as a museum. The station is located at the Cass Avenue crossing of the Grand Trunk in Mt. Clemens.

Train: Nos. 4442 & 4450, 1924 elevated cars, former Chicago Transit Authority; diesel No. 1807. Grand Trunk Western caboose No. 77058, built in 1900, is used as a ticket office.

Schedule: Train: Last Sunday of May through last Sunday of September. Schedule subject to change. Station: Weekends, year-round, 1:00-4:00 p.m. Closed on major holidays.

Fare: Train: Adults $5.00, children (4-12) $2.50, children under 4 ride free. Air Museum: Adults $.50, children (4-12) $.25, children under 4 admitted free.

Locomotives: No. 1807, Alco S-1, former Alco plant switcher; No. 761, 1929 interurban, former Chicago, North Shore & Milwaukee; PCC No. 268, former Detroit Street Railway. (Nos. 761 and 268 are not currently on display.)

Location: Train departs from the Caboose Depot, 3/4 mile north of Mt. Clemens on North Gratiot Avenue. Take the North River Road exit off I-94; the museum is 3/4 of a mile west of Gratiot Avenue on Cass.

🚃 ⊞ 🏠 ✉
🔲 arm 🚆 🔺

Contact: Karl H. Joost
Public Relations

Mailing Address:
P.O. Box 12
Fraser, MI 48026
Telephone: (810) 463-1863
(810) 307-5035

PROJECT 1225

Ride/Operation: Locomotive No. 1225 hauls periodic day-long and local excursions in Michigan and elsewhere in the Midwest. "Engineer for an Hour" operations occasionally permit guests to operate or fire the locomotive.

Displays/Exhibits: No. 1225 is maintained in the former machine shop of the Ann Arbor Railroad at Owosso. The locomotive and tools used to repair it may be seen by visitors.

Train: Air-conditioned coaches and lounge cars.

Schedule: Excursions and Engineer for an Hour: Call for dates and times. Shop: Saturdays, 10:00 a.m.-6:00 p.m., except weekends of major holidays.

Fare: Excursions and Engineer for an Hour: Call for details. Shop: No charge.

Locomotives: No. 1225, 1941 Lima 2-8-4, former Pere Marquette Railway.

Passenger Cars: Baggage car, former Chesapeake & Ohio No. 361.

Location: In yards of the Tuscola and Saginaw Bay Railway, South Oakwood Street, off highway M-71 (Corunna Avenue) in southeast Owosso.

Contact: Aarne Frobom
President

Mailing Address:
P.O. Box 665
Owosso, MI 48867-0665
Telephone: (517) 725-9464

144

KALAMAZOO, LAKE SHORE & CHICAGO RAILWAY
Diesel, scheduled
Standard gauge

COURTESY OF KALAMAZOO, LAKE SHORE & CHICAGO RAILWAY

Ride/Operation: This railway takes passengers past streams, orchards, and woods along Lake Cora and through the area's vineyards over a former Pere Marquette/Chesapeake & Ohio branch line. The *Scenic Train* offers a 12-mile, 1 1/4-hour round trip from Paw Paw to Bonamego Farm; passengers may picnic or hike at the scenic farm and return on a later train. Bicycle rentals are also available. Within walking distance of the Paw Paw depot are two wineries, which offer free tours and tastings year-round.

Train: *Scenic Train:* Former New York Central streamlined coach; two 1910 former Denver & Rio Grande open-window coaches; former Wabash air-conditioned heavyweight; former Elgin, Joliet & Eastern caboose.

Schedule: Weekends and major holidays, April 8-June 30 & November 1-12; Tuesdays-Thursdays & weekends, July-August; daily, October 1-29; certain winter weekends; 2-4 departures per day.

Fare: Adults $8.00, senior citizens $7.00, children $4.00.

Locomotives/Trolleys: No. 104, 1952 EMD GP-7, former Santa Fe No. 2064.

Special Events: Santa Claus Trains: weekends, Thanksgiving to Christmas; a 12-mile, 3-hour round trip with a 1 1/2-hour stopover at a tree farm where passengers may cut their own trees and enjoy wagon rides. Santa Claus boards for the return trip.

Note: Reservations required for Santa trains. Higher fares on Santa trains and Winter Scenic trains.

Location: In southwestern Michigan, 15 miles west of Kalamazoo. Take exit 60 off I-94, then travel north one-quarter mile.

Kalamazoo

Radio Frequency: 160.815

Mailing Address:
P.O. Box 178
Paw Paw, MI 49079
Telephone:
Recorded Information: (616) 657-2423
Reservations: (616) 382-4244

Michigan, Traverse City
R

CITY OF TRAVERSE CITY

CITY OF TRAVERSE CITY
PARKS & RECREATION
Steam, scheduled
1/4 scale

Ride/Operation: No. 400, the "Spirit of Traverse City," is an oil-fired, 1/4-scale replica of a 4-4-2 steam locomotive, which takes passengers around a 4/10-mile loop at the Clinch Park Zoo and Marina on West Bay in Traverse City. The ride provides views of West Grand Traverse Bay, the marina, the beach, and the zoo, which features native Michigan wildlife and the Con Foster Museum.

Train: No. 400 pulls a train of 1/4-scale open-air cars.

Schedule: <u>Daily</u>, May 27-September 4, 10:00 a.m.-4:30p.m.

Fare: Adults $1.00, children (under 13) $.50.

Locomotives: "Spirit of Traverse City," No. 400, 1/4-scale oil-fired 4-4-2.

Passenger Cars: Three open-air cars.

Special Events: <u>Family Fun Day</u>, June 4, 12:00-4:00 p.m., features 25-cent rides, popcorn, and zoo admission.

Location: At Clinch Park Zoo, 100 Grandview Parkway (U.S. 31) and Cass Street.

Contact: Mr. Lauren Vaughn
Parks & Recreation Superintendent

Mailing Address:
625 Woodmere Avenue
Traverse City, MI 49684
Telephone: (616) 922-4910

Michigan, Walled Lake   *MICHIGAN STAR CLIPPER* DINNER TRAIN
R   COE RAIL
                                                 Diesel, scheduled
Standard gauge

Ride/Operation: This line offers 1-hour scenic excursions on Coe Rail and customized 3-hour lunch and dinner excursions on the *Michigan Star Clipper* dinner train. On the *Star Clipper,* passengers can also relax, dine, travel, and sleep aboard two fabulous cars that feature a 50-foot all-mahogany drawing room, a dance floor at the opposite end, and eight suites in between.

Schedule: *Michigan Star Clipper:* year-round; Tuesday-Thursday & Saturday, 7:00 p.m.; Friday, 7:30 p.m.; Sunday, 5:00 p.m. Coe Rail: April-October, Monday-Saturday, 1:00 & 2:30 p.m; children allowed. Open Sundays except major holidays. School groups and bus tours welcomed; buffet or box lunches available. Corporate entertaining, fund-raising events, bus tours welcomed.

Fare: *Michigan StartClipper:* $53.50 (food, ride, tax), $68.50 (food, ride, tax, entertainment). Sleeper cars: please call or write for information. Coe Rail: Adults $6.00, senior citizens (65+) & children (2-10) $5.00.

Locomotives: 1945 Whitcomb, gasoline; 1945 Alco S1; 1947 Alco S1; 1952 Alco S1.

Passenger Cars: *Michigan Star Clipper:* 1952 Pennsylvania Railroad Keystone dining cars; kitchen car; power car; 1950s-vintage stainless steel sleepers. Coe Rail: 1917 coaches, former Erie Lackawanna; 1947 tap car, former Milwaukee Road; 1920 baggage cars; 1945 bay-window cabooses, former PH&D.

Special Events: Hobo Halloween, October 28-29, on Coe Rail. Holiday Specials. New Year's Specials. Many hotel packages available on the *Star Clipper.* Please call or write for more information.

Location: On Pontiac Trail just north of Maple Road; 8 minutes north of Novi exit off I-96.

Contact: J. Coe
Vice President

Mailing Address:
840 North Pontiac Trail
Walled Lake, MI 48390
Telephone: (810) 960-9440
Fax: (810) 960-9444

NORTH STAR RAIL, INC.
Steam, irregular
Standard gauge

RICHARD GRUBER

Ride/Operation: North Star Rail, Inc., operates day-long, steam-powered excursions over various Class I railroads.

Train: Air-conditioned coaches; most trips include deluxe, first-class cars (diners, lounges, domes, and/or observation cars).

Schedule: Varies, depending on trip. Please call or write for information.

Fare: Varies. Advance reservations suggested.

Locomotives: No. 261, 1944 Alco 4-8-4, former Milwaukee Road class S-3, leased to North Star Rail by the National Railroad Museum in Green Bay, Wisconsin.

Contact: Steve Sandberg
Chief Operating Officer

Mailing Address:
1418 Rocky Lane
St. Paul, MN 55122
Telephone: (612) 858-8859

Minnesota, Currie
M-R

END-O-LINE RAILROAD PARK
AND MUSEUM
Railway museum

COURTESY OF END-O-LINE RAILROAD PARK AND MUSEUM

Ride/Operation: Rides on a manually operated turntable and tours are given to all visitors.

Displays/Exhibits: A working railroad yard including a rebuilt enginehouse on its original foundation, an original four-room depot, a water tower, an 1899 section foreman's house, and an outhouse. The turntable, built in 1901 by the American Bridge Company and still operable, is the only one left in Minnesota on its original site. The section-foreman's house is currently undergoing restoration and is scheduled to be completed in 1995. A general store and one-room schoolhouse can also be seen. A replica of the coal bunker, to be built in 1995, will be a picnic shelter and gift shop. The buildings contain various exhibits and displays of railroad artifacts, photographs, memorabilia, and equipment. The freight room in the depot has an HO-scale model-train layout of the railroad yards in Currie, complete with steam engine sound effects, authentic structures, and local countryside. A beautiful wrap-around mural completes the setting. A bicycle/pedestrian paved pathway will be constructed in 1995 to make the railroad park accessible to Lake Shetek State Park (approximately 4 miles, round trip).

Schedule: May 29-September 4, Monday-Friday, 10:00 a.m.-12:00 p.m. & 1:00-5:00 p.m.; Saturday-Sunday, 1:00-5:00 p.m. and by appointment. Last tour of the day begins at 4:00 p.m.

Admission: Adults $2.00, students $1.00, family $5.00.

Rolling Stock/Equipment: Caboose and diesel switcher, former Grand Trunk Western; Fairmont Motors section crew cars; velocipede; ice cart; baggage/milk carts.

Location: Take state highway 30 to Currie, then travel one-half mile north on county road 38.

Contact: Louise Gervais
Director/Curator

Mailing Address:
RR 1, Box 42
Currie, MN 56123
Telephone: (507) 763-3708
Off-season: (507) 763-3113

THE OLD DEPOT RAILROAD MUSEUM
Railway museum

VICTOR VENDING CORPORATION

Displays/Exhibits: A former Great Northern depot built in 1913 is filled with railroad memorabilia and pictures. This 33-foot by 100-foot country depot has two waiting rooms, an agent's office, and a large freight room, as well as a full basement. Authentic recorded sounds of steam locomotives and the clicking of the telegraph key create the realistic feel of an old small-town depot. Items displayed include lanterns, telegraph equipment, semaphores, and other signals; section crew cars, a hand pump car, and a velocipede; tools and oil cans; depot and crossing signs; buttons, badges, service pins, and caps; a large date-nail collection; and many baggage carts. Also included are children's toy trains, an HO-scale model railroad, and many railroad advertising items. Interpretation of the items is provided.

Train: Static one-half-scale train on display.

Schedule: Daily, Memorial Day-October 1, 10:00 a.m.-4:30p.m.

Admission: Adults $2.00, children (under 12) $1.00.

Rolling Stock/Equipment: Two cabooses; one boxcar.

Location: 651 West Highway No. 12, 50 miles west of Minneapolis.

Contact: Howard Page
Manager

Mailing Address:
651 West Highway #12
Dassel, MN 55325
Telephone: (612) 275-3876

LAKE SUPERIOR & MISSISSIPPI RAILROAD
Diesel, scheduled
Standard gauge

DAVE SCHAUER

Ride: A 12-mile, 1 1/2-hour round trip that follows the scenic St. Louis River to New Duluth. The line was first built in 1870 as the Lake Superior & Mississippi Railroad and was later part of the Northern Pacific and the Burlington Northern.

Displays/Exhibits: See the listing of the Lake Superior Transportation Museum (Minnesota, Duluth).

Train: Heavyweight coaches from the Duluth, Missabe & Iron Range.

Schedule: Weekends, July 1-September 3, 11:00 a.m.-2:00 p.m.

Fare: Adults $6.00, senior citizens (60+) $5.00, children (under 13) $4.00. Charter rates available.

Locomotives: No. 46, 1946 General Electric 45-ton diesel.

Passenger Cars: Two heavyweight coaches; open observation car.

Location: Six miles southwest of downtown Duluth on Grand Avenue, route 23, across from the Duluth Zoo and the Lake Superior Zoological Gardens. Train leaves from the Western Waterfront Trail; park in Western Waterfront Trail lot.

♿ ▢ ⊞ ✉ ⏹nearby

🔺 Radio Frequency: 160.380

Contact: Bill Mickelsen
Administrative Assistant

Mailing Address:
506 West Michigan Street
Duluth, MN 55802
Telephone: (218) 727-8025
(seasonal) (218) 624-7549
(218) 727-0687

LAKE SUPERIOR
MUSEUM OF TRANSPORTATION
Railway museum
Standard gauge

BASGEN PHOTOGRAPHY

Displays/Exhibits: A number of interesting and historic locomotives and cars, including the Great Northern's famous "William Crooks" locomotive and cars of 1861; the Northern Pacific's first engine, the "Minnetonka"; Duluth, Missabe & Iron Range 2-8-8-4 No. 227, displayed with revolving drive wheels and recorded sound; Great Northern No. 400, the first production-model SD-45 diesel; an 1887 steam rotary snowplow; other steam, diesel, and electric engines; a Railway Post Office car; a dining-car china exhibit; freight cars; work equipment; an operating electric single-truck streetcar; and much railroadiana.

Schedule: <u>Daily</u>; mid May-mid October, 10:00 a.m.-5:00 p.m. <u>Daily</u>, mid October-mid May; Monday-Saturday, 10:00 a.m.-5:00 p.m.; Sunday, 1:00-5:00 p.m.

Admission: Adults $5.00, children (3-11) $3.00, children under 3 admitted free, family rate $15.00. Price includes admission to adjacent Heritage and Arts Center.

Special Events: The museum sponsors various special excursions each year. Please call or write for details.

Location: 506 West Michigan Street, in the former Duluth Union Depot, now the St. Louis County Heritage & Arts Center; adjacent to North Shore Scenic Railroad station.

Radio Frequency: 160.38

Contact: Tom Gannon
Curator

Mailing Address:
506 West Michigan Street
Duluth, MN 55802
Telephone: (218) 727-0687
(218) 727-8025

NORTH SHORE SCENIC RAILROAD
Steam, scheduled
Standard gauge

TIM SCHANDEL

Ride/Operation: Formerly the Duluth, Missabe & Iron Range Railway's Lake Front Line, this railroad's twenty-six miles of track run between the depot in downtown Duluth, along the Lake Superior waterfront, and through the residential areas and scenic woodlands of northeastern Minnesota to the Two Harbors Depot, adjacent to DM&IR's active taconite yard and ship-loading facility. The line offers 2- and 6-hour round trips with departures from Duluth.

Train: GP-7 locomotive; self-propelled RDC-1; four reconditioned nonpowered RDC-9s, former Boston & Maine; one nonpowered RDC-1.

Schedule: Not available at press time. Please call or write for more information.

Fare: Please call or write for information.

Location: Duluth: Duluth Depot, 5th Avenue West and Michigan Street; parking is at 4th Avenue West, below Michigan Street.

TRAIN 🚂 Radio Frequency: 160.920

Contact: Shaye Moris
Sales

Mailing Address:
506 West Michigan Street
Duluth, MN 55802
Telephone: (218) 722-1273
(800) 423-1273

COMO-HARRIET STREETCAR LINE
MINNESOTA TRANSPORTATION MUSEUM
Electric, scheduled
Standard gauge

Ride/Operation: A 2-mile, 15-minute round trip through a scenic wooded area between Lakes Harriet and Calhoun, on a restored portion of the former Twin City Rapid Transit Company's Como-Harriet line. This is the last operating portion of the 523-mile Twin City Lines system, abandoned in 1954.

Displays/Exhibits: Linden Hills Depot, a re-creation of the 1900 depot at the site, houses historical displays about electric railways in Minnesota. It is open when streetcars operate.

Schedule: <u>Daily</u>, May 26-September 4; Saturdays, Sundays & holidays, 12:30 p.m. to dusk; Monday-Friday, 6:30 p.m. to dusk. <u>Weekends</u>, September 5-30, 12:30 p.m. to dusk. <u>Sundays</u>, May 1-25 & October; 12:30 p.m. to dusk (to 5:00 p.m. in October).

Fare: $1.00, children under 5 ride free. <u>Chartered streetcars</u>: $40 per half hour; please call (612) 291-7588 for charter information and reservations.

Rolling Stock: No. 1300, 1908 Twin City Rapid Transit, and No. 265, 1915 Duluth Street Railway (TCRT Snelling Shops, St. Paul); No. 78, 1893 DSR (Laclede Car Co.); No. 322, 1946 TCRT PCC (St. Louis Car Co.), undergoing restoration; No. 10, 1912 Mesaba Railway Co. (Niles Car Co.), and No. 416, 1949 TCRT PCC (St. Louis Car Co.), awaiting restoration; TCRT motor buses No. 630 (Mack, 1941), No. 1399 (General Motors, 1954), No. 103 (GM, 1962), No. 1303 (GM, 1303), and No. 1488 (AM General, 1974).

Special Events: <u>Linden Hills Neighborhood Fair</u>, May 20-21, features multiple streetcar and bus operation. <u>35th Annual Association of Railway Museums (ARM) Convention</u>, September 20-24; advance registration required.

Note: The museum's Minnehaha Depot is located several miles east in Minnehaha Park; see separate listing (Minnesota, Minneapolis).

Location: The Linden Hills Depot, West 42nd Street & Queen Avenue South, at Lake Harriet in southwest Minneapolis.

&(depot) 🚻 🚗 🏢 🏠

✉ ⛱ ☐ 𝕒𝕣𝕞 🚂 🄰

St. Paul

Radio Frequency: 161.355

Contact: Louis Hoffman
General Superintendent

Mailing Address:
P.O. Box 17240
Nokomis Station
Minneapolis, MN 55417-0240
Telephone: (612) 228-0263
Charter Telephone: (612) 291-7588

MINNEHAHA DEPOT
MINNESOTA TRANSPORTATION MUSEUM
Railway museum

LOUIS HOFFMAN

Displays/Exhibits: Built in 1875, the Minnehaha Depot replaced a smaller Milwaukee Road depot on the same site. Milwaukee Road agents nicknamed the depot the "Princess" because of its intricate architectural details. Closed in 1963, the structure was donated to the Minnesota Historical Society and is staffed by volunteer members of the Minnesota Transportation Museum. Located at the south end of CP Rail System's South Minneapolis branch, once a through route to the south, the depot sees occasional freight movements and often hosts visiting private cars. Visitors may tour the depot, which appears much as it did when in service as a typical railroad station. Exhibits include telegraphy demonstrations and historic photographs of the depot and its environs.

Schedule: Sunday & holidays, May 28-September 4, 12:30-4:30p.m.

Admission: No charge; donations welcomed.

Special Events: Annual Open House featuring refreshments and scenic trips along Minnehaha and West River Parkway using Twin City Rapid Transit Company No. 630 (Mack, 1941) and No. 1399 (General Motors, 1954), May 22, 6:15-9:00 p.m. Fall Colors bus trips using No. 630 and No. 1399 along scenic Minnehaha Parkway from the depot to the Como-Harriet Streetcar Line. Please call or write for dates, schedules, and fares.

Note: The museum's Como-Harriet Streetcar Line is located several miles west at Lake Harriet; see separate listing (Minnesota, Minneapolis).

Location: In Minnehaha Park at 4920 Minnehaha Avenue.

Contact: Corbin S. Kidder
Stationmaster

Mailing Address:
P.O. Box 17240
Nokomis Station
Minneapolis, MN 55417-0240
Telephone: (612) 228-0263
(612) 227-5171

WESTERN MINNESOTA
STEAM THRESHERS REUNION
Steam, scheduled

COURTESY OF WESTERN MINNESOTA STEAM THRESHERS

Ride/Operation: The Western Minnesota Steam Threshers Reunion is a four-day show, lasting from Friday to Monday every Labor Day weekend. In operation are three railroads (full-sized, 1/4-scale, and miniature), thirty-seven steam traction engines, four hundred gas tractors, and many large stationary steam and gas engines.

Displays/Exhibits: Musical entertainment all day and evening. Free rides on a 1920 steam-operated Parker Bros. merry-go-round. Steam plowing and threshing. Morning and afternoon parades of steam and gas tractors. A complete, working horsepower farm, two sawmills, and a flour mill are in operation. An 1895 Great Northern Railway steam forging hammer stamps out souvenir plates.

Schedule: September 1-4, every 20 minutes, 8:00 a.m.-8:00 p.m. (train stops running at 5:00 p.m. on September 4).

Fare/Admission: Gate admission: $7 per day; $10 per season. Children under 15 admitted free. No charge for rides, exhibits, or musical entertainment.

Locomotives: No. 353, 1920 Alco 0-6-0, former Soo Line; Porter 0-4-0; Wagner & Sons 1/4-scale locomotive.

Passenger Cars: Mt. St. Helens (SPS) on display; 5 passenger cars.

Rolling Stock/Equipment: Two former Northern Pacific cabooses; various operating handcars and motor cars; track crane and miscellaneous track-maintenance equipment.

Special Events: Each June, the WMSTR hosts the "University of Rollag College of Steam Traction Engineering," which offers classroom and hands-on instruction on operating steam traction and railroad engines. Students who successfully complete this course fulfill part of the requirements needed to obtain the Minnesota Steam Traction Engineer's license.

Notes: WMSTR is an all-volunteer organization of 3,500 members. Primitive camping is available for $15 per unit for the duration of the show. Area churches serve "threshermen's" meals.

Location: Thirty-two miles southeast of Fargo, North Dakota, just off I-94.

Contact: Lynette Briden
President

Mailing Address:
2610 1st Avenue
North Fargo, ND 58102
Telephone: (701) 232-4484

156

Minnesota, St. Paul
D

TWIN CITY MODEL RAILROAD CLUB, INC.
Model railroad

LARRY VANDEN PLAS

Displays/Exhibits: Three thousand square feet of O-scale operating railroad, featuring a panorama of railroading in Minnesota during the 1940s and 1950s, when steam and diesel shared the rails. The display is located at Bandana Square, the restored Northern Pacific Como Shops that were once used to maintain passenger cars.

Schedule: Monday-Friday, 10:00 a.m.-8:00 p.m.; Saturday, 10:00 a.m.-6:00 p.m.; Sunday, 12:00-5:00 p.m.

Admission: Donations welcomed.

Locomotives: Displayed outside are a former Northern Pacific F-9 and a former Grand Trunk Western 0-8-0.

Passenger Cars: Displayed outside is a former Chicago & North Western wooden combine.

Rolling Stock/Equipment: Boxcar, former Burlington Northern; caboose, former Chicago, Burlington & Quincy

Location: Bandana Square, 1021 Bandana Boulevard East.

St. Paul

Contact: Paul Gruetzman

Mailing Address:
Box 26, Bandana Square
1021 Bandana Boulevard East
St. Paul, MN 55108
Telephone: (612) 647-9628

157

MINNESOTA ZEPHYR LIMITED
Diesel, scheduled
Standard gauge

COURTESY OF *MINNESOTA ZEPHYR LIMITED*

Ride/Operation: The *Minnesota Zephyr* dining train steeps passengers in the ambience of 1940s railroad travel. The 3 1/2-hour journey begins on the Stillwater & St. Paul Railroad, built more than 120 years ago and later acquired by the Northern Pacific Railroad. The 7-mile line first parallels the St. Croix River, then swings west through Dutchtown along scenic Brown's Creek, climbing 250 feet on grades up to 2.2 percent. The tracks pass open fields to the Oak Glen Country Club, the summit area, then head onward to Duluth Junction. The *Zephyr* stops at the junction to prepare for the return to Stillwater.

Displays/Exhibits: Stillwater Depot, which opened in 1993, features displays about the history of Stillwater and the logging and rail industry.

Train: Two 1951 diesel-electric engines: No. 788, a 1750-horsepower FP9, and No. 787, a 1500-horsepower F7; five dining cars.

Schedule: Monday-Saturday, 7:30 p.m; Sunday and afternoon trips, 12:00 p.m. Call for more information on afternoon excursions and group charters.

Location: Follow Highway 36 east from the Twin Cities to Stillwater. Boarding for the *Zephyr* is at the Stillwater Depot at 601 North Main Street.

Fare: $52.50 for excursion and dinner. Reservations required. Call for group/charter prices.

Locomotives: FP9 No. 788, 1750-horsepower diesel; FP7 No. 787, 1500-horsepower diesel.

Passenger Cars: Two dome cars; "The Grand Dome" was built in 1938 and refurbished in 1954 by the Southern Pacific Railroad. Five dining cars; "The Northern Winds" was built in 1949.

Note: Semiformal attire requested.

Contact: David L. Paradeau

Mailing Address:
601 North Main Street
P.O. Box 573
Stillwater, MN 55082
Telephone: (612) 430-3000
(800) 992-6100

LAKE COUNTY HISTORY
& RAILROAD MUSEUM
Railway museum
Standard gauge

COURTESY OF LAKE COUNTY HISTORY & RAILROAD MUSEUM

Displays/Exhibits: The "3-Spot," former Duluth & Iron Range 2-6-0 No. 3, the first engine on the D&IR; a 2-8-8-4, former D&IR No. 229; a 1907 D&IR depot with exhibits relating to the early railroad, logging, and shipping history of the area. Visitors can also see the *Edna G.*, the last coal-fired tug on the Great Lakes; ore-loading docks; and Great Lakes ore boats.

Schedule: Daily, April 15-October 31, 9:00 a.m.-6:00 p.m. Weekends after November 1.

Admission: Adults $2.00, children (7-12) $.75.

Location: One block from the 1st Avenue shopping area. Turn off 7th Avenue (highway 61) at Waterfront Drive and head towards the lake.

Contact: Jeff McMorrow
Administrator

Mailing Address:
P.O. Box 313
Two Harbors, MN 55616
Telephone: (218) 834-4898

SMOKY HILL RAILWAY
Diesel, scheduled
Standard gauge

COURTESY OF SMOKY HILL RAILWAY

Ride/Operation: An 6-mile, 45-hour round trip on former Frisco trackage from downtown Belton, Missouri, through scenic farmland along the western Missouri high ridge. The line was built in 1871 by the Kansas City, Osceola & Southern; the Frisco acquired it in 1921 to gain access to Kansas City. The line parallels the old Kansas City, Clinton & Springfield right-of-way ("The Leaky Roof"). The Smoky Hill Railway is approximately five miles south of the original Santa Fe Trail.

Displays/Exhibits: Static steam locomotive; operating diesel locomotive; freight and passenger cars from Midwestern railroads. A collection of refrigerator cars shows their development from all-wood to all-steel.

Train: 1920 former Erie-Lackawanna open-window coach; 1969 former Santa Fe caboose; wide-vision cupola caboose No. 13562.

Schedule: Weekends, April 8-October 31, 2:00 p.m. Group specials available by reservation. Call or write for information.

Fare: Adults $5.75, senior citizens (55+) $5.25, children (under 12) $4.50. Group rates available.

Locomotives: No. 5, 1933 Alco 2-8-0, former Okmulgee Northern; No. 1632, 1918 Baldwin "Russian" Decapod 2-10-0, former Frisco; No. 630, 1942 EMD E-6, former Rock Island *Rocket*.

Passenger Cars: Heavyweight business car No. 3, "Oklahoma," former Frisco; 1920 open-window coach No. 4364, former Erie-Lackawanna; 1920 heavyweight parlor car "City of Peru," former *Wabash Cannonball*; heavyweight baggage car No. 873, former Wabash; heavyweight RPO-baggage car No. 6, former Chicago Great Western; heavyweight observation-instruction car No. 80, former Santa Fe; 1940 tavern-lounge-observation car No. 55, "Hospitality"; former Kansas City Southern "Southern Belle."

Rolling Stock/Equipment: Class CA-1 wood caboose No. 25752, former UP; Sunray-DX tank car No. 410; FGEX wood refrigerator car No. 55907;

URTX wood/steel refrigerator car No. 26679; SRLX mechanical refrigerator car No. 25034; Wilson Meat Co. refrigerator car No. 2711.

Special Events: Belton Community Days. Halloween train rides.

Location: 502 South Walnut. Belton is 30 minutes south of Kansas City on highway 71.

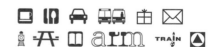

Contact: Kevin Love
General Superintendent

Mailing Address:
502 South Walnut Street
Belton, MO 64012
Telephone: (816) 331-0630

STAN GAYUSKI

Ride/Operation: This railway operates a 40-mile, 1 3/4-hour round trip through the Ozark foothills over the former Missouri Pacific White River Route, now owned by the Missouri & North Arkansas Railroad. Most trips take passengers south into Arkansas, across Lake Taneycomo and two high trestles and through two tunnels. Branson, home to three theme parks and 36 theaters featuring many well-known stars, is known as the live-entertainment capital of the country.

Displays/Exhibits: The original 1906 Branson depot houses the railway's ticket office, waiting room, gift shop, and business offices.

Train: Luxury dome cars, lounge cars, and coaches, air-conditioned and heated.

Schedule: Wednesday-Saturday, March 15-31 & November 1-December 16; 8:30 & 11:00 a.m., 2:00 p.m. Monday-Saturday, April 1-September 30, plus May 28, July 2 & September 3; 8:30 & 11:00 a.m., 2:00 p.m.; 4:30 p.m. train added May 26-September 4. Daily, October; 8:30 & 11:00 a.m., 2:00 & 4:30 p.m.; no 4:30 p.m. train October 29-31. Closed Thanksgiving Day.

Fare: Adults $17.50, senior citizens (55+) $16.50, children (3-12) $9.75. Group rates available for parties of 15 or more; please call or write for information. Fares subject to change without notice.

Locomotives: No. 6527, GP-35, Missouri & North Arkansas, former Southern Pacific; GP-35s Nos. 2912 & 2913, former Norfolk & Western, former Wabash; No. 9913, E-9A, former Chicago, Burlington & Quincy, former Burlington Northern.

Passenger Cars: Tavern-lounge-observation No. 48, former New York Central; dome-lounge-coach "Silver Garden," dome-lounge-observation "Silver Solarium," and dome-lounge-coach "Silver Castle," all former CB&Q; dome-lounge No. 503, "Plaza Santa Fe," former Atchison, Topeka & Santa Fe; tavern-lounge-observation "Westport," former Atlantic Coast Line; 60-seat coach No. 461, former

Texas & Pacific; 48-seat coach No. 4725, former AT&SF; 32-seat buffet-lounge No. 8703, former Pennsylvania Railroad.

Location: 206 East Main Street in historic downtown Branson, 3/4 mile east of U.S. 65. Branson is 40 miles south of Springfield.

Kansas City, St. Louis

Mailing Address:
206 East Main Street
Branson, MO 65616
Telephone:
Tickets and schedules: (417) 334-6110
(800) 2-TRAIN-2
Business info:
Paul Lasky, (417) 336-2895

161

SIX FLAGS OVER MID-AMERICA
Steam, scheduled
36" gauge

COURTESY OF SIX FLAGS OVER MID-AMERICA

Ride/Operation: The narrow-gauge Six Flags Railroad was built and first operated in 1971. It consists of one 25-ton steam locomotive, a tender, four passenger cars, and a caboose. The engine is a propane-fueled steam locomotive manufactured by Crown Metal Company.

Schedule: Runs continuously around park, stopping at two stations.

Fare/Admission: Free.

Locomotive: One 25-ton narrow-gauge steam locomotive.

Passenger Cars: Open.

Rolling Stock/Equipment: One enclosed caboose.

Location: I-44 and Allentown Road, west of St. Louis.

St. Louis

Contact: John Donnelly
Operations Supervisor

Mailing Address:
P.O. Box 60
Eureka, MO 63025
Telephone: (314) 938-5300

WABASH FRISCO & PACIFIC RAILWAY
"THE UNCOMMON CARRIER"
Steam, scheduled
12" gauge

Ride/Operation: The WF&P, founded in 1939, moved to its present location in 1961. The ride is a 2-mile, 30-minute round trip over a former Missouri Pacific right-of-way along the scenic Meramec River, upgrade through wooded areas and across three bridges. Despite its small size, the railroad is authentically operated. Standard crossing signals protect a street crossing in downtown Glencoe. Fourteen regularly scheduled departures are possible via radio-dispatched, two-train operations using three locomotives, with meets at either Bluffs, one-quarter mile out of Glencoe, or Mohan, one-half mile out. The WF&P is visited regularly by tourists from all nations.

Train: Passenger cars; wooden-benched flatcars; equal to two eight-car trains.

Schedule: Sundays, May 7-October 29, 12:00-4:15 p.m.

Fare: $2.00, children under 3 ride free.

Locomotives: No. 102, 1983 Peoria, IL, 2-6-2 (coal); No. 171, 1907 Elgin, IL, 4-4-0 (coal); No. 180, 1922 4-4-0 (coal); No. 300, 1958 Alton, IL, 4-4-2 (oil); No. 350, 1959 Plainfield, IL, 4-4-4 (coal); No. 400, 1925 Shalford, United Kingdom, CPR prototype 4-6-2 (oil); No. 802, 1982 Wood River, IL, SW-11 (gasoline); No. X-41, 1945 Berkeley, Missouri, 5-horsepower 0-4-0 (gas); No. 82, 1992 rebuilt Pacific, MO, 11-horsepower "B-B" (gas); No. 5205, 1992 Bel-Ridge, MO, 22-horsepower "A" unit (gas); Alco FA style "diesel"; No. 92, 1992 rebuilt TB-11.

Passenger Cars: No. 1300, 1950 passenger coach; No. 1201, 1942 coach. The fleet of 26 cars includes three gondola cars, a tank car, boxcar, and two cabooses; two vehicles were built by full-sized railroads: 1950 gondola No. 51999, former Frisco (Springfield, Missouri, shops); and 1946 aluminum hopper No. 301, former Missouri Pacific (Sedalia, Missouri, shops).

Note: There is frequent train operation at nearby Eureka, where the main lines of the Union Pacific and the Burlington Northern railroads parallel each other.

Location: Halfway between Eureka and Ellisville, about 25 miles west of St. Louis. Take exit 264 (Eureka) off I-44, travel 3.5 miles north on route 109 to Old State Road, and make two right turns to the depot on Washington Street-Grand Avenue.

 (nearby)

Kirkwood

Radio Frequency: 151.955

Contact: David J. Neubauer
President, Operations & Publicity

Mailing Address:
1569 Ville Angela Lane
Hazelwood, MO 63042-1630
Telephone (recorded message):
(314) 587-3538

Missouri, Jackson
R

ST. LOUIS, IRON MOUNTAIN & SOUTHERN RAILWAY
Steam, scheduled
Standard gauge

COURTESY OF ST. LOUIS, IRON MINE & SOUTHERN RAILWAY

Ride/Operation: Steam-powered train takes passengers on their choice of three different round trips over a former Missouri Pacific branch line: a 10-mile, 1 1/4-hour sightseeing trip to Gordonville; a 20-mile, 2-hour dinner trip to Dutchtown; or a 36-mile, 5-hour dinner trip to Delta.

Train: Two 1920 steel coaches, former Illinois Central; former Missouri Pacific cupola caboose; former New York Central Pullman.

Schedule: Weekends, April-October. Sightseeing trip: Saturday, 11:00 a.m. & 2:00 p.m.; Sunday, 1:00 & 3:00 p.m. Dinner train: Saturday, 4:00 or 6:00 p.m., depending on destination. Saturdays, November-March, sightseeing trip, 12:30 p.m. Weekday charters available.

Fare: Sightseeing trip: Adults $8.00, children (3-12) $4.00. Dinner train: $22.00 or $34.50, depending on destination.

Locomotives: No. 5, 1946 Porter 2-4-2, former Central Illinois Public Service, former Crab Orchard & Egyptian; No. 300, 1926 Alco 2-6-0, former Augusta Railway; No. 911, 1952 Baldwin-Lima-Hamilton diesel-electric, former Pittsburg Plate Glass Co.; 1949 14-inch-gauge live-steam 4-6-4.

Rolling Stock/Equipment: Open-air observation car (former piggyback car); two bay-window cabooses.

Special Events: Candlelight Dinner, February 14. Murder Mystery, March 11. Mickey Mouse Days, May 27-28. Train Robberies, June 24-25. Karaoke Weekend, July 15-16. Victorian Weekend, September 9-10. Fall Foliage Breakfast, October 15. Santa Express, December 2, 9, 16 & 23. New Year's Eve Murder Mystery, December 31.

Location: West of I-55 in southeast Missouri, a few miles from Cape Girardeau at the intersection of highways 61, 25, 72, and 34.

Radio Frequencies: 160.845, 161.070

Contact: Amy Philipps
Manager

Mailing Address:
P.O. Box 244
Jackson, MO 63755
Telephone: (314) 243-1688

PATEE HOUSE MUSEUM
Railway museum

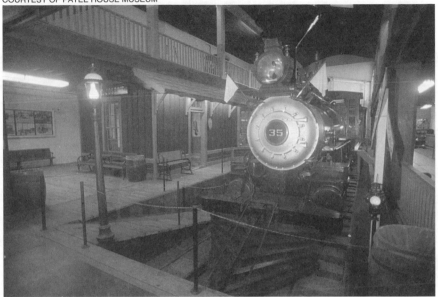

Displays/Exhibits: A communications and transportation museum with exhibits including an 1860 Hannibal & St Joseph steam locomotive and a Railway Post Office, invented by a St. Joseph postmaster to speed the mail on the Pony Express. The train is inside, beside the 1877 depot from Union Star, Missouri. Patee House, opened by John Patee in 1858 as a 140-room luxury hotel, is a National Historical Landmark, having served as a Pony Express headquarters in 1860. The museum also houses antique cars, trucks, fire trucks, telephones, radios, and furniture. Inside are the "Streets of Old St. Jo," antique buggies and wagons, and a 1920s service station.

Admission: Adults $2.00, students (under 18) $1.00.

Locomotives: Baldwin 4-4-0.

Rolling Stock/Equipment: 1960 Pacific track-maintenance motor car, former Union Pacific; 1860 Railway Post Office.

Special Events: Pony Express rerun between St. Joseph, Missouri, and Sacramento, California, the second and third weeks of June each year, in conjunction with the National Pony Express Association. Annual Jesse James Model Railroad Show, last week of June and first week of July.

Notes: The Jesse James Home, where outlaw Jesse James was shot and killed on April 3, 1882, is located next door.

Location: Five minutes from I-29, at 12th and Penn streets. Take U.S. 36 west to 10th Street exit, then travel 6 blocks north and 2 blocks east.

Contact: Gary Chilcote
Museum Director

Mailing Address:
Box 1022
St. Joseph, MO 64502
Telephone: (816) 232-8206

MUSEUM OF TRANSPORTATION
Railway museum
Standard gauge

Displays/Exhibits: One of the country's largest, this transportation museum displays an extensive, important collection of all forms of transportation equipment. On the grounds are more than seventy locomotives, from ancient 4-4-0s to some of the largest, newest steam and diesel engines in the country, including Frisco Lines No. 1522, which has been restored to operating condition. There are also passenger and freight cars, motor trucks, aircraft, streetcars, buses, and fire apparatus.

Schedule: Daily, 9:00 a.m.-5:00 p.m. Closed Thanksgiving, Christmas, and New Year's Day.

Admission: Adults $4.00, senior citizens (65+) $1.50, children (5-12) $1..50.

Locomotives/Trolleys: Thirty-five steam locomotives, including 1858 4-4-0 "Daniel Nason"; 1889 Black Diamond 2-2-2, former Reading; 4-6-0 No. 173, former Baltimore & Ohio; and 4-8-8-4 No. 4006, former Union Pacific. Twenty-three internal-combustion locomotives, including EMD FT-103 No. 50, former B&O; Centennial No. 6944, former UP; and gas-turbine No. 1149, former U.S. Army. Nine electric locomotives, including General Electric No. 1; No. 113, former New York Central; and P5 No. 4700, former Pennsylvania Railroad. Thirty interurbans, including an 1889 mule-drawn streetcar; test car No. 2611; No. 890, former St. Louis; and railbus No. 206, former Illinois Terminal.

Passenger Cars: Twenty-three, including parlor car, former Gulf, Mobile & Ohio; Pullman Colonial No. 94; No. A-252, former Mississippi Central; observation car No. 750, former Missouri Pacific.

Rolling Stock/Equipment: Fifty-four pieces, including poultry palace car; vinegar car No. 1634, GATY No. 96500; and composite gondola, former Chicago, Burlington & Quincy.

Location: From the north, take Big Bend Road exit off I-270, turn right and travel to Barrett Station Road. From the south, take Dougherty Ferry Road exit off I-270, turn left and travel to Barrett Station Road.

Kirkwood

Contact: Wayne Schmidt
Director

Mailing Address:
3015 Barrett Station Road
St. Louis, MO 63122
Telephone: (314) 965-7998

Missouri, St. Louis
R

ST. LOUIS & CHAIN OF ROCKS RAILROAD
Diesel, scheduled
Standard gauge

RICHARD A. EICHHORST

Ride: A 6-mile, 1-hour round trip on the tracks of the St. Louis Water Works Railway. The Southern Division connects with the Burlington Northern in North St. Louis, offering a view of the downtown skyline and the Gateway Arch. The Northern Division runs along the bank of the Mississippi River, offering a view of Dam No. 27, the largest rock-fill dam in the United States.

Train: Consist from locomotive and passenger-car pool.

Schedule: April 9, May 14, June 11, July 9, August 13, September 10, October 8; 1:00-4:00 p.m.

Fare: Coach and open car: Donations welcomed. Private car (combine): $3.00.

Locomotives: EMD F7A No. 406, former Chicago & North Western; 80-ton Whitcomb, former Missouri Portland Cement.

Passenger Cars: Combine, former CC&H, former Bessemer & Lake Erie; coach, former Central of New Jersey; open-air car, former St. Louis Southwestern flatcar; cabooses, former Norfolk & Western and former Illinois Central; RDC-1, former New Jersey Department of Transportation.

Rolling Stock/Equipment: Stored equipment includes the "Hayride Car," a former St. Louis Southwestern gondola; former Baltimore & Ohio and Chesapeake & Ohio baggage cars; a former Western Maryland exhibit car; former B&O, Alton & Southern, Frisco, Chicago Great Western, Manufacturers Railway, Rock Island, C&NW, and TRRA cabooses; motor cars; handcar; Illinois Central, Essex Terminal & Union Pacific cabooses.

Special Events: Hayride On A Train, November 12. Santa Claus Train, December 10. These events are sponsored by the American Association of Railroaders Inc., as a benefit for the SL&CR.

Location: Riverview Boulevard at Spring Garden Drive, 1.5 miles south of I-270 bridge over the Mississippi River. A boat landing on the Mississippi River is adjacent to the station.

Contact: Richard A. Eichhorst
President & General Manager

Mailing Address:
4351 Holly Hills Boulevard
St. Louis, MO 63116-2255
Telephone: (314) 752-3148

167

Missouri, Springfield
M

FRISCO RAILROAD MUSEUM
Railway museum
Standard gauge

COURTESY OF FRISCO RAILROAD MUSEUM

Displays/Exhibits: This museum, located at station 238 on the Frisco's former Lebanon Subdivision, Eastern Division, is housed in a building originally constructed by the Frisco Railway in 1943 as a Centralized Traffic Control command center. It is the only facility in the country devoted exclusively to the preservation and display of the history and memorabilia of the Frisco Railway. The facility displays more than 2,000 items of Frisco and Frisco-related memorabilia, representing a wide range of operations, equipment, and services. In addition, it has the largest archive of historical, technical, and photographic information about the Frisco currently available to the public through its "Frisco Folks" membership program.

Schedule: Tuesday-Saturday, 10:00 a.m.-5:00 p.m.

Admission: Adults $2.00, children (under 12) $1.00. Group discounts available.

Rolling Stock/Equipment: Caboose No. 139 and boxcar No. 10055, both former Frisco.

Special Events: Frisco Days, April. Christmas Open House, featuring large collection of train-related Christmas ornaments, two weeks before Christmas.

Note: Frisco steam locomotive No. 4254 is on display in a city park near the museum.

Location: At 543 East Commercial Street. Take exit 80 A/B off I-44, travel south on business 65 1.3 miles to Commercial Street (third light), then travel west 1.3 miles.

Contact: Alan Schmitt
President

Mailing Address:
543 East Commercial Street
Springfield, MO 65803
Telephone: (417) 866-SLSF (7573)
800-N-FRISCO (637-4726)

FREMONT & ELKHORN VALLEY RAILROAD
Diesel, scheduled
Standard gauge

COURTESY OF FREMONT & ELKHORN VALLEY RAILROAD

Ride/Operation: The Fremont & Elkhorn Valley, Nebraska's longest and largest excursion railroad and designated the State Railroad Museum of Nebraska, offers a 30-mile, 3-hour round trip to the historic town of Hooper, including a 30-minute stopover. The train crosses the Mormon Trail and runs through the beautiful Elkhorn River valley on a portion of the former Chicago & North Western main line to the Black Hills. The railroad also hosts the *Fremont Dinner Train*, which operates year-round.

Train: 1920s heavyweight coaches, former C&NW; 1940s lightweight coaches, former Milwaukee Road; steel and wood cabooses; RPO car, former Burlington.

Schedule: Hooper: Weekends, May-October; Saturday, 12:00p.m., Sunday, 2:00p.m.; Sunday only, by reservation, November-December (heated coaches). Nickerson (16-mile round trip): Saturdays, June-August, 2:00p.m.

Fare: Hooper: First class: adults $12.75, children (under 13) $6.75. Tourist class: adults $10.75, children (under 13) $5.75. Nickerson: adults $6.50, children (under 13) $4.50.

Locomotives: No. 1219, 1962 EMD SW-1200, former C&NW.

Passenger Cars: 1947 dining car, former Illinois Central; 1942 dining car, former Canadian National; 1949 coach, former Milwaukee; two 1925 coaches, former C&NW.

Special Events: Hooper "Old Fashioned" Fourth of July. Santa Train.

Location: At 1835 North Somers. Fremont is about 35 miles west of Omaha.

Radio Frequency: 160.245

Contact: Bruce Eveland
Manager

Mailing Address:
1835 North Somers
Fremont, NE 68025
Telephone: (402) 727-0615

THOMAS R. SCHULTZ

STUHR MUSEUM
OF THE PRAIRIE PIONEER
Railway display
Standard gauge, narrow gauge

Displays/Exhibits: The Stuhr Museum preserves and interprets the history of steam railroading in Nebraska. Southeast of the museum's main building is "Railroad Town," a re-created prairie railroad community with sixty turn-of-the-century structures that focus on a large railyard exhibit consisting of the 1887 Kearney & Black Hills depot; stationary standard- and narrow-gauge steam locomotives, rolling stock, and equipment; and miscellaneous memorabilia. Standard-gauge equipment on display includes 1902 Baldwin 2-8-0 No. 437, a 1912 caboose, Pullman car "Lake Crystal," and other passenger equipment, all former Union Pacific; and 1872 St. Joseph-Grand Island boarding car. Narrow-gauge equipment on display includes No. 69, 1908 Baldwin 2-8-0, former White Pass & Yukon; 1897 coach, former Florence & Cripple Creek No. 65; 1874 baggage car, former Colorado & Southern; and three gondolas, former Denver & Rio Grande Western.

Schedule: Daily, May 1-October 15.
Admission: Adults $6.40, students (7-16) $3.75, children under 7 admitted free.

Location: Four miles north of I-80, at the junction of U.S. routes 281 and 34.

Contact: Gail Stoklasa
Marketing Director

Mailing Address:
3133 West Highway 34
Grand Island, NE 68801
Telephone: (308) 385-5316

OMAHA ZOO RAILROAD
Steam, scheduled
30" gauge

WILLIAM W. KRATVILLE

Ride/Operation: Passengers take a guided, 2 1/2-mile, 20-minute trip through the zoo grounds, seeing hundreds of animals, including many rare and endangered species.

Displays/Exhibits: Exotic animals featured at the zoo include white tigers, leopards, lions, polar bears, elephants, rhinos, gorillas, and monkeys. Visitors can also experience a trip through Lied Jungle, the world's largest indoor rain forest. A new aquarium is opening in 1995, featuring king penguins, sharks, and thousands of fish. Also new is a state-of-the-art engine house, funded by donations from the Union Pacific Railroad.

Train: Weekends: No. 395-104, five open-air coaches, caboose. Weekdays: No. 119, four open-air coaches.

Schedule: Train: Daily, May 30-September 5; weekends, April 1-May 29 and September 6-October 31; 11:00 a.m.-4:00 p.m. Zoo: Daily, year-round.

Fare/Admission: Train: Adults $2.50, children (3-11) $1.50, children under 3 ride free. Zoo: Adults $7.00, children (5-11) $3.50, children under 5 admitted free, senior citizens $5.50, family membership $55.00.

Locomotives: No. 395-104, 1890 Krauss 0-6-2T; No. 119, 1968 Crown 4-4-0, replica of Union Pacific 4-4-0 No. 119.

Passenger Cars: Five open-air coaches; caboose.

Rolling Stock/Equipment: Ballast maintainer; Fairmont MT14 motor car.

Special Events: Members' Day, with free train rides to zoo members. Halloween Terror Train during zoo-sponsored Halloween Party—children in costume ride free.

Location: Henry Doorly Zoo, 3701 South 10th Street.

Contact: Cyndy T. Andrews

Mailing Address:
3701 South 10th Street
Omaha, NE 68107
Telephone: (402) 733-8401

171

UNION PACIFIC HISTORICAL MUSEUM
Railway museum

UNION PACIFIC HISTORICAL MUSEUM COLLECTION

Displays/Exhibits: This museum tells the story of the Union Pacific Railroad and the role it played in building the West from the days of Abraham Lincoln and General Grenville Dodge to the present. Displays include a life-sized model of Lincoln's funeral car; mementos of the driving of the Golden Spike at Promontory; a stuffed buffalo; General Dodge's surveying instruments; an O-gauge model railroad; a railroad auditor's office from the 1880s; historic Union Pacific model trains, cars, and locomotives; lanterns; china; silver; and other artifacts and photos showing the growth and operations of the Union Pacific.

Schedule: Monday-Friday, 9:00 a.m.-3:00 p.m. Saturdays, 9:00 a.m.-12:00 p.m.
Admission: No charge.

Location: On the first floor of the Union Pacific Railroad's twelve-story headquarters building in downtown Omaha.

            Omaha

Contact: Peggy Shepherd
Information Coordinator

Mailing Address:
1416 Dodge Street
Omaha, NE 68179
Telephone: (402) 271-3530

NEVADA STATE RAILROAD MUSEUM
Railway museum
Standard gauge

GEORGE A. FORERO, JR.

Ride/Operation: A steam locomotive or motor car operates on selected weekends during the summer.

Displays/Exhibits: The museum owns more than sixty locomotives, passenger cars, and freight cars, including the largest collection of nineteenth-century railroading equipment in the country. Featured are thirty pieces from the famous Virginia & Truckee railroad, many seen in movies and on television. The museum also houses exhibits, photos, and artifacts of Nevada's railroad heritage. The state of Nevada owns an additional forty-seven pieces, stored in southern Nevada.

Schedule: Museum: Wednesday-Sunday, 8:30 a.m.-4:30 p.m. Steam train: selected weekends, May 30-September 5, plus October 22-23; call or write for schedule. Motor car: selected weekends, May 30-September 5; call or write for schedule.

Fare/Admission: Museum: adults $2.00, children under 18 admitted free. Steam train: adults $2.50, children (6-11) $1.00, children under 6 ride free. Motor car: Adults $1.00, children (6-11) $.50, children under 6 ride free.

Locomotives: No. 25, 1905 Baldwin 4-6-0; No. 18, "Dayton," 1873 Central Pacific 4-4-0; and No. 22, "Inyo," 1875 Baldwin 4-4-0; all former V&T. No. 1, "Glenbrook," 1875 Baldwin narrow-gauge 2-6-0, former Carson & Tahoe Lumber & Fluming Co.; No. 8, 1888 Cooke 4-4-0, former Dardanelle & Russellville.

Rolling Stock/Equipment: Coaches Nos. 3, 4, 8, 11, 12, 17 & 18, express/mail Nos. 14 & 21, caboose-coaches Nos. 9 & 10, and eleven freight cars, all former V&T; French "40 & 8" boxcar; chair car No. 30, former Las Vegas & Tonopah; coaches Nos. 24 & 52, former Nevada-California-Oregon; narrow-gauge freight cars Nos. 4, 159 & 162, former Southern Pacific; baggage-mail-express No. 3, former Carson & Colorado; caboose No. 3, former Nevada Copper

Belt; caboose No. 402, former Tonopah & Tidewater; caboose No. 449, former Western Pacific; hopper No. 409, former Nevada Northern; motor car "Washoe Zephyr," former Tucson, Cornelia & Gila Bend No. 401.

Special Events: Nevada State Handcar Championships, August. Virginia & Truckee Railroad History Symposium, October 13-15.

Location: 2180 South Carson Street (highways 50 & 395) at the south end of town.

Contact: Kyle Wyatt
Assistant Curator

Mailing Address:
Capitol Complex
Carson City, NV 89710
Telephone: (702) 687-6953

173

NEVADA NORTHERN RAILWAY MUSEUM
Steam, diesel, scheduled
Standard gauge

JACK SWANBERG

Ride/Operation: Keystone Route: A 14-mile, 1 1/2-hour round trip to the historic mining district of Keystone, passing downtown Ely, tunnel No. 1, the ghost town of Lane City, and Robinson Canyon. Highline Route: A 22-mile, 1 1/2-hour round trip with exciting overviews of the scenic Steptoe Valley, high in the foothills.

Displays/Exhibits: Steam, diesel, and electric locomotives; 1907 steam rotary snowplow; 1910 Jordan spreader; more than sixty pieces of antique passenger, freight, and work equipment; general offices; depot; machine shops; roundhouse.

Train: 1890s Pullman coach; 1908 St. Louis coach; open car with benches.

Schedule: Museum: daily, May 27-September 3, 45-minute walking tours at 9:00 & 11:30 a.m. and 2:00 & 4:00 p.m. Steam excursions: May 27-28, June 3, 10, 17 & 24, July 1-3, 8, 15, 22 & 29, August 5-6, 12, 19 & 26, September 2-3; 1:30 & 3:30 p.m. Diesel excursions along the Highline Route depart at 5:30 p.m. Call for more information.

Fare/Admission: Museum: $2.50, children under 10 admitted free. Steam train: Adults $14.00, senior citizens & youths $12.00, children $6.00. Diesel trains: adults $10.00, senior citizens & youths $8.00, children $4.00. Group discounts and charters available.

Locomotives: No. 40, 1910 Baldwin 4-6-0, Nevada Northern Railway; No. 93, 1909 Alco 2-8-0; No. 105, Alco RS-2, and No. 109, Alco RS-3, both former Kennecott Copper Co.

Special Events: 1995 "Raildays," Labor Day weekend. Fireworks Train, July 4 (evening). Locomotive rental programs available.

Location: In eastern Nevada on U.S. 93; trains leave from the East Ely Depot at 1100 Avenue A at 11th Street East.

(during Raildays)

Contact: Lorraine Ulibarri
Executive Director

Mailing Address:
P.O. Box 150040
East Ely, NV 89315
Telephone: (702) 289-2085

VIRGINIA & TRUCKEE RAILROAD CO.
Steam, scheduled
Standard gauge

GEORGE A. FORERO, JR.

Ride/Operation: A 5-mile round trip from Virginia City to the town of Gold Hill through the heart of the historic Comstock mining region. A knowledgeable conductor gives a running commentary of the area and of the 126-year-old railroad.

Displays/Exhibits: 1888 Northwestern Pacific combine and coach; former Tonopah & Tidewater coach; former Northern Pacific caboose; No. 30, 1919 0-6-0, former Southern Pacific.

Train: Open car; two semiclosed cars.

Schedule: Daily, May 28-October 2; weekends, October; 10:30 a.m.-5:45 p.m. Cab rides available; inquire at ticket office.

Fare: Adults $4.50, children (5-12) $2.25, children under 4 ride free. All-day pass $9.00.

Locomotives: No. 29, 1916 Baldwin 2-8-0, former Longview, Portland & Northern; No. 8, 1907 Baldwin 2-6-2, former Hobart Southern.

Note: Special excursion and party trains available. Please call or write for details.

Location: At Washington and "F" Streets.

Contact: Robert C. Gray
President

Mailing Address:
P.O. Box 467
Virginia City, NV 89440
Telephone: (702) 847-0380

HOBO RAILROAD
Diesel, scheduled
Standard gauge

COURTESY OF HOBO RAILROAD

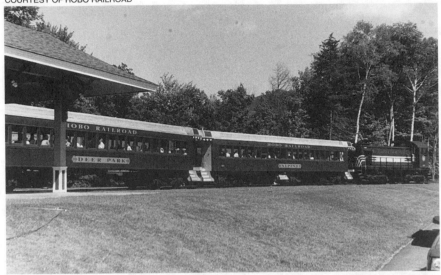

Ride/Operation: A 1 1/4-hour train ride in a woodsy setting along the Pemigewasset River on former Boston & Maine track. On most trips passengers glimpse a variety of wildlife, including a golden eagle, ducks, a blue heron, beavers, and other small creatures. Passengers may also enjoy lunch or dinner on the train. The Hobo Picnic Lunch is a unique specialty, served in a souvenir hobo bindle stick. Fine dining is also offered on the 7:00 p.m. train aboard the "Cafe Lafayette," a restored 1924 Pullman dining car.

Train: Open-platform coaches; dining car.

Schedule: Daily, May 29-late October; Wednesday-Sunday, 11:00 a.m., 1:00, 3:00, 5:00 & 7:00 p.m.; Monday & Tuesday, 11:00 a.m., 1:00, 3:00 & 5:00 p.m. As needed, mid March-May 29 & November 1-December 31; please call or write for information. Group tours available mid-March to December; call or write for more information.

Fare: Adults $7.00, children $4.50, children under 4 ride free. Food service priced separately. Reservations suggested for all trains.

Locomotives: No. 1008, 1949 Alco S-1, former Portland Terminal; No. 959, 1949 Alco S-1, former North Stratford.

Rolling Stock/Equipment: Four modified motors, former Erie & Lackawanna; modified Pullman day coach, former New York Central; two kitchen cars, former U.S. Army; several Budd cars; others.

Special Events: Easter Bunny Trains, April 8-9 & 15. Track Car Weekend, June 3-4. Fourth of July Family Party Train. Gold Panning, July & August. Halloween Specials, late October. Santa Trains, November 24-25, December 2-3, 9-10 & 16-17. Others. Please call or write for details.

Note: Many unadvertised trains are operated. The Hobo Railroad is under the same ownership and management as the Winnipesaukee Scenic Railroad in Meredith, New Hampshire. The general office for both operations is in Lincoln.

Location: On Kancamagus Highway, in the heart of the scenic White Mountains. Take exit 32 off I-93.

Radio Frequencies: 160.47, 161.55

Contact: Eddie or Brenda Clark

Mailing Address:
P.O. Box 9
Lincoln, NH 03251
Telephone: (603) 745-2135

WHITE MOUNTAIN CENTRAL RAILROAD
Steam, scheduled
Standard gauge

Ride/Operation: A 2-mile, 30-minute ride through the scenic White Mountains, leaving from a beautiful depot at Clark's Trading Post. The train crosses a 120-foot covered bridge and climbs a 2-percent grade into the woods.

Displays/Exhibits: A facsimile of an 1890s railroad station, a wooden caboose, boxcars, and flatcars. Other exhibits include trained bears; a fire museum; an Americana museum; a haunted house; an antique photo parlor; a 1920s-era garage; an illusion building, "Merlin's Mansion"; and much more.

Train: Climax steam locomotive; open excursion cars.

Schedule: Daily, July & August; weekends, May 29-June 30 & September 1-October 9; six trains per day.

Fare: Adults $7.00, children (6-11) $6.00, children (3-5) $1.00, children under 3 ride free. Group discounts available.

Locomotives: No. 4, 1927 2-truck Heisler, former International Shoe Co.; No. 6, Climax, former Beebe River Railroad; No. 3, former East Branch & Lincoln.

Rolling Stock: Caboose; boxcar.

Location: On route 3, one mile north of North Woodstock.

Contact: W. Murray Clark
Vice President & Treasurer

Mailing Address:
Box 1
Lincoln, NH 03251
Telephone: (603) 745-8913

177

New Hampshire, Meredith
D-R

WINNIPESAUKEE SCENIC RAILROAD
Diesel, scheduled
Standard gauge

GEORGE A. FORERO, JR.

Ride/Operation: This line operates 1- and 2-hour excursions over former Boston & Maine track between Meredith and Lakeport. Passengers view unsurpassed scenery along the shores of New Hampshire's largest lake, Lake Winnipesaukee, in the comfort of climate-controlled coaches. Dining service is available during the summer, and the Ice Cream Parlor Car offers a make-your-own-sundae bar aboard the train. Fall foliage tours are 3-hour round trips to Plymouth.

Displays/Exhibits: An 1893 former B&M baggage car serves as the ticket office; cabooses and other rolling stock are also on exhibit.

Train: Diesel locomotives; coaches, former B&M, New Haven, and SEPTA.

Schedule: Daily, July 1-September 4; departures from Weirs at 11:00 a.m., 12:00, 1:00, 2:00, 3:00, 4:00 & 5:00 p.m.; departures from Meredith at 10:30 a.m., 12:30, 2:30 & 4:30 p.m., with a 6:30 p.m. dinner train on weekends. As needed, May 1-June 30 & September 5-October 31; please call or write for information. Fall foliage: September 24 & 30, October 1, 7-9 & 14-15; 9:30 a.m. & 1:00 p.m. Reservations required for fall foliage trips; please call or write for information. Groups: please call or write for information.

Fare: One-hour trip: adults $6.50, children $5.50, children under 4 ride free. Two-hour trip: adults $7.50, children $5.50, under 4 ride free. Food service priced separately; reservations suggested for food service.

Locomotives: No. 2, 1943 44-ton General Electric, former U.S. Government; No. 1186, 1952 Alco S-3, former B&M.

Rolling Stock/Equipment: Five Budd RDC-1 coaches; 1893 baggage car, former B&M, serving as ticket office; cabooses; others.

Special Events: Track Car Weekend, June 3-4. Caboose Fun Trains. Others. Please call or write for details.

Note: Many unadvertised trains are operated. The Winnipesaukee Scenic Railroad is under the same ownership and management as the Hobo Railroad in Lincoln, New Hampshire. The general office for both operations is in Lincoln.

Location: In the Lakes Region of New Hampshire, with boarding at Meredith or Weirs Beach. Free parking at Meredith, just off route 3.

Radio Frequencies: 160.47, 161.55

Contact: Eddie or Brenda Clark

Mailing Address:
P.O. Box 9
Lincoln, NH 03251
Telephone:
Year-round - (603) 745-2135
In season - (603) 279-5253

New Hampshire, Mt. Washington
R

GEORGE A. FORERO, JR.

MOUNT WASHINGTON RAILWAY CO.
Steam, scheduled
4' 8" gauge (cog)

Ride/Operation: The world's first mountain-climbing railway, completed in 1869, is still 100-percent steam-powered. The train ascends New England's highest mountain on a breathtaking right-of-way with grades as steep as 37.41 percent. The average grade is 25 percent to the summit, elevation 6,288 feet.

Displays/Exhibits: "Old Peppersass," the world's first cog engine, on display at the Base Station; museum with historical exhibits.

Train: Open- or closed-platform coach.

Schedule: <u>Daily</u>, early May-October, on the hour from 8:00 a.m. <u>Spring and fall</u> schedules vary; call for information. Last train leaves three hours before sunset in summer. <u>All trains are subject to cancellation</u> because of weather conditions or lack of passengers.

Fare: <u>Round trip</u>: $35.00. <u>Group rates</u> available. <u>Family rates and senior citizens'</u> discounts available. Reservations recommended.

Passenger Cars: Four new wooden coaches have been built since 1990 by the Cog Railway shops.

Locomotives: Eight 0-2-2-0 cog-wheel locomotives with inclined boilers: six built by Manchester Locomotive Works, 1870-1908; No. 10, "Col. Teague," built in Mt. Washington shops, 1972; No. 8, constructed in the Cog Railway shops, placed in service in 1983.

Note: Historic Cog Railway video is available.

Location: Off U.S. route 302 east of Twin Mountain.

Contact: Bobby Trask
General Manager

Mailing Address:
Mount Washington, NH 03589
Telephone: (603) 846-5404
Advance ticket purchases:
(800) 922-8825

179

CONWAY SCENIC RAILROAD
Steam, scheduled
Standard gauge

LES MACDONALD

Ride/Operation: Rides of varying duration originate at North Conway's historic 1874 railroad station and take passengers over a former Boston & Maine branch line through farmlands in the Mount Washington Valley. New for 1995 is a trip west on the Crawford Notch line to Bartlett Village.

Displays/Exhibits: A museum of railroad memorabilia is located within the 120-year-old Victorian railroad station. An old-time roundhouse and operating turntable are highlights of the railroad yard, which also displays many pieces of restored rolling stock and maintenance-of-way equipment.

Train: Coaches; open observation cars; extra-fare 1898 Pullman parlor-observation car; dining car.

Schedule: <u>Daily</u>, May 13-October 29; <u>weekends</u>, April 15-May 12 & November 4-December 17. <u>Fine dining</u> available on dining car from mid June to late October. Please call for information.

Fare: Adults from $7.50, children (4-12) from $5.00, children under 4 ride free when not occupying a seat in coach. <u>Coach and first-class service</u> available. <u>Group and charter rates available</u> upon request.

Locomotives: No. 7470, 1921 Grand Trunk 0-6-0, former Canadian National; No. 15, 1945 44-ton General Electric, former Maine Central; No. 1055, 1950 Alco-General Electric S-4, former Portland Terminal Co.; No. 4266, 1949 EMD F-7, former Boston & Maine; No. 4268, 1949 EMD F-7 (display); No. 108, 1920 Baldwin 2-6-2, former Reader Railroad (display); No. 501, 1910 Alco 2-8-0, former Maine Central (display).

Passenger Cars: Restored wood and early steel cars.

Special Events: <u>Annual Railfan's Day</u>, September 16. Thanksgiving <u>"Turkey Trotter,"</u> November 24-26. <u>"Santa Claus Express,"</u> December 2-3, 9-10 & 16-17.

Location: The depot faces the village park. North Conway is on routes 16 and 302 in New Hampshire's Mount Washington Valley.

Boston, MA, or White River Jct., VT

Radio Frequency: 161.250

Contact: Russell G. Seybold
President & General Manager

Mailing Address:
P.O. Box 1947
North Conway, NH 03860
Telephone: (603) 356-5251

HARTMANN MODEL RAILROAD LTD.

Displays/Exhibits: A display for all ages, this site features many operating layouts, from G to Z scales, including a replica of Crawford Notch, New Hampshire, in the mid 1950s to early 1960s. Visitors can see several other detailed operating layouts with trains winding through tunnels, over bridges, and past miniature stations and buildings, and Thomas the Tank Engine operates by a light-sensor system. Also on display are about 2,500 to 3,000 model locomotives and coaches, American and European, from the site's extensive collection; included is a unique handmade brass locomotive and car display from the 1930s. Displays change constantly.

Schedule: Daily, 11:00 a.m.-5:00 p.m.

Admission: Adults $5.00, senior citizens $4.00, children (5-15) $3.00. Group rates available upon request.

Location: At Norcross Place, 300 feet from the depot of the Conway Scenic Railroad, on routes 16/302 in the heart of town.

COURTESY OF KLICKETY KLACK MODEL RAILROAD

Displays/Exhibits: This model railroad, housed in a 30-foot by 76-foot building, features model trains in H, O, and N gauges. Visitors are invited to operate eleven trains and can push fifteen buttons to operate accessories.

Schedule: July 1-September 5, Monday-Saturday, 10:00 a.m.-5:30 p.m. September 6-June 30, Thursday-Saturday, 10:00 a.m.-5:00 p.m. Closed the last week in April.

Admission: Adults $4.00, children (3-12) $3.00.

Location: At the junction of routes 28 and 109A.

Contact: Richard Parshley
Owner

Mailing Address:
P.O. Box 205
Wolfeboro Falls, NH 03896
Telephone: (603) 569-5384

NEW JERSEY MUSEUM OF TRANSPORTATION
Steam, diesel, scheduled
36" gauge

GEORGE A. FORERO, JR.

Ride/Operation: This museum, which operates the Pine Creek Railroad at Allaire State Park, offers a 10-minute, 1 1/2-mile ride over a loop track.

Displays/Exhibits: A variety of narrow-gauge engines and cars either on display or being restored in the railroad shop. Allaire Park is the site of a restored early-1800s iron-making community.

Train: No. 502, 1902 open-platform wood coach, former Newfoundland Railway; No. 91155, 1874 wooden caboose, former Central of New Jersey; open excursion car.

Schedule: Steam: weekends & holidays, May-mid October. Diesel: weekdays, July & August. Trains run every 30 minutes from 12:00 to 5:00 p.m. Locomotives and schedules may be changed when required by operating conditions.

Fare: $2.00, children under 3 and members ride free on non-special-event days. Fares slightly higher during special events.

Locomotives: No. 6, 1927 2-truck Shay, former Ely-Thomas Lumber Co.; No. 3L, "Lady Edith," 1887 Stephenson 4-4-0T, former Cavan & Leitram Railway (Ireland); No. 26, 1920 Baldwin 2-6-2, former Surrey, Sussex & Southampton Railway; No. 1, 1942 12-ton Plymouth, former Haws Refractories; No. 40, 1940 25-ton Whitcomb, former Midvale Steel Corp.; No. 7751, 1942 25-ton General Electric, former U.S. Army; 1953 25-ton General Electric, former Kerr-McGee.

Special Events: Great Locomotive Chase/Civil War Reenactment, June 18; 12:00-4:00 p.m. Railroaders' Day, September 10, 12:00-4:30 p.m. Christmas Express, November 25-26, December 2-3, 9-10 & 16-17, 12:00-3:00 p.m.

Location: On route 524, Wall Township, Monmouth County. Take exit 98 off the Garden State Parkway and travel west, or take exit 31 off I-195 and travel east.

Contact: John P. Lyle II
General Manager

Mailing Address:
P.O. Box 622
Allaire, NJ 07727-0622
Telephone: (908) 938-5524
FAX: (908) 918-0742

BLACK RIVER & WESTERN RAILROAD
Steam, diesel, scheduled

JOHN E. HELBOK

Ride/Operation: This railroad offers a 10-mile round trip from Ringoes to Flemington on a former branch of the Pennsylvania Railroad and a 14-mile round trip between Ringoes and Lambertville, passing through some of New Jersey's most scenic farm country. Passengers on the Ringoes-Flemington trip may board at either town.

Displays/Exhibits: Museum and railroad equipment stored in Ringoes yard; the Ringoes station, built in 1872; and the Lambertville station, built in 1887.

Train: No. 60, Alco 2-8-0, used on weekend trips between Flemington and Ringoes; diesel used on all other trips. Former Delaware, Lackawanna & Western, Central of New Jersey, and Canadian National passenger cars.

Schedule: Ringoes-Flemington: weekends, April 1-June 30 & September 1-December 15; daily, July 1-August 31; lv. Ringoes 10:45 a.m., 12:15, 1:45 & 3:15 p.m.; lv. Flemington 11:30 a.m., 12:15, 1:45 & 3:15 p.m.; lv. Flemington 11:30 a.m., 1:00 & 2:30 p.m. Ringoes-Lambertville: Sundays, May 1-October 31; call for departure times.

Fare: Adults $6.00, children (4-12) $3.00, children under 4 ride free. Season passes available.

Locomotives: No. 60, 1937 Alco 2-8-0; No. 752, 1956 EMD GP-9; No. 780, 1950 EMD GP-7; No. 42, EMD CF7 rebuilt in 1978, former Atchison, Topeka & Santa Fe.

Passenger Cars: Nos. 320-323, commuter cars, former Central of New Jersey; Nos. 301-305, "Wyatt Earp" cars, former Delaware, Lackawanna & Western; Nos. 491-494, heavyweight cars, former Canadian National; No. 2066, lounge converted to diner.

Rolling Stock/Equipment: Caboose No. 645, former Maine Central; caboose No. C-140, former Erie; wreck crane No. 197, former Long Island.

Special Events: Easter Bunny Train. Shad Festival. Train Robbery. July 4th. Railroad Days. Pumpkin Festival. *Santa Express*. Please call for schedules.

Location: The Ringoes depot is on county route 579, 3/4 mile from the junction of highways 31 and 202. The Flemington depot is in the center of town near Liberty Village.

184

WHIPPANY RAILWAY MUSEUM
Railway museum
Standard gauge

STEVE KAY

Operation: The Whippany Railway Museum, with headquarters in the restored 1904 freight house of the Morristown & Erie Railway, is the only museum in the north Jersey area devoted to railroading. Inside are displays and artifacts from many area railroads, including headlights, bells, whistles, photos, tickets, and a large Lionel O-gauge layout. New for 1995 is a one-hundredth-anniversary tribute to the Whippany River Railroad, the predecessor of the present-day Morristown & Erie Railway. The 1995 special transportation exhibit commemorates the eightieth anniversary of the torpedoing of the passenger liner *Lusitania* in May 1915. The loss of this ship and twelve hundred of its passengers hastened the U.S.'s entry into World War I. Outdoor exhibits include a replica of a small suburban retail coal yard as well as several pieces of historic railroad rolling stock and equipment.

Schedule: Sundays and holidays, April-October, 12:00-4:00 p.m.

Admission: Suggested donation: adults $1.00, children (under 12) $.50.

Rolling Stock/Equipment: New additions to the museum's growing collection include 0-6-0 No. 4039, 1942 Alco, former Morris County Central, former Virginia Blue Ridge; commuter observation car "Jersey Coast," former Jersey Central, restored to the appearance of a *Blue Comet* observation car; and a wreck crane and idler car, former Erie. Additional equipment includes a 1918 White railbus, former M&E, former MCC; and assorted passenger and freight cars from many Northeast anthracite carriers, including the Delaware & Hudson; the Delaware, Lackawanna & Western; the Erie; the Erie Lackawanna; and the Central of New Jersey.

Special Events: Annual Railroad Festival, fall. *Easter Bunny Express* and *Santa Claus Express* operate during holiday seasons with Morristown & Erie power and equipment. Please call or write for details.

Location: 1 Railroad Plaza, at the intersection of route 10 & Whippany Road.

🚗 ⊞ 🚏 ✉ ♿ 𝕒𝕣𝕞

 Newark, Metropark Station

Radio Frequency: 160.230 (Morristown & Erie Railway)

Contact: Joseph Krygoski
Vice President

Mailing Address:
P.O. Box 16
Whippany, NJ 07981-0016
Telephone: (201) 887-8177

TOY TRAIN DEPOT
16" gauge
Model railroads

COURTESY OF TOY TRAIN DEPOT

Ride/Operation: Visitors can take a 3-mile ride through Alameda Park on a 16-inch-gauge passenger train led by an F-3 diesel.

Displays/Exhibits: This museum of toy and model trains is housed in a refurbished 1898 Southern Pacific depot. Exhibits include operating layouts in N, TT, HO, S, and O gauge. The HO layout has more than twelve hundred feet of track; there are also displays of models from Z to G gauge and a 7 1/2-inch-gauge live-steam engine.

Schedule: Wednesday-Monday, 12:00-5:00 p.m.; train operates 12:00-4:30 p.m. Closed New Year's Day, Thanksgiving, and Christmas.

Admission: Museum: adults $1.50, children $1.00. Train: adults $2.00, children $1.00. Children under 6 must be accompanied by an adult.

Location: At the north end of Alameda Park on highway 54/70. Take U.S. 70 north from I-10 in El Paso, Texas, south from I-40 in Santa Rosa, New Mexico, or east from I-25 in Las Cruces, New Mexico.

El Paso, Texas

Contact: John Koval
President

Mailing Address:
1991 North White Sands Boulevard
Alamogordo, NM 88310
Telephone: (505) 437-2855

New Mexico, Chama	CUMBRES & TOLTEC SCENIC RAILROAD
Colorado, Antonito	*Steam, scheduled*
R	*36" gauge*

Ride/Operation: Steam trains travel over highly scenic former Denver & Rio Grande Western narrow-gauge trackage. The 64-mile line crosses Cumbres Pass (elevation 10,015 feet) and goes through spectacular Toltec Gorge, over high bridges, and through two tunnels. Passengers may choose to ride either the *Colorado Limited* from Antonito to Osier, Colorado, via Toltec Gorge or the *New Mexico Express* from Chama, New Mexico, to Osier via Cumbres Pass. The two trains meet at Osier for a lunch stop, and the trains exchange locomotives for the return trip.

Train: Coaches; snack bar; souvenir-shop car; open observation car.

Schedule: Daily, May 28-mid October; lv. Chama 10:30 a.m., return 4:30 p.m.; lv. Antonito 10:00 a.m., return 5:00 p.m. Passengers are advised to dress warmly, since sudden and dramatic changes in the weather may occur.

Location: Terminals at Chama, New Mexico, and Antonito, Colorado.

Fare: Round trip: adults $32.00, children (under 12) $16.00. Through trips from either terminal with return by van: adults $50.00, children $26.00. Reservations recommended for all trips.

Locomotives: Nos. 463, 484, 487, 488, 489, 497, 1925 Baldwin 2-8-2s, former D&RGW.

Notes: The C&TS is a joint undertaking of the states of Colorado and New Mexico. The line is leased to Kyle Railways, Inc.

Contact: Joe C. Vigil
General Manager

Mailing Address:
P.O. Box 668
Antonito, CO 81120
P.O. Box 789
Chama, NM 87520
Telephone:
Antonito: (719) 376-5483
Chama: (505) 756-2151

ARCADE & ATTICA RAILROAD
Steam, scheduled
Standard gauge

PETER SWANSON

Ride/Operation: The A&A, a common-carrier railroad that has been in existence since 1881, offers a 15-mile, 2-hour round trip over the historic trackage to Curriers.

Displays/Exhibits: Grover Cleveland's "Honeymoon Car," former New York, Ontario & Western Railway, is on display at Arcade and contains its original dishes and glassware. It may be visited on days that the passenger train operates.

Train: Open-end steel coaches and combination cars from the Delaware, Lackawanna & Western Railroad; open gondola car.

Schedule: Weekends and holidays, May 27- October 29; Wednesdays and Fridays, July-August; Wednesdays, 12:30 & 3:00 p.m; Fridays, 1:00 p.m. Fall Foliage Runs: September 30, October 1, 7-8, 14-15 & 21-22, 12:00, 2:00 & 4:00 p.m.; October 6, 13 & 20, 1:00 p.m.

Fare: Adults $8.00, senior citizens $7.25, children (3-11) $5.00, children under 3 ride free. Group rates available for parties of 25 or more.

Locomotives: No. 14, 1917 Baldwin 4-6-0, former Escanaba & Lake Superior; No. 18, 1920 Alco (Cooke) 2-8-0, former Boyne City Railroad.

Special Events: Civil War Train Capture, August 19-20. Mixed Train Runs, to be scheduled; please call for information.

Location: In western New York, midway between Buffalo and Olean. Train departs from the Arcade depot in the center of town, at routes 39 and 98.

Contact: Linda Kempf
Agent

Mailing Address:
278 Main Street
P.O. Box 246
Arcade, NY 14009
Telephone: (800) 841-2418

New York, Arkville
D-R

DELAWARE & ULSTER RAIL RIDE
Diesel, scheduled
Standard gauge

GEORGE A. FORERO, JR.

Ride/Operation: A 10-mile, 50-minute round trip from Arkville to Fleischmanns over the route of the historic Ulster & Delaware Railroad. Longer special trips may also operate on occasion.

Displays/Exhibits. The Arkville station and yards have been restored; in the depot is a free video show and railway exhibits.

Train: Former Pennsylvania Railroad MP-54 coaches and open cars (heated coaches subject to availability). Dining car with catering available for charter. Brill railcar may also operate.

Schedule: <u>Weekends</u>, May 27-July 2 and September 9-October 29; <u>Wednesdays-Sundays</u>, July 5-September 4; 11:00 a.m., 1:00 & 3:00 p.m. Depot opens at 10:00 a.m. on operating days.

Fare: Adults $7.00, senior citizens $5.50, children (5-11) $4.00, children under 5 ride free.

Locomotives. No. 5106, 1953 Alco S-4, former Chesapeake & Ohio; No. 1012, 1954 Alco S-4, former Ford Motor Co.; M-405, 1928 J.G. Brill Co. diesel-electric railcar, former New York Central.

Rolling Stock/Equipment: Two flatcars with benches, former Cumberland & Pennsylvania; N-5 caboose, former PRR; two boxcars, former NYC; 44-ton locomotive, former Western Maryland.

Special Events: Train Robberies. Teddy Bear Runs. Tractor Pull. Antique Engine Gas-Up. Motor-Car Convention. Fall Foliage Runs. Halloween Train.

Location: Route 28.

 ♿ 🅿 🍴 🎦 🚗 🚐

♨ ✉ 🍴 🪟 TRAIN

Radio Frequency: 161.385

Contact: Vic Stevens
General Manager

Mailing Address:
Box 310
Stamford, NY 12167
Telephone: (914) 586-3877
(800) 225-4132

New York, Bath
D-R

CHAMPAGNE TRAIL EXCURSION TRAIN
Diesel, scheduled

COURTESY OF STEUBEN COUNTY *HISTORIAN*

Ride/Operation: A 15-mile, 2 3/4-hour round trip between Cohocton and Bath, crossing the Cohocton River several times as the train wends its way down New York's beautiful Cohocton Valley, which is rich in lush foliage and scenic vistas.

Displays/Exhibits: The Cohocton Valley Farm Museum, next to the Cohocton Depot, features eight dioramas depicting farming from 1790 to 1840, as well as a large collection of antique farm tools.

Train: The cars, dating from the 1920s and 1930s and originally used as circus cars to transport entertainers and animals around the country, have been completely restored, but a collection of antique posters inside them was left intact.

Schedule: Weekends, May 1-June 30 and September 1-October 31; Wednesdays and weekends, July 1-August 31; lv. Cohocton 10:00 a.m., arr. Bath 11:15 a.m.; lv. Bath 11:30.am., arr. Cohocton 12:45 p.m.; lv. Cohocton 1:00 p.m., arr. Bath 2:15 p.m.; lv. Bath 2:30 p.m., arr. Cohocton 3:45 p.m. Tour-bus groups may schedule to visit any day. Schedule subject to change; please call or write to confirm.

Fare: Adults $10.00, children $5.00.

Locomotives: Two 1950 Alcos; Davenport steam locomotive being restored.

Passenger Cars: Two 80-passenger coaches; dining-lounge car with tables and chairs for lunch and beverage service.

Special Events: Birthday, anniversary, company, or private parties.

Note: A restaurant and lounge are located in restored railroad cars at Bath. The restaurant serves lunch and dinner from a full menu.

Location: Bath Station is located at 31 Lackawanna Avenue. Cohocton Depot is located at 55 Maple Avenue.

Contact: Stanley Clark
Owner

Mailing Address:
31 Lackawanna Avenue
Bath, NY 14810
Telephone: (607) 776-1616
(716) 384-9187

190

NEW YORK TRANSIT MUSEUM
Railway museum

Displays/Exhibits: Located in an actual 1936 subway station, this museum houses one hundred years of transit lore and memorabilia, including eighteen vintage subway and elevated cars, antique turnstiles, a working signal tower, a unique gift shop, and much more. The story of the subway is the story of the city, and the New York Transit Museum offers visitors an opportunity both to discover the past and to see the present and future of public transportation in New York City.

Schedule: Tuesdays-Sundays; Tuesday-Friday, 10:00 a.m.-4:00 p.m.; weekends, 12:00-5:00 p.m. Closed major holidays.

Admission: Adults $3.00, senior citizens and children (under 17) $1.50.

Locomotives/Electric Cars: Eighteen completely restored subway and elevated cars dating from 1903.

Rolling Stock/Equipment: Working signal tower.

Location: Corner of Boerum Place and Schermerhorn Street, Brooklyn Heights.

Contact: Richard A. Madigan
Deputy Director

Mailing Address:
130 Livingston Street, 9th Floor
Brooklyn, NY 11201
Telephone: (718) 330-5839
Recorded Information: (718) 330-3060

ALCO BROOKS RAILROAD DISPLAY
Railway display
Standard gauge

COURTESY OF HISTORICAL SOCIETY OF DUNKIRK

Displays/Exhibits: Horatio Brooks, once superintendent of the Dunkirk Shops of the Erie Railroad, founded the Brooks Locomotive Works in 1869, when the Erie moved its shops to Hornell, New York. In 1901 the Brooks Locomotive Works became part of the American Locomotive Company, producing steam locomotives until 1929. The plant manufactured other heavy industrial and military materials until its closing in 1963. The ABRD, located at the Chautauqua County Fairgrounds since 1987, owns an original Alco-Brooks steam locomotive, a wood-sided boxcar housing displays of Chautauqua County commerce and railroads along with a gift shop, and a restored wooden caboose. Other items of interest at the site are a Nickel Plate work cart, an Erie Railroad concrete telephone booth, a New York Central harp switch stand, a Pennsylvania Railroad cast-iron crossing sign, a DAV&P land line marker, and an operating crossing flasher.

Schedule: <u>Saturdays</u>, June 1-August 31, 1:00-3:00 p.m. (weather permitting). <u>Daily</u> during special events or by appointment.

Admission: Donations welcomed.

Locomotives: No. 444, 1916 Alco-Brooks 0-6-0, former Boston & Maine No. 444, former Fletcher Granite Co. (West Chelmsford, Massachusetts).

Rolling Stock/Equipment: 1907 wood-sided boxcar No. 22020, former Delaware & Hudson; 1905 wooden caboose No. 19224, former New York Central.

Special Events: <u>Chautauqua County Antique Automobile Show & Flea Market</u>, May 19-20. <u>Chautauqua County Fair</u>, July 24-30.

Location: Chautauqua County Fairgrounds, 1089 Central Avenue.

Contact: Roy A. Davis
Vice President

Mailing Address:
Historical Society of Dunkirk
513 Washington Avenue
Dunkirk, NY 14048
Telephone: (716) 366-3797

New York, Gowanda
R

NEW YORK & LAKE ERIE RAILROAD
Diesel, scheduled
Standard gauge

KEVIN ARGUE

Ride/Operation: This railroad serves freight customers and operates two excursions over former Erie Railroad trackage: the *South Dayton Flyer,* which makes a 20-mile, 2 1/2-hour round trip to South Dayton over a steep grade and through an old stone tunnel; and *The Blue Diamond,* which makes a 30-mile, 4-hour round trip to Cherry Creek, featuring a full-course dinner. Depending upon the excursion, intermediate station stops are made at South Dayton or Cherry Creek. The depot in South Dayton was featured in the motion pictures *The Natural* and *Planes, Trains and Automobiles.*

Train: Coaches, former Baltimore & Ohio; commuter cars, former Delaware, Lackawanna & Western; open-air car; dining car "City of Salamanca," former Canadian National; dining car "The Daniel Webster," rebuilt from a B&O cafe-coach by the NY&LE.

Schedule: *South Dayton Flyer:* May-June & September, weekends, 1:00 p.m.; July-August, Wednesday & Friday, 12:00 p.m., weekends, 1:00 p.m.; October, weekends, 1:00 & 3:30 p.m. *The Blue Diamond:* May-November, Saturdays, 6:30 p.m., Sundays, 2:00 p.m.; February-March, selected dates. Weekday group tours scheduled for Cherry Creek; write or call for schedule and group rates.

Fare: *South Dayton Flyer:* adults $8.00, senior citizens $7.50, children (3-11) $4.00. *The Blue Diamond:* call or write for reservations and fares.

Locomotives: No. 85, 1950 Alco S-2; No. 1013, 1965 Alco C-425, former Norfolk & Western; No. 6101, the "Charles E. Hensel"; Alco C-425, former Pennsylvania Railroad.

Special Events: Murder Mystery Dinner Train, third Saturday of each month. *Peter Cottontail Express.* Kids' Day. Ghosts and Goblins. *Santa Claus Express.* Other special trips throughout the year.

Notes: All trains except the *South Dayton Flyer* require advance reservations.

Location: Gowanda is on U.S. route 62 and state route 39, thirty miles south of Buffalo. All trains depart from 50 Commercial Street.

Contact: Director
Passenger Operations

Mailing Address:
P.O. Box 309
Gowanda, NY 14070-0309
Telephone: (716) 532-5716

193

TROLLEY MUSEUM OF NEW YORK
Electric, scheduled
Standard gauge

GEORGE A. FORERO, JR.

Ride/Operation: This museum was established in 1955 and moved to its present location in 1983, becoming part of the Kingston Urban Cultural Park. A 2 1/2-mile, 40-minute round trip takes passengers from the foot of Broadway to Kingston Point, with stops at the museum in both directions. A gas-powered railcar operates on private right-of-way and in-street trackage along Rondout Creek to the Hudson River over part of the former Ulster & Delaware Railroad main line.

Displays/Exhibits: An exhibit hall features trolley exhibits and a theater.

Train: Railcar No. 120, 1919 gasoline-powered Brill car, former Sperry Rail Service, former Remington Arms.

Schedule: Weekends & holidays, May 27-October 9, 12:00-4:00 p.m. Additional dates may be scheduled; call for information. Charters available.

Fare: Adults $3.00, children $1.00. Museum: donations welcomed.

Trolleys: Whitcomb diesel-electric; seven rapid-transit cars; eleven trolleys; one interurban.

Special Events: Shamrock Run, March 12. Easter Bunny Run, April 16. Shad Festival, May 7. Mother's Day, May 14. Father's Day, June 18. Independence Day, July 4. Labor Day, September 4. Columbus Day, October 9. Hobo Day, October 29. Teddy Bear Run, November 12. Santa Claus Runs, December 2-3.

Note: Adjacent to the museum are the Hudson River Maritime Museum and the Kingston Urban Cultural Center; visitors may want to schedule a boat ride along with the trolley ride, or visit the shops and restaurants. This section of Kingston is being restored to its original late-nineteenth-century appearance.

Location: In the historic Rondout Waterfront area of Kingston. Call or write for specific directions.

Rhinecliff

Radio Frequency: 462.175

Contact: President

Mailing Address:
89 East Strand
P.O. Box 2291
Kingston, NY 12401-0227
Telephone: (914) 331-3399

194

CATSKILL MOUNTAIN RAILROAD
Diesel, scheduled
Standard gauge

GEORGE A. FORERO, JR.

Ride/Operation: This railroad, which operates over trackage of the former Ulster & Delaware Railroad (later the Catskill Mountain branch of the New York Central), offers a 6-mile, 1-hour round trip to Phoenicia along the scenic Esopus Creek, through the heart of the beautiful Catskill Mountains. Tourists, inner-tubers, and visitors interested in canoeing or fishing may ride one way or round trip; round-trip passengers may stay at Phoenicia to visit shops and restaurants and return on a later train.

Displays/Exhibits: 1894 wooden baggage car, former Delaware & Hudson; 1937 caboose, former Lehigh Valley No. 94071.

Train: Open flatcars; wooden caboose, former Delaware & Hudson.

Schedule: Weekends and holidays, May 27-October 15, 11:00a.m.-5:00p.m.

Fare: Round trip: adults $5.00, children (4-11) $1.00, children under 4 ride free. One way: adults $4.00, children (4-11) $1.00, children under 4 ride free.

Locomotives: No. 1, "The Duck," 1942 Davenport 38-ton diesel-mechanical, former U.S. Air Force; No. 2, "The Goat," H.K. Porter 50-ton diesel-electric, former U.S. Navy.

Rolling Stock/Equipment: No. 2361, 1952 Alco RS-1, former Wisconsin Central (Soo Line); No. 8301, 1942 self-propelled diesel crane, former U.S. Army.

Special Events: Fall Foliage Trains and others; call for schedule.

Location: Take exit 19 (Kingston) off the New York State Thruway and travel west 22 miles on route 28 to the railroad depot in Mt. Pleasant.

Contact: Gladys Gilbert
Treasurer

Mailing Address:
P.O. Box 46
Shokan, NY 12481
Telephone: (914) 688-7400

TIOGA SCENIC RAILROAD
Diesel, scheduled
Standard gauge

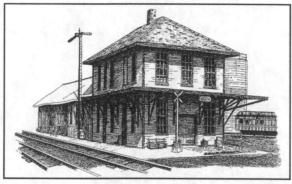

Ride/Operation: A 1 3/4-hour round trip from Owego to Newark Valley over tracks of the former Southern Central, constructed beginning in 1868 to connect southern New York with the Great Lakes. Breakfast, lunch, and dinner trains, as well as fall foliage and other special-event excursions, travel farther north to Berkshire.

Displays/Exhibits: Trains operate between the historic Owego and Newark Valley depots, which date from the earliest days of the Southern Central; the Owego depot, the headquarters of the SC, is being completely restored. The Newark Valley depot, refurbished by the Newark Valley Historical Society, features offices and dispatch areas as they were circa 1910, in addition to historical and railroad exhibits and a model layout of the Lehigh Valley Railroad. The Bement-Billings Farmstead, a circa 1840 living museum featuring costumed interpreters demonstrating skills of that time in a home, blacksmith shop, barn, sawmill, and gristmill, can be reached via a free shuttle bus from the Newark Valley depot.

Train: GP-9; two 1920 coaches, former Delaware, Lackawanna & Western; two 1940s dinner cars, former Illinois Central.

Schedule: Weekends, May 27-October 29; lv. Owego 11:00 a.m., 1:00 & 3:00 p.m.; lv. Newark Valley 12:00, 2:00 & 4:00 p.m. Breakfast, lunch, and dinner trains: please call or write for information.
Fare: Adults $7.00, children (4-11) $5.00, children under 3 ride free. Breakfast, brunch, lunch, and dinner trains: please call or write for information. Group rates and charters available.
Special Events: Easter. Mother's Day. Father's Day. Fall Foliage. Halloween. Christmas. New Year's.

Location: Owego is off exit 64 of New York route 17; Newark Valley is north of Owego on route 38.

Contact: Ticket Agent

Mailing Address:
25 Delphine Street
Owego, NY 13827
Telephone: (800) 42-TIOGA

New York, Phoenicia
M

EMPIRE STATE RAILWAY MUSEUM
Railway museum

Ride/Operation: First chartered in 1960, the all-volunteer Empire State Railway Museum moved to the 1899 former Ulster & Delaware depot in Phoenicia in 1984. Museum members have restored the station and are raising funds to begin restoration of four historic pieces of rolling stock: circa 1923 flatcar No. 7704 and 54-inch, wooden-sided, end-door boxcar, both former Central Vermont; 1912 four-wheel wood-bodied bobber caboose, former Pennsylvania Railroad; and 1890s express Railway Post Office car, former Boston & Maine. Visitors can board the train of the Catskill Mountain Railroad at Mt. Pleasant and ride to the museum in Phoenicia.

Displays/Exhibits: Archival photographs, films, and artifacts of the Ulster & Delaware and other regional branch lines.

Schedule: Weekends and holidays, May 27-September 4, 11:00 a.m.-4:00 p.m.

Admission: Suggested donation: adults $3.00, senior citizens & students $2.00, children (under 12) $1.00

Rolling Stock/Equipment: No. 23, 1910 Alco 2-8-0, former Lake Superior & Ishpeming; 1915 Pullman dining car "Lion Gardiner," stored in Kingston. Rolling stock described above is being restored in Phoenicia.

Special Events: Lectures, slide shows, videos at monthly membership meetings throughout the year. Santa Claus Special. Members' picnics. Other special events.

Note: Membership includes a free copy of the *Steam Passenger Service Directory* and quarterly newsletters.

Location: Off High Street.

Mailing Address:
P.O. Box 455
Phoenicia, NY 12464
Telephone (recorded message):
(914) 688-7501

New York, Rochester
D

COURTESY OF EDGERTON MODEL RAILROAD CLUB

Displays/Exhibits: Four operating O-gauge tinplate layouts, each depicting one of the seasons of the year. The layouts feature operating log loaders, coal loaders, a gantry crane, bascule bridges, and a water tower. The autumn layout has a drive-in theater featuring real movies. Each layout has its own diorama, illustrating local scenery, buildings, and landmarks.

Schedule: Individual and group tours: year-round. Continuous tours, Tuesday and Thursday evenings, 6:00 p.m. (except holidays).

Admission: Adults $1.25, senior citizens $.50, children (6-16) $.75, children under 6 admitted free.

Special Events: Open House/Model Train Show, fall and spring.

Note: Individuals with an interest in model railroading can volunteer to maintain and help operate the exhibit through the Edgerton Model Railroad Club. Membership is open to adults (18 and older). Members will be trained in the operation of the exhibits and are welcome to participate in the many layout projects, including scenery construction, wiring, painting, and cleaning.

Location: Corner of Phelps and Backus streets, off 400 Lake Avenue, in the Edgerton Park Community Center.

A **Rochester**

Contact: Tom Herlihy
Curator

Mailing Address:
41 Backus Street
Rochester, NY 14608
Telephone: (716) 458-5132

New York, Rochester
M-R

JIM DIERKS

NEW YORK MUSEUM
OF TRANSPORTATION
Railway museum
Standard gauge

Ride/Operation: Round-trip track-car rides are offered over a loop of track that circles the museum and extends to the Rochester & Genesee Valley Railroad Museum.

Displays/Exhibits: A comprehensive collection of artifacts from upstate New York State and elsewhere, including 1914 interurban No. 157, former Rochester & Eastern; Philadelphia snow sweeper C-130; wooden caboose No. 8, former Delaware, Lackawanna & Western; a bus; antique automobiles; and railroad photos and memorabilia. Under restoration are a Plymouth gasoline locomotive, an H.K. Porter 0-4-0 steam locomotive, and several trolleys. Video/photo gallery includes a rare color film of the Rochester subway.

Schedule: Museum: Sundays, 11:00 a.m.-5:00 p.m. Track-car rides: mid-May to late October, weather permitting. Group visits by appointment.

Admission: Adults $4.00, senior citizens $3.00, students (5-15) $2.00, family maxium (two adults with four or more children ages 5-15) $15.00. Includes admission to NYMT and R&GVRRM and track-car ride between the museums. From November to mid May, includes entry only to NYMT, and prices are lower.

Location: On East River Road about twenty minutes south of Rochester. Take exit 46 off the New York State Thruway and travel south two miles on I-390 to exit 11. Take state route 251 west 1 1/2 miles to East River Road, turn right, and travel 1 mile to the museum entrance.

🚗 🚙 ⊞ ✉ ♿(limited)
📷 ⛽ 📖 TRAIN 🔺
⫸Rochester

Contact: Theodore H. Strang, Jr.
Director

Mailing Address:
P.O. Box 136
West Henrietta, NY 14586
Telephone: (716) 533-1113

ROCHESTER & GENESEE VALLEY RAILROAD MUSEUM
Railway museum
Standard gauge

Ride/Operation: Track-car rides originate at the New York Museum of Transportation and operate to this museum.

Displays/Exhibits: Railroad artifacts from area railroads are housed in a restored 1900-era Erie Railroad station; a number of railroad cars and locomotives are on display on outdoor tracks. The combined tours and track-car ride offer a comprehensive and unique transportation experience. For further information, see the listing of the New York Museum of Transportation (New York, Rochester).

Schedule: Museum: Sundays, mid May to late October, 11:00 a.m.-5:00 p.m. Track-car rides: mid May to late October, weather permitting. Group visits by appointment.

Admission: Adults $4.00, senior citizens $3.00, students (5-15) $2.00, family maximum (two adults with four or more children ages 5-15) $15.00. Includes admission to NYMT and R&GVRRM and track-car ride between the museums. November through mid May, includes entry only to NYMT, and prices are lower.

Locomotives: 1946 80-ton General Electric, former Eastman Kodak No. 6; 1953 Alco RS-3, former Lehigh Valley; 1953 Alco S-4, former Nickel Plate No. 79; 1941 45-ton General Electric, former Rochester Gas & Electric; No. 1843, Fairbanks-Morse H12-44, former U.S. Army.

Rolling Stock/Equipment: 1909 70-ton hopper car No. 747803, former Pennsylvania Railroad class H-21a; baggage car No. 633 and caboose No. C-2631, both former Baltimore & Ohio; MU car No. 4628, former Delaware, Lackawanna & Western; caboose No. 19877 and flatcar, both former New York Central; 1940 sleeper-lounge "Pine Falls," former Long Island Railroad/Pennsylvania Railroad; baggage car No. 489022, former Erie-Lackawanna; Stillwell coach No. 2328, caboose No. C-254, and milk car No. 6603, all former Erie; 1958 MDT ice refrigerator car; speeder; section car; tamper; assorted maintenance-of-way equipment.

Location: Take exit 11 off Route 390 (2 miles south of New York State Thruway), travel west on Route 251 two miles to the flashing signal at East River Road, turn right, travel 1.5 miles north to the entrance of the Rochester & Genesee Valley Railroad Museum and the New York Museum of Transportation, and turn left to enter grounds.

⊞ 卉 TRAIN ♿(limited)

Rochester

Contact: Michael M. Byrne
Public Relations Coordinator

Mailing Address:
P.O. Box 664
Rochester, NY 14603
Telephone:
Recorded Message: (716) 533-1431

200

ONTARIO & WESTERN RAILROAD MUSEUM
Railway museum

Ride/Operation: This museum was established under the charter of the Ontario & Western Railway Historical Society in 1984 in a former Erie Railroad caboose. The O&W railway festival, first held in August of that year, has since become an annual event.

Displays/Exhibits: The museum complex consists of a restored O&W caboose, watchman's shanties, and the O&W station motif building. The museum contains displays of O&W memorabilia and other railroadiana, as well as local-history displays that show the impact of the O&W on community life, hunting, fishing, farming, tourism, and local industry.

Schedule: May 26-October 8, weekends, 11:00 a.m.-3:00p.m.

Fare: Donations welcomed.

Special Events: O&W Golden Spike Rededication, July 9. Hobo Celebration & Parade, July 15. O&W Festival & Craft Fair, July 29-30.

Location: Railroad Avenue.

Contact: Wilmer E. Sipple
Director & Curator

Mailing Address:
P.O. Box 305
Roscoe, NY 12776-0305
Telephone: (607) 498-5500
(607) 498-5289

NORTHEAST RAIL
BATTEN KILL RAILROAD
Diesel, scheduled
Standard gauge

Ride/Operation: On this line, the *Batten Kill Rambler* takes passengers on a scenic, 2-hour, 14-mile round trip along the Batten Kill, crossing the river eight times. Most trips lay over in Shushan for one hour. A secluded riverfront picnic park, accessible only by train or river, is available to groups by advance arrangement.

Train: Two 1940s Budd coaches; Budd RDC used as a control car.

Schedule: May 12-June 25, Friday-Sunday; June 29-October 22, Thursday-Sunday; also May 29, July 4, and October 9.

Fare: Adults $8.00, children (3-12) $4.00, children under 3 ride free if not occupying a seat. Group rates and charters available.

Locomotives: No. 605, 1950 Alco RS-3; No. 4116, 1952 Alco RS-3.

Passenger Cars: Nos. 2106 & 2108, 1941 Budd, former New York Central, built for the *Empire State Express;* No. M-403, Budd RDC, former Pennsylvania/Reading Seashore Lines.

Special Events: Spectacular Fall Foliage trips.

Location: Route 22, Main Street.

🚗 🚌 ⊞ 🏠 ✉ ⅋ ▲

 Saratoga Springs or Ft. Edwards

Radio Frequency: 160.905

Contact: Karl Pingree
Administrator

Mailing Address:
1 Elbow Street
Greenwich, NY 12834
Telephone:
Operating days: (518) 854-3787
Other times: (518) 692-2191

New York, Sodus
R

ONTARIO-MIDLAND RAIL EXCURSIONS
Diesel, scheduled
Standard gauge

DUNCAN RICHARDS

Ride/Operation: The Rochester Chapter of the National Railway Historical Society offers 34-mile, 1 3/4-hour round-trip fall foliage excursions from Sodus to Newark in rural upstate New York over the former New York Central Hojack and Pennsylvania Railroad Sodus Point lines.

Schedule: Sundays, September 24, October 1 & 22; weekends, October 7-8 & 14-15; 12:00 & 2:00 p.m.

Fare: Adults $9.75, children (3-15) $6.00, children under 3 ride free. Family discounts on September 24: children (3-15) $3.00. Advance ticket purchase recommended; send an SASE and a check payable to "NRHS Rochester" to the address below. Call or write for additional information.

Locomotives: No. 40, 1962 Alco RS36, and No. 36, 1957 Alco RS11, both former Norfolk & Western.

Rolling Stock/Equipment: Five former NYC *Empire State Express* stainless-steel Budd cars, used in revenue service until 1987 by Metro North.

Special Events: 1940s Big Band Review, October 1.

Location: Take the Maple Street exit off route 104 and travel south one-half mile. Sodus is 23 miles east of Rochester.

Contact: Mike Byrne
Publicity Director

Mailing Address:
P.O. Box 1161
Webster, NY 14580
Telephone: (716) 224-0581

New York, Syracuse
R

NEW YORK, SUSQUEHANNA & WESTERN RAILWAY CORP. (ONTRACK)

Steam, diesel, scheduled
Standard gauge

NEW YORK, SUSQUEHANNA & WESTERN RAILWAY CORP.

Ride/Operation: This line offers two trips: a scenic, 44-mile, 2-hour round trip between Syracuse and Tully, New York, over former Lackawanna Railroad trackage with steam and/or diesel locomotives; and 5-mile *City Express* shuttle service between Syracuse University, Armory Square, and Carousel Center with restored rail diesel cars.

Schedule: Excursion: Weekends and most Thursdays and Fridays, April 1-December 31, 12:00 & 3:00 p.m. *City Express:* Daily, April 1-December 31, 11:00a.m.-6:00p.m.

Fare: Excursion: Adults $12.00 first class (limited seating), $9.00 coach; children (under 13) $8.00 first class, $5.00 coach. Tickets may be purchased in advance with credit card by mail or telephone. Group rates and charters available. *City Express:* $1.00 one way; pay upon boarding.

Locomotives: No. 142, 2-8-2; Nos M-5, M-7 & M-8, Budd RDCs; Alco C430s; General Electric B40-8s; EMD E8s, F45s, GP18s, GP38s, SD45s & SD70s.

Passenger Cars: Nos. 520-524, 1947-48 long-distance coaches, former New York Central; Nos. 530-533, 1956 commuter coaches, former Long Island.

Special Events: Dinner trains. Murder Mystery trips. *Orange Express* shuttles for Carrier Dome events. School field trips. Fall foliage excursions. Halloween trains. Santa Claus trains. Please call or write for a complete listing.

Location: West Jefferson Street, off South Clinton Street, in Armory Square, downtown Syracuse.

 Syracuse

Contact: Robert Colucci
General Manager

Mailing Address:
P.O. Box 1245
Syracuse, NY 13201
Telephone:
(800) FOR-TRAIN (367-8724)
(315) 424-1212

204

ADIRONDACK SCENIC RAILROAD
Diesel, scheduled
Standard gauge

DOUGLAS ELLISON

Ride/Operation: This line, operated by the Adirondack Railway Preservation Society, offers a 9-mile, 1-hour round trip over a section of the former Adirondack Division of the New York Central. The ride takes passengers along the Middle Branch of the Moose River through rock cuts and forests, past lakes and ponds, and through some of the most scenic areas of the Adirondack Park.

Displays/Exhibits: A small museum in the front waiting room of the century-old Thendara Station focuses primarily on the Adirondack Division and also features the New York Central and railroading in general.

Train: Six former Canadian National open-window coaches; former New York Central Pacemaker caboose; former Pennsylvania Railroad baggage/open-air car; former Pullman 12-1 sleeper, being converted to an open-air car.

Schedule: Weekends and Memorial Day, May; Saturday-Thursday, June; daily, July 1-October 31; weekends, November; 11:30a.m. & 2:30p.m.

Fare: Adults $6.00, children (2-12) $4.00. Groups of 15 or more, 20 percent off regular fare. October 30-31: 50 percent off if in Halloween costume.

Locomotives: No. 8223, first Alco RS3 on the New York Central; SW-1 No. 68, former Louisville & Nashville.

Special Events: Loomis Gang Train Robberies, Tuesdays, July-August. Halloween Special, October 30-31. Santa Special, November 27-28. Please call for details and schedules.

Note: Schedule is subject to changes or cancellations without notice.

Location: On New York route 28, 1 mile south of Old Forge and Fulton Chain of Lakes, 2 miles south of Enchanted Forest/Water Safari, 30 miles south of Adirondack Museum at Blue Mountain Lake, and 50 miles north of New York State Thruway exit 31 (Utica).

Utica

Contact: Douglas J. Ellison
Executive Director

Mailing Address:
P.O. Box 84
Thendara, NY 13472
(315) 369-6290

RENSSELAER MODEL RAILROAD EXHIBIT
Model railroad

JEFF ENGLISH

Displays/Exhibits: This five-hundred-foot serpentine layout occupies a 120-foot by 30-foot area and depicts actual 1950 scenes of Troy, Vermont, and the Champlain Valley. The exhibit is the largest historically accurate operating diorama of its kind, illustrating the interconnection of yesterday's smokestack industries from the gathering of raw materials in the Adirondacks and the Green Mountains, through the manufacturing processes, to the distribution of finished products to market. The exhibit thus demonstrates how Troy was such a pivotal area in the country's industrial history. Begun in 1972, the layout is approximately sixty percent completed, so visitors can see all phases of construction, from bare benchwork to finished, detailed scenes. The layout, a sophisticated historical exhibit rather than a toy-train display, is not recommended for children under twelve years old.

Schedule: Fridays, 1:00-4:00 p.m.; Saturdays, 10:00 a.m.-4:00 p.m. Closed Christmas and New Year's weekend.

Admission: $4.00, children under 5 admitted free.

Note: The Rensselaer Model Railroad Society has set up a combination gift shop/HO hobby shop to help defray the enormous costs needed to build and maintain the layout. This shop specializes in high-quality and hard-to-find kits and supplies with which the society has had firsthand experience.

Location: In the basement of Davison Hall dormitory on the Rensselaer Polytechnic Institute campus. Davison Hall is opposite Troy High School on Burdett Avenue. Follow route 7 into Troy, turn south onto Burdett just east of Dunkin' Donuts, and turn right into the last parking lot.

Contact: Joe Sagmore
Visitor Coordinator

Mailing Address:
RPI Student Union
Troy, NY 12180-3590
Telephone: (518) 276-2764

TWEETSIE RAILROAD
Steam, scheduled
36" gauge

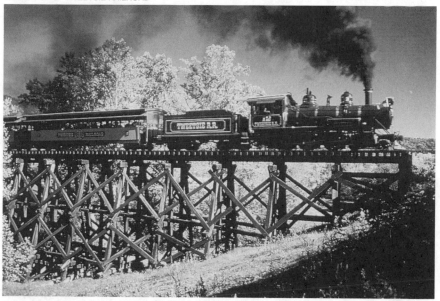

Ride/Operation: The Tweetsie Railroad is a theme park centered on a three-mile train ride. Visitors can enjoy the train show, live entertainment, rides, mountain crafts, and a petting zoo.

Train: Open excursion cars; wooden combine; coach.

Schedule: Daily, May 20-October 31, 9:00 a.m.-6:00 p.m. Please call for weekday schedule after Labor Day.

Admission: Adults $14.95, senior citizens (60+) and children $12.95, children under 4 admitted free. Group rates available. Admission includes train ride and other park attractions.

Locomotives: No. 12, 1917 Baldwin 4-6-0, former Tennessee & Western North Carolina; No. 190, 1943 Baldwin 2-8-2, former White Pass & Yukon.

Special Events: Railroaders' Day, June 17.

Location: Between Boone and Blowing Rock on U.S. 221-321. Take Mile Post 291 exit off the Blue Ridge Parkway.

Contact: Marketing Director

Mailing Address:
P.O. Box 388
Blowing Rock, NC 28605
Telephone: (704) 264-9061

North Carolina, Dillsboro
R

FLOYD MCEACHERN
HISTORICAL MUSEUM
Railway museum

FLOYD MCEACHERN HISTORICAL MUSEUM

Ride/Operation: More than 3,000 articles of railroad memorabilia, spanning more than 140 years of railroad history, are on display at this site. Model trains also operate on a beautifully landscaped layout.

Schedule: Please call or write for information.   **Location:** 1 Front Street.
Admission: Adults $3.00, children $2.00.

Contact: Floyd McEachern

Mailing Address:
P.O. Box 180
Dillsboro, NC 28725
Telephone: (704) 586-4085

208

North Carolina, Dillsboro
R

GREAT SMOKY MOUNTAINS
RAILWAY
Steam, diesel, scheduled

Ride/Operation: This railway offers scenic round-trip excursions ranging from 3 1/2 to 4 1/ 2 hours over its 67 miles of track from Dillsboro to Andrews. The scenic mountain line follows rivers and mountainsides and goes through villages and valleys, over trestles, and through tunnels. Mixed trains are frequently operated.

Train: No. 1702, former U.S. Army 2-8-0; GP35s; GP7s; lightweight and heavyweight coaches; open-air cars; cabooses.

Schedule: April-December; schedules vary with seasons. Lunch, dinner, and rail-raft trips are available. Please call or write for schedules.

Location: Excursion trains leave from Dillsboro, Bryson City, and Andrews, North Carolina.

Fare: Varies depending on trip: adults, from $16.00 and $23.00; children (under 13), from $7.00. Reservations recommended.

Locomotives: No. 1702, 1942 Baldwin 2-8-0, former U.S. Army; Nos. 711 & 777, EMD GP-7s; Nos. 210 & 223, EMD GP-35s.

Contact: Malcolm G. MacNeill
President

Mailing Address:
P.O. Box 397
Dillsboro, NC 28725
Telephone : (704) 586-8811
(800) 872-4681

NATIONAL RAILROAD MUSEUM
AND HALL OF FAME
Railway display

Displays/Exhibits: This museum's displays feature photographs, maps, a model-railroad layout, and four pieces of rolling stock.

Schedule: Please call or write for information.

Admission: No charge.

Rolling Stock/Equipment: Motor car No. 1114 and caboose No. 5241, both former Seaboard Air Lines; replica of engine "Raleigh"; motor car.

Location: 2 Main Street.

Hamlet

Radio Frequency: 160.590 (CSX)

Contact: J. A. Crowell
President

Mailing Address:
2 Main Street
Hamlet, NC 28345
Telephone: (919) 582-3317

NORTH CAROLINA TRANSPORTATION MUSEUM AT HISTORIC SPENCER SHOPS

Transportation museum
Standard gauge

Ride/Operation: Steam and diesel locomotives operate April to mid December.

Displays/Exhibits: Spencer Shops was the largest railroad repair facility on the Southern Railway; more than twenty-five hundred people were employed in the fifty-seven-acre complex. The massive backshop, thirty-seven-stall roundhouse, and nine other major buildings are being restored to chronicle the history of transportation in North Carolina. Two buildings are currently open: the former Master Mechanic's Office and the Flue Shop.

Train: Open and closed coaches, former Reading and former Canadian National.

Schedule: Museum: Daily, April 1-October 31; Monday-Saturday, 9:00 a.m.-5:00 p.m.; Sunday, 1:00-5:00 p.m. Tuesday-Saturday, November 1-March 31; Tuesday-Saturday, 10:00 a.m.-4:00 p.m.; Sunday, 1:00-4:00 p.m. Train: Daily, April 1-September 5; Monday-Saturday, 11:00 a.m., 1:00, 2:00 & 3:00 p.m.; Sunday, 1:30, 2:30 & 3:30 p.m. Weekends, September 6-mid December; Saturday, 11.00 a.m., 1:00, 2:00 & 3:00 p.m.; Sunday, 1:30, 2:30 & 3:30 p.m.

Fare/Admission: Steam train: adults $4.00, senior citizens and children (3-12) $3.00. Diesel train: adults $3.50, senior citizens and children (3-12) $2.50. Museum: no charge.

Locomotives: No. 604, 1926 Baldwin 2-8-0, former Buffalo Creek & Gauley No. 4; No. 542, 1903 2-8-0, No. 6900, EMD E-8, and No. 6133, EMD FP-7, all former SR; No. 1925, 1925 Lima 3-truck Shay, former Graham County Railroad; No. 1616, AS-416 diesel, former Norfolk Southern; No. 620, EMD GP-9 diesel, former Norfolk & Western.

Rolling Stock/Equipment: RPO and baggage car, both former SR; maintenance-of-way car, former NS; cabooses, former SR, former Seaboard Railway, former NS, and former N&W; 40 & 8 boxcar.

Special Events: Rail Days, June 10-11.

Location: Spencer is just off I-85 about 3 miles north of Salisbury. Spencer Shops is at 411 South Salisbury Avenue (U.S. 29-70).

Salisbury

Contact: Kelly Wrinn
Programs Specialist

Mailing Address:
P.O. Box 165
Spencer, NC 28159
Telephone: (704) 636-2889

211

CHARLES KERNAN

Displays/Exhibits: Maintenance-of-way exhibits, dining-car china, timetables, safety awards, labor exhibit, photos, O-scale exhibit, and extensive HO-model history exhibit. Displays primarily represent the Atlantic Coast Line Railroad, but others are featured.

Schedule: Tuesday-Sunday; Tuesday-Saturday, 10:00a.m.-5:00p.m.; Sunday, 1:00-5:00p.m.

Admission: Adults $2.00, children (6-11) $1.00, children under 6 admitted free.

Locomotives: 1910 Baldwin 4-6-0.

Rolling Stock/Equipment: Boxcar, former Richmond, Fredericksburg & Potomac; caboose, former ACL; caboose, former Norfolk & Western; motor cars.

Location: 501 Nutt Street.

 (limited)

Contact: Kelly S. Verhelle
Executive Director

Mailing Address:
501 Nutt Street
Wilmington, NC 28401
Telephone: (910) 763-2634

BONANZAVILLE, U.S.A.
Railway display
Standard gauge

COURTESY OF BONANZAVILLE, U.S.A.

Displays/Exhibits: Bonanzaville, U.S.A., a pioneer village, museum, and interpretive center, includes more than forty buildings (mostly original). At the Railroad Complex is the former Embden, North Dakota, depot, which has been completely refurbished to its turn-of-the-century appearance. Also at the site is former Northern Pacific 4-4-0 No. 684, the only remaining locomotive of the first eleven purchased when the NP began operations. Visitors can also see a caboose, passenger coaches, and a railroad snowplow. A second station, from Kathryn, North Dakota, is the headquarters for the Spud Valley Railroad Club. The station agent's former living quarters have been transformed by the club into a model-train complex that shows the Fargo-Moorhead area in the 1950s, including the Union Stockyards, the Northern Pacific Depot, Dilworth, and many other buildings along Front Street (now Main Avenue).

Schedule: Late May-late October, daily; please call for schedule. November-April: museum only; 9:00a.m.-5:00p.m.

Admission: Please call for information.

Location: On U.S. highway 10. Travel west from I-29 exit 65; travel east from I-94 exit 343.

Campground adjacent

Contact: Margo Lang
Operations Manager

Mailing Address:
P.O. Box 719
West Fargo, ND 58078
Telephone: (701) 282-2822
Fax: (701) 282-7606

MAD RIVER & NKP RAILROAD SOCIETY
Railway museum
Standard gauge

DENNIS BRANDAL

Displays/Exhibits: A depiction of small-town railroading, including buildings, rolling stock, locomotives, and many items pertaining to everyday railroad life, with many hands-on items. Cars contain exhibits and photographs about railroad history; depots and other structures appear as they did in use; and several passenger and freights trains are on display. On loan from the B&O Museum in Baltimore is the wooden scale-model replica of the Mad River & Lake Erie's "Sandusky," the first locomotive to operate in Ohio and reportedly the first to have a whistle.

Schedule: <u>Daily</u>, May 30-September 5; <u>weekends</u>, May, September & October; 1:00-5:00 p.m.

Admission: Suggested donation: Adults $2.00, senior citizens and children $1.00, family $5.00.

Locomotives/Trolleys: Lake Shore electric interurban under restroration; Alco RSD 12 No. 329 and EMD GP30 No. 900, both former Nickel Plate; EMD F-7A No. 671, former Wabash; Fairbanks-Morse H12-44 No. 740, former Milwaukee Road; Brooks 0-6-0 No. 1190, former Buffalo, Rochester & Pittsburgh; Porter fireless 0-6-0 No. 7, former Cleveland Electric Illuminating.

Passenger Cars: Former Chicago, Burlington & Quincy "Silver Dome," the first dome car built in the U.S.; coach No. 105, former NKP; diner, former Seaboard Air Lines; sleeper "Tiger River," former Southern; RPO, former Pennsylvania Railroad; Pullman sleeper "Donizetti"; coach No. 618, former Milwaukee Road; two baggage cars, former Wabash and former Louisville & Nashville.

Rolling Stock/Equipment: Cabooses, freight cars, track speeders, and specialty equipment such as former New York Central wedge snowplow, former NKP dynamometer car, former N&W 200-ton wreck crane, and more.

Special Events: The society sponsors <u>main-line excursions and common-carrier trips</u>; please call or write for information. <u>Annual Flea Market</u>.

Note: Many pieces of railroad-related highway equipment are on display or under restoration.

Location: 253 Southwest Street, two blocks from downtown.

Contact: Dennis J. Brandal
Curator

Mailing Address:
233 York Street
Bellevue, OH 44811-1377
Telephone: (419) 483-2222

CINCINNATI RAILROAD CLUB
Railway display

DOYLE W. BROWN

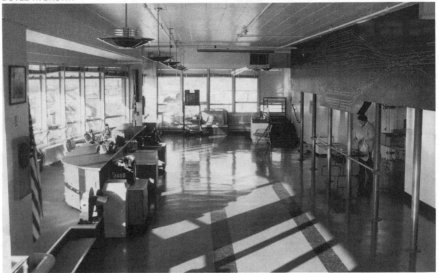

Displays/Exhibits: Founded in 1938, this club has a new exhibit in Cincinnati Union Terminal's former Control Tower A, the former operating and dispatching center for terminal operations from 1933 to 1973. The tower, which overlooks the busy Norfork Southern and CSX yards and main lines and the former Southern Railway bridge to Kentucky, has been restored by CRC members as their display and meeting location. Displays include the former track-diagram board, with lights showing track occupancy and the location of switches; the dispatcher's desk; the train starting board; and railroadiana, headlights, bells, whistles, lanterns, and photos related to Cincinnati railroading. The club has an extensive library and photo collection in its archives at the tower.

Schedule: Saturdays, July 1-September 30, 10:00 a.m.-5:00 p.m.; October 1-June 30, 10:00 a.m.-4:00 p.m. Third Sunday of the month, July-September, 12:00-5:00 p.m.; October-June, 12:00-4:00 p.m.

Admission: No charge. Parking is $3.00 per day in Union Terminal lot.

Locomotives/Trolleys: Curve-sided car No. 2435, former Cincinnati Street Railway, is on display at the south ramp of the terminal.

Special Events: The club sponsors field trips to local railroads and may sponsor excursions on a main-line or local railroad. The monthly buisness meeting is held the first Thursday of the month at 8:00 p.m.; special slide and video programs are offered throughout the year. Please call or write for information.

Location: 1301 Western Avenue at Ezzard Charles Drive. Take exit 1H or 1G off I-75.

Cincinnati

Contact: Dale W. Brown
Trustee and Librarian

Mailing Address:
P.O. Box 14157
Cincinnati, OH 45250-0157
Telephone: (513) 651-RAIL (7245)

CONNEAUT RAILROAD MUSEUM
Railway museum
Standard gauge

PAUL W. PRESCOTT

Displays/Exhibits: The Conneaut station, built by the Lake Shore & Michigan Southern in 1900, is adjacent to Conrail (former New York Central) tracks. Inside are extensive displays of timetables, passes, lanterns, old photos, builder's plates, telegraph instruments, and models of locomotives, cars, and structures. An HO-scale model railroad operates on weekends. On display outside are a train, section cars, track equipment, and a ball signal. On the station platform are baggage trucks, hand carts, and old trunks. A stready parade of Conrail trains passes the station.

Schedule: <u>Daily</u>, May 30-September 5, 12:00-5:00 p.m.

Admission: Donations welcomed.

Locomotives/Trolleys: No. 755, 1944 Lima 2-8-4, former Nickel Plate.

Rolling Stock/Equipment: A 90-ton hopper car and a wooden caboose, both former Bessemer & Lake Erie.

Location: In the old New York Central station at Depot and Mill streets, north of U.S. 20 and I-90. Blue-and-white locomotive signs point the way to the museum.

Mailing Address:
P.O. Box 643
Conneaut, OH 44030
Telephone: (216) 599-7878

CARILLON HISTORICAL PARK
Railway display

PATRICIA PORTER

Ride/Operation: Twice a month, the Carillon Park Rail and Steam Society, an auxiliary organization of Carillon Historical Park, operates a scale-model layout at the western edge of this outdoor historical museum. Associate members and their families may ride (membership is $5).

Displays/Exhibits: Rail-related exhibits include an 1835 Baltimore & Ohio "grasshopper" locomotive; a 1903 Barney and Smith wood-bodied passenger car; a 1904 G.C. Kuhlman Co. interurban; a 1903 J.G. Brill summer trolley; an H.K. Porter locomotive, 0-6-0 No. 6721, former New York Central; a Baltimore & Ohio caboose; a 1909 Lima fireless locomotive; the 1894 Bowling Green, Ohio, train depot; and a 1907 railroad watchtower. Inside the depot is original equipment as well as a model of the "Cincinnati," the first locomotive to enter Dayton, in 1851.

Schedule: May 1-October 31; Tuesday-Saturday, 10:00a.m.-6:00p.m.; Sundays and holidays, 1:00-6:00 p.m.

Admission: Adults $1.00, children under 18 admitted free. Carillon Historical Park members admitted free.

Location: Take exit 51 off I-75; travel east on Edwin C. Moses Boulevard, then turn right onto Stewart Street, right onto Patterson Boulevard, and right onto Carillon Boulevard. Park entrance is on the left.

Contact: Mary Mathews
Executive Director

Mailing Address:
2001 South Patterson Boulevard
Dayton, OH 45409-2023
Telephone: (513) 293-2841
Fax: (513) 293-5798

Ohio, Dennison
M

RUSTY FOX

THE DENNISON RAILROAD
DEPOT MUSEUM
Railway museum

Ride/Operation: This museum sponsors excursions ranging from 1-hour to all-day trips, through an arrangement with the Columbus & Ohio River Railroad in Coshocton.

Displays/Exhibits: Restored 1873 Pennsylvania Railroad station, once the site of a World War II canteen that served more than one million GIs. The depot was part of a complex begun in the mid-1860s by the Pittsburgh, Cincinnati & St. Louis Railroad; at its peak, the Dennison yards and shops employed three thousand workers. Exhibits include a canteen room; a large N-scale layout of Dennison during its heyday; original waiting rooms (men's and women's) filled with railroad displays; a ticket booth; a cargo room; a Railway Express building and office; a 1950 former Norfolk & Western caboose; and a 1946 "Thermos Bottle" engine.

Train: Steam locomotive No. 1551, 1912 Montreal Locomotive Works, former Canadian National; historic passenger coaches.

Schedule: Museum: Tuesday-Saturday, 10:00 a.m.-5:00 p.m.; Sunday, 11:00 a.m.-5:00 p.m. Excursions: All-day trips on May 21 (Jewett to Roscoe Village), June 18 (Father's Day; Dennison to Gould Tunnel), July 16 (Dennison to Roscoe Village), August 19 (Murder Mystery Ride), September 30 (to Sugarcreek for Swiss Festival), October 8 (Fall Foliage; Newark to Dennison), October 15 (Fall Foliage; Dennison to Dresden), and December 3 (Santa Train Ride). Please call or write for more detailed information.

Fare/Admission: Museum: adults $3.00, senior citizens $2.50, students $1.75, children under 7 admitted free. Excursions: fare varies; 1-hour rides are generally $7.00 for adults and $5.00 for students. Please call or write for more specific information.

Special Events: Railroad Festival, May 17-21. Forties Fest, September 30 & October 1.

Location: 400 Center Street where routes 36, 250 and 800 meet, 18 miles east of I-77.

Contact: Wendy Zucal
Museum Director

Mailing Address:
P.O. Box 11
400 Center Street
Dennison, OH 44621
Telephone: (614) 922-6776

218

ASHTABULA, CARSON & JEFFERSON SCENIC LINE
Diesel, scheduled
Standard gauge

ASHTABULA, CARSON & JEFFERSON SCENIC LINE

Ride/Operation: An 11-mile, 1-hour round trip over the last remaining portion of the former New York Central's Ashtabula-to-Pittsburgh "High Grade" passenger main line. The train travels through scenic woods and farmland from the quaint village of Jefferson to Carson, a staging yard for Conrail's coal and iron-ore operations in historic Ashtabula Harbor.

Train: Air-conditioned coach, former Erie No. 1022; baggage cars, former Erie Lackawanna Nos. 200 and 201; open-window coach, former NYC; caboose, former Nickel Plate No. 425.

Schedule: Weekends, June 3-October 29; 12:30, 2:00 & 3:30 p.m. Reservations required in October. Charters available May 1-November 1

Fare: Adults $6.50, senior citizens $5.50, children $4.50.

Locomotives: No. 107, 1950 Alco S-2, former Nickel Plate, former Fairport, Painesville & Eastern.

Special Events: Halloween train, featuring haunted baggage car; reservations required.

Location: In northeastern Ohio, accessible from I-90 and I-80 via state route 11. Trains depart from Jefferson Street, two blocks east of state route 46.

➤➤ Cleveland, Ohio, or Erie, Pennsylvania

Contact: Frank Rueter
General Manager

Mailing Address:
P.O. Box 222
Jefferson, OH 44047-0222
Telephone: (216) 576-6346

I&O SCENIC RAILWAY
Diesel, scheduled
Standard gauge

COURTESY OF I&O SCENIC RAILWAY

Ride/Operation: A working, common-carrier freight and passenger railroad, this line offers a 12-mile, 1-hour round trip through the rolling hills of southwest Ohio over a former Pennsylvania Railroad branch line.

Train: Four electric commuter cars built in 1930 for the Delaware, Lackawanna & Western Railroad; open gondola car.

Schedule: <u>April 29-December 23</u>.

Fare: Adults $9.00, senior citizens $8.00, children $5.00.

Locomotives: No. 55, 1950 EMD GP-7, former Chesapeake & Ohio.

Special Events: <u>Golden Lamb Sunday dinner packages. Ice Cream Social on Rails. Mystery Dinner Tours. Train Rides with Santa.</u>

Location: In southwestern Ohio, between Dayton and Cincinnati. Take I-71 or I-75 to Lebanon and follow the signs to the station on South Broadway.

TRAIN ⟫ Cincinnati

Radio Frequency: 161.385

Contact: Passenger Service Representative

Mailing Address:
198 South Broadway
Lebanon, Ohio 45036
Telephone: (513) 398-8584

HOCKING VALLEY SCENIC RAILWAY
Steam, scheduled
Standard gauge

COURTESY OF HOCKING VALLEY SCENIC RAILWAY

Ride/Operation: This historic railroad offers a 12-mile round trip to Haydenville and a 25-mile round trip to Logan with a visit to an 1860s settlers' village at Robbin's Crossing. The train operates over a former Chesapeake & Ohio route that was once a part of the original Hocking Valley Railway, listed on the National Register of Historic Places. Special trains include the Canal Winchester 100-mile round trip Steam Specials; please call or write for information.

Train: Coaches, former Rock Island and former Baltimore & Ohio; open-air car.

Schedule: Weekends and holidays, May 27-October 29. Haydenville train: 12:00 p.m. Logan train: 2:30 p.m.

Fare: Haydenville: adults $6.50, children (2-11) $4.00. Logan: adults $9.50, children (2-11) $6.50.

Locomotives: No. 33, 1916 Baldwin 2-8-0; No. 5833, 1952 EMD GP-7, former Chesapeake & Ohio; No. 7318, 1942 General Electric; No. 3, 1920 Baldwin 0-6-0.

Special Events: Santa Claus Trains, December 2-3, 9-10 & 16-17; only Logan train in operation. Canal Winchester Steam Specials; please call or write for information.

Location: On route 33 in southeastern Ohio, 60 miles southeast of Columbus.

Contact: Passenger Agent

Mailing Address:
P.O. Box 427
Nelsonville, OH 45764
Telephone (weekdays): (513) 335-0382
Weekends during operating season:
(614) 753-9531

Ohio, Newark
R

BUCKEYE CENTRAL SCENIC RAILROAD
Diesel, scheduled
Standard gauge

COURTESY OF BUCKEYE CENTRAL SCENIC RAILROAD

Ride/Operation: A 12-mile round trip over part of the former Shawnee Branch of the Baltimore & Ohio Railroad, through Licking County to Heath. The train winds its way through the countryside, passing over two trestles and a long steel bridge over the Licking River.

Displays/Exhibits: Station built just after the Civil War; railroad memorabilia.

Train: Passenger cars, gondola, caboose.

Schedule: Weekends, May 30-October 15, 1:00 & 3:00 p.m. Charters available May 15-October 31.

Fare: Adults $6.00, children (3-11) $5.00, children under 3 ride free when accompanied by an adult.

Locomotives: No. 8599, 1948 Electro-Motive SW-1, former Penn Central Railroad.

Rolling Stock/Equipment: Seven passenger cars, two circa 1910, three 1958, one 1941, and one 1956; 1941 gondola; three cabooses, former Norfolk & Western, former Chesapeake & Ohio, 1941 former Pere Marquette.

Special Events: Halloween Nite Train Rides. Santa Specials. Civil War Encampment. Train Robberies. Hobo Parties. Please call for schedules.

Location: Three miles east of Hebron on U.S. 40.

Contact: Robert H. Miller
President

Mailing Address:
P.O. Box 242
Newark, OH 43055
Telephone: (614) 366-2029

222

TROLLEYVILLE, U.S.A.
Electric, scheduled
Standard gauge

A. D. YOUNG

Ride/Operation: A 2 1/2-mile ride over a scenic residential and park route; optional carbarn tour to view Trolleyville's complete collection.

Displays/Exhibits: Rare photos, streetcar memorabilia, and novelties in the ticket office; Harry Christiansen Library (by appointment); restored Baltimore & Ohio depot from Berea, Ohio, housing the Morris Stone collection of O-gauge traction equipment, along with an operating O-gauge layout, under wire.

Schedule: Weekends & holidays, May 6-May 25 & October 2-October 28; Friday-Sunday and holidays, May 26-June 6; Wednesday, Friday-Sunday & holidays, June 7-October 1; 12:00-5:00 p.m.

Fare: Adults $3.00, senior citizens $2.70, children (4-12) $2.25, children under 4 ride free.

Trolleys: Two Brill Vera Cruz open summer trolleys; three wooden and five steel heavyweight interurbans, former Chicago, Aurora & Elgin; two lightweight interurbans, former Aurora, Elgin & Fox River; city cars, former Cleveland, Pittsburgh, Cincinnati, Shaker Heights, and Blackpool, England; Dallas double-ended PCC; three box motors from Iowa and Michigan; others.

Rolling Stock/Equipment: 1968 boxcar, former Chesapeake & Ohio; 1965 boxcar, former Pennsylvania Railroad; 1914 caboose, former Norfolk & Western; 1875 four-wheel caboose, former New York & Ontario.

Special Events: Moonlight Rides. Popsicle Fridays. Train Shows. Murder Trains. Bus Tours. Halloween Party. Flea Market. Trolleys on Parade. Festival of Lights. Please call or write for information.

Location: At 7100 Columbia Road (state route 252-S), east of exit 9 of the Ohio Turnpike. Off I-480, two miles south of Great Northern Mall. Six miles west of the Bagley Road exit of I-71, and one mile north on Columbia Road.

Contact: Cliff Perry
General Manager

Mailing Address:
7100 Columbia Road
Olmsted Township, OH 44138
Telephone: (216) 235-4725
Fax: (216) 235-6556

Ohio, Orrville
D-R

ORRVILLE RAILROAD HERITAGE SOCIETY
Steam, irregular
Railway display

COURTESY OF ORRVILLE RAILROAD HERITAGE SOCIETY

Ride/Operation: This society sponsors periodic main-line passenger excursions, often behind former Nickel Plate 2-8-4 No. 765. Destinations have included Pittsburgh, Pennsylvania, and Bellevue, Fremont, Toledo, Ashtabula, Vermilion, Coshocton, and Zanesville, Ohio. Excursions are typically powered by steam, if available.

Displays/Exhibits: A restored 1868 depot that served the Pittsburgh, Fort Wayne & Chicago and the Cleveland, Akron & Columbus railroads, both later part of the Pennsylvania Railroad, contains railroad artifacts and Orrville historical items. Also on display, unrestored, is the interlocking tower that controlled the junction.

Schedule: Depot: April-mid October, Saturdays, 10:00 a.m.-4:00 p.m.; please call to confirm schedule. Depot is not open when excursions are operated. Excursions: please call or write for schedule.

Fare/Admission: Depot: no charge; donations welcomed. Excursions: varies; please call or write for prices.

Locomotives: No. 82C, 1951 EMD F9 A-unit, former Milwaukee Road; No. 781, 1956 EMD F9 B-unit, and No. 817, 1954 EMD F9 B-unit, both former Northern Pacific.

Passenger Cars: No. 101 "William B. Baer," 1947 Budd, former PRR No. 4064; No. 102, "H.H. Wade," 1947 Budd, former New York Central No. 2905; No. 103, "Robert S. Bixler," 1946 Budd, former Atchison, Topeka & Santa Fe No. 3155; No. 104, "City of Orrville," 1940 Budd, former Atlantic Coast Line No. 214; No. 105, concession car, former Amtrak baggage car No. 1370; No. 106, "Ohio Presidents," 1939 Budd, former Seaboard Air Line No. 6203. Not restored are 1940 Budd dining car "Baltimore," former ACL, and two other Budd coaches. Cars are located at Pine Street siding, east of route 57.

Rolling Stock/Equipment: Former Chesapeake & Ohio boxcar, used as tool car; PRR N5C cabooses.

Special Events: Main-line excursions. Depot Days, June 10-11, with equipment and artifact displays, Operation Lifesaver displays, track-car rides, entertainment, souvenirs, and refreshments.

Location: 145 Depot Street. Orrville is southwest of Akron on state route 57, three miles north of U.S. route 30.

 Akron and Alliance

Contact: Richard Hull
President

Mailing Address:
P.O. Box 11
Orrville, OH 44667
Telephone: (216) 683-2426

224

CUYAHOGA VALLEY SCENIC RAILROAD
Diesel, scheduled
Standard gauge

CUYAHOGA VALLEY SCENIC RAILROAD

Ride/Operation: Built in 1880 as the Cleveland Terminal & Valley Railway, the CVS offers up to a 52-mile round trip from Independence to Akron, paralleling the Ohio & Erie Canal and the Cuyahoga River through the scenic Cuyahoga Valley National Recreation Area. Shorter rides are available.

Train: Air-conditioned and heated coaches; snack-bar cars; round-end observation car.

Schedule: Varies; please call or write for information.

Fare: Varies; please call or write for information.

Locomotives: Nos. 15 & 6777, Alco FPA-4s; Nos. 4088 & 4099, Alco FPA-4s, former Delaware & Hudson.

Location: Train departs from the parking area on Old Rockside Road in Independence, one mile east of the intersection of I-77 and Rockside Road (exit 155).

Cleveland and Akron

Contact: P. R. Birgeles
Executive Director

Mailing Address:
P.O. Box 158
Peninsula, OH 44264-0158
Telephone: (800) 468-4070

Ohio, Sugarcreek
R

OHIO CENTRAL RAILROAD
Steam, diesel, scheduled
Standard gauge

DOYLE YODER

Ride/Operation: The Ohio Central, a 70-mile-long working railroad, operates the diesel- and steam-powered Sugarcreek Service, a 1-hour round trip over former Wheeling & Lake Erie trackage in the Amish country known as the "Switzerland of Ohio."

Train: Passenger coaches, former Burlington, former Grand Trunk, and former Lackawanna.

Schedule: <u>Monday-Saturday</u>, May 2-October 29, 11:00 a.m., 12:30, 2:00 & 3:30 p.m. <u>Extra trains added</u>, Saturdays, July, August & October, 9:30 a.m. & 5:00 p.m.

Fare: Adults $7.00, children (3-12) $4.00, children under 3 ride free.

Locomotives: No. 1551, 1912 Montreal 4-6-0, former Canadian National; No. 13, 1920 Alco 2-8-0, former Buffalo Creek & Gauley; No. 12, 1950 Alco S-1, former Timken Roller Bearing; No. 6325, 1942 Alco 4-8-4, former Grand Trunk Western.

Special Events: <u>Swiss Festival</u>, September 29-30.

Location: Ohio Central Station, 111 Factory Street.

Contact: Laura Jacobson
Manager

Mailing Address:
P.O. Box 427
Sugarcreek, OH 44681
Telephone: (216) 852-4676

TOLEDO, LAKE ERIE & WESTERN RAILWAY
Diesel, scheduled
Standard gauge

GEORGE A. FORERO, JR.

Ride/Operation: A 20-mile, 2-hour round trip over a portion of the former Cloverleaf Division of the Nickel Plate Road. The train travels through villages, fields, and woodlands and over a 900-foot-long bridge over the Maumee River and the old Miami & Erie Canal.

Displays/Exhibits: Cars that are not part of the train; World War II troop sleeper; freight cars; maintenance-of-way equipment.

Train: Electric commuter cars, former New York Central and former Lackawanna; coaches, former Baltimore & Ohio and NYC; parlor car; Pullman car; cabooses.

Schedule: Weekends and holidays, May 6- October 29; Waterville round trip, 1:00 & 4:00 p.m.; Grand Rapids round trip, 2:30 p.m.; one-way trip, 5:30 p.m. Tuesdays and Thursdays, May 29-September 4; Waterville round trip, 10:30 a.m. & 1:30 p.m.; Grand Rapids round trip, 11:45 a.m.; one-way trip, 2:45 p.m. Charters may be scheduled any time.

Fare: Round trip: adults $8.00, senior citizens $7.00, children (3-12) $4.50. One-way fare and group rates available. Caboose and parlor-car seats available on some trains for $1.00 extra each way per person.

Locomotives: No. 5109, 1948 Alco S-4, former Chesapeake & Ohio; No. 112, 1946 Alco S-2, former U.S. Steel; No. 202, 1920 Baldwin 0-6-0, former Detroit Edison Co.; No. 1, 1941 44-ton Whitcomb, former Ann Arbor Railroad; No. 15, 1908 Porter 0-6-0T, former Brooklyn Eastern District Terminal.

Note: Stopovers are permitted at each terminal.

Location: Waterville Depot: take U.S. 24 to state route 64 north and turn right on Sixth Street. Grand Rapids: take state route 65 to Mill Street, then travel south on Mill Street one block.

Toledo

Contact: Terri Harrison
Charter Director

Mailing Address:
P.O. Box 168
Waterville, OH 43566
Telephone:
Waterville Depot: (419) 878-2177

LORAIN & WEST VIRGINIA RAILWAY
Diesel, scheduled
Standard gauge

MARK CHAPPO

Ride/Operation: This line offers an 8 1/2-mile round trip over original Lorain & West Virginia trackage, which is being restored after having been out of service for 25 years.

Displays/Exhibits: Mid-nineteenth-century former New York Central freight station.

Train: Restored Pullman heavyweight cars; two cabooses.

Schedule: <u>Weekends</u>, July 15-August 20 & August 28-October 29, 1:00, 3:00 & 5:00 p.m. <u>Daily</u>, August 21-27, 1:00 to 8:30 p.m.

Fare: <u>Adults</u>: "Mount Baxter" $6.00, caboose $4.00, coach $3.00. <u>Children (2-11)</u>: "Mount Baxter" $5.00, caboose $3.00, coach $2.00. <u>Children under 2</u> not occupying a seat ride free.

Locomotives: No. 123, 1950 Alco RS-3, former U.S. Steel No. 574, 1950 EMD SW-1, former LTV Steel.

Passenger Cars: No. 1, "Mount Baxter," 1924 Pullman 10-section sleeper-lounge; coaches No. 90, 1926 Pullman, and No. 62, 1934 Pullman, both former Nickel Plate.

Rolling Stock/Equipment: No. C-2423, wagon-top caboose, former Baltimore & Ohio; No. 293, cupola caboose, former Chesapeake & Ohio.

Special Events: <u>Lorain County Fair</u>, August 21-27; passengers may board train at Main Gate No. 1. <u>Haunted Train Rides</u>; October 13-14, 8:00, 9:00 & 10:00 p.m.; October 20-21 & 27-28, 7:00, 8:00, 9:00 & 10:00 p.m.; adults $5.00, children (under 12) $4.00.

Location: One mile west of town on state route 18.

Elyria

Radio Frequency: 464.425

Contact: Paul W. Quayle
Treasurer

Mailing Address:
6548 Edgerton Road
North Royalton, OH 44133-5735
Telephone: (216) 237-4395

228

Ohio, Youngstown
D

MAHONING VALLEY
RAILROAD HERITAGE ASSOCIATION
Railway display

BRUCE LIGHTCAP

Ride/Operation: This organization was founded in 1985 to establish an operating railroad museum and to preserve the railroading heritage of greater Youngstown and Warren, Ohio. It focuses on the railroads that served the area, including the Pennsylvania, the New York Central, the Erie, and the Baltimore & Ohio, and in the specialized breed of railroading used by the steel industry. The organization is planning construction of a regional rail museum to be located on the west side of Youngstown.

Displays/Exhibits: Former YS&T No. 301 is on public display at the Canfield Fairgrounds with a Youngstown & Southern wooden caboose. No. 301 is in the Western Reserve Village, a re-creation of a pioneer village comprising historic buildings that have been moved to the fairgrounds, which includes the former Erie station from Canfield, Ohio, and a crossing watchman's tower. Other equipment owned by the organization is in storage and can be toured by prior arrangement.

Schedule: Rolling stock can be seen only by prior arrangement. YS&T No. 301 can be visited every day from dawn to dark and during the Canfield fair in early September. Call for a guided tour of rolling stock or locomotive.

Admission: No charge, except during fair days or special events. Fair: $4.00 per person.

Locomotives: 1915 Baldwin 0-6-0 No. 301, former Youngstown Sheet & Tube Co.

Passenger Cars: No. 454017 and No. 3617, troop sleepers converted to camp cars, former Delaware, Lackawanna & Western; No. 6519, Railway Post Office, former PRR.

Rolling Stock/Equipment: Pugh-type hot-metal cars and slag car, former Youngstown Sheet & Tube Co.; N5c cabin car, former PRR; caboose/hot metal spacer car, former Monongahela Connecting Railroad; A-6 Fairmont motor car, former Bessemer & Lake Erie; Pollock Co. hot metal car; transfer caboose, former Pittsburgh & Lake Erie; 250-ton steam wrecking derrick, former P&LE; 40-ton locomotive crane, former U.S. Steel.

Location: At the Canfield Fairgrounds, south of Canfield, Ohio.

Youngstown

Contact: J. Richard Rowlands
Historian

Mailing Address:
P.O. Box 3055
Youngstown, OH 44511
Telephone: (216) 568-0328

229

RAILROAD MUSEUM OF OKLAHOMA
Railway museum

LANCE CHESTER

Displays/Exhibits: This museum, housed in a 1926-27 former Santa Fe freight house, has one of the largest collections of railroad artifacts in the Midwest. Memorabilia pertaining to all railroad professions can be found here: one room is devoted to more than 400 pieces of dining-car china; another holds a library that includes many books as well as postcards, railroad money, and items of local history. The former loading dock, now enclosed, contains HO- and N-gauge model-railroad layouts. Enid was known as the railroad hub of Oklahoma; 10 main tracks radiated outward from it, more than were found in the much larger cities of Tulsa and Oklahoma City.

Schedule: Tuesdays-Fridays, 1:00-4:00 p.m.; Saturdays, 10:00 a.m.-1:00 p.m. Also by appointment.
Admission: Donations welcomed.
Locomotives: No. 1519, former St.Louis-San Francisco 4-8-2, located in Enid City Park and scheduled to be moved to the museum this year; No. VMCX1, 50-ton General Electric class BB switcher, former Vulcan Chemicals.
Passenger Cars: No. 968186MWX, 86-foot RPO/combination car, former Chicago, Burlington & Quincy.
Rolling Stock/Equipment: Cabooses No. 25323, former Union Pacific; No. 1281, former Frisco; No. 132, former Missouri-Kansas-Texas; No. 1139, former Northern Pacific; No. 12433, former Burlington Northern; and No. 999567, former Santa Fe. No. CONX50004, 1928 automobile boxcar, former Santa Fe/Continental Oil Co.; No. CONX190, tank car, former COC; two section cars; Herbard shop mule; White trackmobile.
Special Events: Two model-railroad swap meets each year. Annual Christmas Party.

Location: Thirty miles west of I-35 in north-central Oklahoma, on U.S. routes 60, 81, 64 & 412. The museum is 6 blocks northwest of the downtown square.

Contact: Robert E. Chester
Vice President

Mailing Address:
3805 North Lincoln
Enid, OK 73703
Telephone: (405) 233-3051

230

Oklahoma, Hugo
M-R

HUGO HERITAGE RAILROAD
Diesel, scheduled
Standard gauge

COURTESY OF CHOCTAW COUNTY HISTORICAL SOCIETY

Ride/Operation: This operation offers a 2 1/2-hour round trip from Hugo (Circus City, U.S.A.) to points north and south, including Paris, Texas.

Displays/Exhibits: A museum located in the former 1915 Frisco depot, the largest one left on Frisco's southwest lines. Displays include an HO-gauge model railroad on a mountain layout, railroad artifacts, turn-of-the-century memorabilia, rare photographs, and a working Harvey House restaurant.

Train: Climate-controlled coaches pulled by the Kiamichi Railroad's engines on the Kiamichi right-of-way.

Schedule: Saturdays, April-November, 2:00 p.m.

Fare/Admission: Train: adults $15.00, children (4-12) $10.00. Museum: no charge. Group specials available.

Passenger Cars: Two 1940s coaches: No. 1001, "Kiamichi Country," former Norfolk & Western; No. 1002, "Circus City U.S.A."

Rolling Stock/Equipment: Baggage car No. 372, former Frisco (stored); circa 1950 Railway Express truck; Kiamichi No. SL1, 1949 F-7A, former Kansas City Southern No. 70-A.

Special Events: Railroad Days, October 15-16. Fall Color Runs.

Note: The Hugo Heritage Railroad is a project of the Choctaw County Historical Society.

Location: 300 Block West Jackson.

Contact: Noel Pence
President, Board of Directors

Mailing Address:
P.O. Box 577
Hugo, OK 74743
Telephone: (405) 326-6630

231

HUGH SCOTT

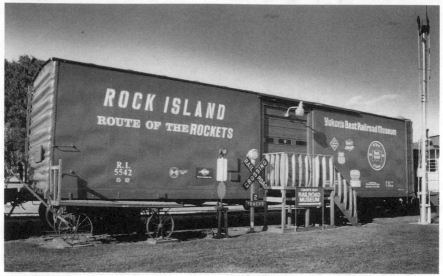

Displays/Exhibits: This museum contains an extensive display of railroad antiques and artifacts. Emphasis is placed on the Rock Island Line, but many other railroads are represented.

Schedule: Please call or write for information.

Admission: No charge.

Rolling Stock/Equipment: Boxcar No. 5542 and caboose No. 17039, both former Rock Island; caboose No. 13724, former Missouri Pacific; caboose No. 25865, former Union Pacific.

Location: Third and Main streets.

Contact: John A. Knuppel
Curator

Mailing Address:
1020 West Oak Street
Yukon, OK 73099
Telephone: (405) 354-5079

Oregon, Baker City
D-R

SUMPTER VALLEY
RAILROAD RESTORATION
Steam, scheduled
36" gauge

COURTESY OF SUMPTER VALLEY RAILROAD RESTORATION

Ride/Operation: A 10-mile round trip takes passengers through a wildlife area to the city of Sumpter. Views include the rugged Elkhorn Mountains, beautiful Sumpter Valley, and dredge tailings left from gold-mining days.

Displays/Exhibits: Original SVR boxcars and stock cars, old boilers, and an original SVR 2-8-2 steam locomotive. Members are also establishing an SVR museum at the Sumpter depot, which they hope to open to the public this season.

Train: Two-truck, 40-ton Heisler; plans also call for operation of an original SVR 2-8-2 this summer.

Schedule: Weekends and holidays, May 28-September 30.

Fare: Round trip: adults $8.00, children $6.00, family $20.00. One way: adults $5.00, children $4.00, family $13.00.

Passenger Cars: Original SVR 1890s Pullman coach; two open-air cars; open-sided boxcar.

Rolling Stock/Equipment: Original SVR-built caboose; six hopper cars; two flatcars; tank car.

Special Events: Founders' Day Celebration. Moonlight Dinner Rides, three times a year.

Location: In the Blue Mountains of eastern Oregon. Take I-84 to Baker City, then take highway 7 along the Powder River to Railroad Park.

Contact: Ron Brinton
President

Mailing Address:
P.O. Box 389
Baker City, OR 97814
Telephone: (503) 894-2268

233

OREGON ELECTRIC RAILWAY MUSEUM
Electric, scheduled
Standard gauge

STEVE MORGAN

Ride/Operation: The OERM's 47-acre site includes picnic facilities; cars travel on 1 1/2 miles of track through woods and fields. Take an old-fashioned family outing by trolley to the picnic grove!

Displays/Exhibits: Museum display, "How the Trolley Changed America"; a number of streetcars on display in the Car Barn.

Schedule: Weekends and holidays, May 1-October 31, 11:00a.m.-5:00p.m.

Location: 38 miles west of Portland on route 6.

Admission: Adults $3.00, children $2.00, children under 5 admitted free, family $9.00. Includes unlimited trolley rides, carbarn tours, and use of the picnic grounds for the day.

Trolleys: 1904 double-deck No. 48, former Blackpool, England; No. 503, 1904 Brill semi-convertible, and No. 813, 1932 Brill master unit, both former Portland; No. 1159, 1946 St. Louis/San Francisco PCC car; open car No. 1187, former Sydney, Australia; 1911 interurban No. 1304, former British Columbia.

Contact: Director

Mailing Address:
P.O. Box 702
Forest Grove, OR 97116
Telephone (evenings): (503) 642-5097

Oregon, Hood River
R

MOUNT HOOD RAILROAD
Diesel, scheduled
Standard gauge

Ride/Operation: A 44-mile, 4-hour round trip to Parkdale, following the Hood River up a 3-percent grade to a switchback and climbing through forests to an upper valley carpeted with fruit orchards. The ride offers unparalleled views of Mount Hood and Mount Adams.

Train: Pullman heavyweight coaches; concession car; newly refurbished caboose.

Schedule: April-June & September-October; Wednesday-Friday, 10:00 a.m. & 3:00 p.m.; weekends, 3:00 p.m. July-August; Tuesday-Friday, 10:00 a.m. & 3:00 p.m.; weekends, 3:00 p.m.

Fare: Adults $19.95, senior citizens (60+) $16.95, children (2-11) $11.95. Weekday discount, April-May & October-December: $1.00 off.

Locomotives: Nos. 88 and 89, EMD GP-9s.

Special Events: Easter Egg Train, April 16. Fruit Blossom Special, April 22-23. Mother's Day Special, May 14. Train Robbery and Western Celebration, May 21-22, June 17-18, July 15-16, August 19-20 & September 16-17. Memorial Day Train Ride, May 29. Independence Day Train Ride, July 3. Labor Day Train Ride, September 4. Hood River Harvest Festival, October 14-15. Halloween Spook Train, October 28. Thanksgiving Holiday Special, November 25. Annual Christmas Tree Train, December 9-10.

Note: The Mount Hood Railroad depot, constructed in 1911 and recently restored, has been designated a National Historic Site.

Location: Hood River is 63 miles east of Portland on I-84. The railroad is in the heart of the Columbia River Gorge National Scenic Area, only a few minutes from Bonneville Dam and Multnomah Falls.

Hood River and Bingen

Contact: Diane Martin-Langley
Marketing Director

Mailing Address:
110 Railroad Avenue
Hood River, OR 97031
Telephone: (503) 386-3556

SAMTRAK
Diesel, irregular
Standard gauge

SAMTRAK

Ride/Operation: Traveling over the former Portland Traction Company's interurban right-of way along the Willamette River, this line offers a 1-hour round trip between two of Portland's most popular attractions: the Oregon Museum of Science & Industry; and the historic Oaks Amusement Park, dating from 1905. Passengers may stop to visit these sites at either end and return on a later train.

Train: "Little Toot," 1942 diesel-electric; tank car converted to passenger car; former Simpson Timber Company logging caboose.

Schedule: May 6-October 15, 11:00 a.m.-5:00 p.m. Schedule varies; please call or write for information.

Fare: Adults $4.00, children (1-4) $1.50, children under 1 ride free.

Locomotives: The line's freight operations use No. 100, SW-1, former Portland Traction Co.; No. 5100, 70-ton, former Southern Pacific; No. 602, SW-8, former Oregon, Pacific & Eastern.

Rolling Stock/Equipment: Various pieces of work equipment are stored at the freight headquarters.

Special Events: Annual "Oktoberfest" at Oaks Amusement Park, September 23-24; passengers are shuttled to the park at no charge.

Location: Boarding locations are at SE 5th & Spokane Streets; at Oaks Amusement Park; and at the Oregon Museum of Science & Industry, 1945 SE Water Avenue.

Portland

Radio Frequency: 160.575

Contact: Donna Samuels
Director, Passenger Operations

Mailing Address:
P.O. Box 22548
Portland, OR 97222
Telephone: (503) 659-5452

WASHINGTON PARK & ZOO RAILWAY
Steam, diesel, scheduled
30" gauge

COURTESY OF WASHINGTON PARK & ZOO RAILWAY

Ride/Operation: A 4-mile round trip around the zoo and through forested hills to Washington Park, passing the elephant enclosure for a close-up view of the zoo's world-famous pachyderm herd and overlooking the Alaska Tundra exhibit. The stop at Washington Park station offers a panoramic view of Mount Hood, the city of Portland, and Mount St. Helens, and passengers may obtain a stopover pass there to visit the Rose Test Gardens and the Japanese Garden, located nearby.

Train: Streamlined cars and open coaches; two trains are wheelchair-accessible. The train is one of the last registered Postal Railway Stations in the United States.

Schedule: Full round trip: weekends, April 15-May 21; daily, May 27-September 30. Zoo loop trip: weekdays, March 18-May 26, weather permitting. Trains depart at frequent intervals.

Fare/Admission: Full round trip: adults $2.75, senior citizens and children (3-11) $2.00, children under 3 ride free. Zoo loop trip: adults $1.75, senior citizens and children (3-11) $1.25, children under 3 ride free. Zoo admission is required to ride railway.

Locomotives: 4-4-0 No. 1, replica of Virginia & Truckee "Reno"; *Zooliner,* replica of General Motors *Aerotrain;* diesel-powered *Orient Express;* gas-powered switcher and fire train.

Rolling Stock/Equipment: Two work trains.

Location: 4001 S.W. Canyon Road.

⬚ ⊞ ⫯ ᴛᴿᴬᴵᴺ ⟫ Portland

Radio Frequency: 151.655

Contact: Mark Dillon
Retail Manager

Mailing Address:
4001 S.W. Canyon Road
Portland, OR 97221
Telephone: (503) 226-1561

WILLAMETTE SHORE TROLLEY
Electric, scheduled
Standard gauge

CLAUDIA BROWN

Ride/Operation: Trolleys operate along the former Portland, Eugene & Western "Red Electric" interurban line, running 6 6/10 miles between Portland and Lake Oswego beside the Willamette River. The line starts from a former industrial area and first runs through five blocks of city streets, then private rights-of-way, passing two beautiful riverside parks, crossing three long, high trestles beside the river, penetrating Elk Rock via a quarter-mile curved tunnel, and ending at the foot of "A" Avenue in Lake Oswego.

Schedule: Weekends, March 1-December 31, 10:00 a.m., 12:00, 2:00 & 4:00 p.m. Tuesday-Sunday, May 30-September 13, 10:00 a.m., 12:00, 2:00, 6:00 & 8:00 p.m.; additional trips Friday-Sunday, 4:00 p.m.

Fare: Adults $7.75, senior citizens (55+) & children (under 13) $5.75. Family fares available.

Trolleys: "Old 300," 1913 enclosed car with underseat heating, former San Antonio; 1930s open parade car "Blackpool Belle," former Blackpool, England, is shaped like a Mississippi paddle wheel boat and features more than eight hundred lights (used when weather permits).

Location: Sheridan Street Station at 2511 SW Moody Avenue; a few blocks south of downtown Portland, under the Marquam bridge near the Riverplace Marina.

Portland

Contact: P. V. Class
Operations Manager

Mailing Address:
61635 Agaard Road
Gales Creek, OR 97116
Telephone: (503) 222-2226

HORSESHOE CURVE
NATIONAL HISTORIC LANDMARK
Railway display

COURTESY OF RAILROADERS MEMORIAL MUSEUM

Displays/Exhibits: When Altoona's Horseshoe Curve opened in 1854, it revolutionized rail travel and cleared the way for westward expansion. The Curve's story is now told at the modern, interpretive Visitor Center, located in a picturesque setting. A seven-minute film describes the role of Pennsylvania transportation in America's move to the West; guests may ride to track elevation aboard a single-track funicular or walk the 194 stairs.

Horseshoe Curve is located on Conrail's busy East-West Main Line, with more than fifty trains passing each day. Trains climbing or descending the 1.8-percent grade can be viewed and photographed safely from the trackside park.

Schedule: Summer hours: daily, April 2-October 28, 9:30a.m.-7:00p.m. Winter hours: Tuesday-Sunday, October 29-April 1, 10:00a.m.-4:30p.m.

Admission: Visitor Center and grounds: No charge. Funicular: $1.50. Groups: please call ahead.

Rolling Stock/Equipment: Former Pennsylvania Railroad GP-9 No. 7048 is on display at track elevation.

Location: On Kittanning Point Road, state route 4008. Follow the Heritage Route.

Altoona

Contact: Peter D. Barton
Executive Director

Mailing Address:
1300 Ninth Avenue
Altoona, PA 16602
Telephone: (814) 941-7960

RAILROADERS MEMORIAL MUSEUM
Railway museum
Standard gauge

COURTESY OF RAILROADERS MEMORIAL MUSEUM

Displays/Exhibits: Altoona built the Pennsylvania Railroad, and the Pennsylvania Railroad built Altoona. More than sixty-seven hundred steam locomotives were built and maintained in the Altoona shops; peak railroad employment in Altoona was nearly eighteen thousand. The Railroaders Memorial Museum is dedicated to the memory of the men and women of the PRR, telling stories of the people who laid the track, built the locomotives, and guided trains through Altoona and across the Horseshoe Curve. Various exhibits and special programs are featured throughout the year; currently, guests can view an exhibit detailing train wrecks in the Altoona area. A new museum, scheduled to open in September 1996, will be housed in the former PRR Master Mechanics Building; construction is under way on this project.

Schedule: Summer hours: daily, April 2-October 28, 10:00 a.m.-6:00 p.m. Winter hours: Tuesday-Sunday, October 29-April 1, 10:00 a.m.-5:00 p.m.

Admission: Adults $2.50, senior citizens $2.00, children $1.50, family rate $7.00. Groups of more than 10: two weeks' advance notice required; ask about special rates.

Locomotives: 1918 Juniata Shops K-4s 4-6-2 No. 1361 and GG-1 No. 4913, both former PRR (No. 1361 is not currently on public view); 1918 Vulcan 0-4-0T switcher "Nancy"; two diesel locomotives.

Passenger Cars: The "Loretto," private railroad car of Charles M. Schwab; dining car; two coaches; three sleeping cars; other equipment.

Rolling Stock/Equipment: Express refrigerator car.

Location: Downtown Altoona. Take the 17th Street exit off U.S. route 220.

Altoona

Contact: Peter D. Barton
Executive Director

Mailing Address:
1300 9th Avenue
Altoona, PA 16602
Telephone: (814) 946-0834

PIONEER TUNNEL
COAL MINE RAILROAD
Steam, scheduled
42" gauge

GEORGE A. FORERO

Ride/Operation: A 1 1/2-mile ride along Mahaney Mountain to an abandoned strip mine. A battery-operated mine motor provides an interesting tour of an anthracite mine. A large community park adjoins the mine entrance.

Displays/Exhibits: "Henry Clay," 1927 Vulcan steam locomotive.

Train: Open mine cars with seats; red caboose.

Schedule: Daily, May 30-September 5; weekends, May, September & October; 10:00 a.m.-6:00 p.m. On September 3 the railroad closes at 4:00 p.m.

Fare: Train: adults $2.25, children (under 12) $1.25. Mine tour: adults $5.00, children (under 12) $2.75.

Special Events: Pioneer Day, August 26; tour of coal mine, steam train ride, variety of events in adjoining community park.

Location: 19th and Oak Streets.

Contact: Dorothy Hornung
Business Manager

Mailing Address:
19th & Oak Streets
Ashland, PA 17921
Telephone: (717) 875-3850
(717) 875-3301

241

AVONDALE RAILROAD CENTER
Railway museum
Standard gauge

BRIAN R. WOODCOCK

Displays/Exhibits: This museum is located in historic Chester County, Pennsylvania, on the former Pennsylvania Railroad Octoraro Branch, extending from Chadds Ford, Pennsylvania, to the Maryland state line. The display consists of four former PRR passenger cars and a former Atlanta, Birmingham & Atlantic Baldwin steam locomotive. Iron Horse Antiques is an antique shop located inside the train, and nearby is a former Pomeroy & Newark Railroad freight station (the only surviving structure of this line) and the original Avondale former PRR passenger station.

Schedule: Display: daily. Iron Horse Antiques: Wednesday-Sunday, 10:00 a.m.-5:00 p.m.
Admission: No charge.
Locomotives: 1907 Baldwin slope-back steam locomotive.
Rolling Stock/Equipment: Four MP-54 passenger cars.
Special Events: Seasonal events. Please call or write for information.
Note: Other area attractions include Longwood Gardens, the Brandywine River Museum, the Brandywine Battlefield, the Hagley Museum, the Winterthur Museum, the Delaware Natural History Museum, and the Delaware Art Museum. A local airport features rides in restored vintage aircraft.

Location: On U.S. 1 and route 41, two miles off the U.S. 1 bypass, six miles from Longwood Gardens and twelve miles from Wilmington, Delaware.

Wilmington, Delaware

Contact: Brian Woodcock

Mailing Address:
State and Pomeroy Streets
P.O. Box 809
Avondale, PA 19311
Telephone: (215) 268-2397

242

BELLEFONTE HISTORICAL RAILROAD
Diesel, scheduled
Standard gauge

MICHAEL BEZILLA

Ride/Operation: Scheduled and special trips over the 60-mile Nittany & Bald Eagle Railroad to Lemont, Vail (Tyrone), and Mill Hall. Regular service includes stopovers at Lemont, Bellefonte, Curtin Village, and Julian Glider Port. Fall foliage and railfan runs cover up to 120 miles; all-inclusive restaurant runs to Tyrone are also offered.

Displays/Exhibits: The Bellefonte Station, a restored former Pennsylvania Railroad structure built in 1888, houses an operating N-gauge layout of the Bellefonte-Curtin Village route, as well as historical photos and memorabilia of area railroading. A snowplow and caboose under restoration are displayed beside the station.

Train: No. 9167, 1952 RDC-1, and 1962 No. 1953; air-conditioned passenger cars. Can be configured for meal service.

Schedule: Weekends and holidays, May 30-September 5, 1:00, 2:15, & 4:00 p.m. Destinations vary. Charters are available any time, year-round. Tyrone restaurant runs: last Friday of the month, January-October.

Location: Central Pennsylvania, a short distance from I-80.

Fare: Varies depending on destination. Minimum: adults $5.00, children (2-11) $2.00.

Special Events: Spring, fall, and Christmas runs.

Mailing Address:
The Train Station
Bellefonte, PA 16823
Telephone: (814) 355-0311

ALLEGHENY PORTAGE RAILROAD
NATIONAL HISTORIC SITE
Railway display
Standard gauge

ALLEGHENY PORTAGE RAILROAD

Displays/Exhibits: This site was established in 1964 to commemorate the first railroad to cross the Allegheny Mountains, in 1834. The Portage Railroad, considered a technological wonder of its day, played a role in opening the interior of the United States to trade and settlement. Today's park, covering fifteen hundred acres, preserves remains of this railroad and reveals its interesting story. The visitor center features a twenty-minute motion picture and exhibits that help tell the story of the railroad. A new feature is the Engine House 6 Exhibit Building, which protects the remains of the original engine house and includes a full-sized model of a stationary steam engine. The Lemon House, a tavern during the days of the railroad, is being restored to its nineteenth-century appearance and will open in 1996.

Train: Ranger-guided historic rail tours are offered between Johnstown and Altoona on Amtrak's *Pennsylvanian* (see the listing for "Tracks Through Time" [Pennsylvania, Johnstown]).

Schedule: Visitor Center: daily, May 29-September 4, 9:00 a.m.-6:00 p.m.; daily, September 5-May 26, 9:00 a.m.-5:00 p.m. Closed Christmas Day. Ranger-guided Train Tours: Thursday-Saturday, June-mid October.

Admission: Visitor Center: no charge. Ranger-guided Train Tours: for information on Amtrak fares and tickets, contact your local Amtrak agent or call 1-800-USA-RAIL.

Locomotives: A full-sized model of the 1837 steam locomotive "Lafayette" is on display in the Visitor Center.

Location: Off the Gallitzin exit of U.S. 22, between Altoona and Cresson.

Altoona

Contact: Superintendent

Mailing Address:
P.O. Box 189
Cresson, PA 16630
Telephone: (814) 886-6150

244

GETTYSBURG RAILROAD
Steam, scheduled
Standard gauge

DEANE MELLANDER

Ride/Operation: This railroad operates over a former Reading Company branch line. The regular ride is a 16-mile, 1 1/2-hour round trip to Biglerville; special 50-mile, 5-hour dinner trips are made on selected dates to Mt. Holly Springs.

Train: Open-side excursion cars; steel coaches; double-deck open car.

Schedule: Biglerville: weekends, April, 1:00 & 3:00 p.m. Thursday-Sunday, May 1-June 30; Thursday-Friday, 10:00 a.m. & 12:30 p.m.; weekends, 1:00 & 3:00 p.m. Daily, July 1-August 31; weekdays, 11:00 a.m. & 1:00 p.m.; weekends, 11:00 a.m., 1:00 & 3:00 p.m. Thursday-Sunday, September 1-October 30; Thursday-Friday, 11:00 a.m. & 1:00 p.m.; weekends, 1:00 & 3:00 p.m. Also September 4, 11:00 a.m. & 1:00 p.m. Mt. Holly Springs: May 6, 2:00 p.m. (Apple Blossom Trip); June 16, 6:00 p.m. (Summer's Eve Trip); July 15, 5:00 p.m. (Hobo Special); August 18, 6:00 p.m. (Moonlight Trip); September 23, 2:00 p.m. (Fall Harvest Trip). Reservations suggested for these trips.

Fare: Biglerville: adults $8.00, children (3-12) $3.50. Mt. Holly: adults $17.00, children (3-12) $9.00.

Locomotives: No. 76, 1920 Baldwin 2-8-0, former Mississippi Railway; No. 1278, 1948 Canadian 4-6-2, former Canadian Pacific.

Special Events: Easter Bunny Train, April 15, 1:00 & 3:00 p.m. Civil War Train Raids; July 1-2, 11:00 a.m. & 1:30 p.m.; September 16-17, 1:00 p.m. & 3:30 p.m. Lincoln Train, August 6-7, 1:00 & 3:00 p.m. Photo Trip (to Mt. Holly Springs), September 9, 10:00 a.m.

Fall Foliage Trips (to Mt. Holly Springs), October 7-8, 14-15 & 21, 10:00 a.m. Halloween Train, October 28-29, 1:00 & 3:00 p.m. Christmas Train, December 2-3 & 9-10, 1:00 & 3:00 p.m.

Location: At the former Reading Station on Washington Street.

Contact: Station Master

Mailing Address:
Passenger Service
106 North Washington Street
Gettysburg, PA 17325
Telephone: (717) 334-6932

BIG BEAR FARM
Steam, scheduled
24" gauge

HOWARD J. WALTON

Ride/Operation: A half-mile ride (eventually to be a one-mile loop) on a two-foot-gauge railroad through forest and pasture, where deer and other animals roam.

Displays/Exhibits: Steam engines, gas engines, precision models, coal-mining equipment, an antique reciprocating-saw display, antique tractors, and other mechanical antiques, as well as a former Delaware & Hudson battery-powered coal-mine locomotive, a 1920 wooden Central Vermont caboose, and other railroad artifacts. Also located here is a performing-bear show, a game farm, and a museum.

Train: 1922 Krauss 24-inch-gauge 0-4-0; 1936 Whitcomb gas locomotive; 1948 Brookville gas locomotive; open cars with bench seats, made from narrow-gauge flatcars.

Schedule: May 1-July 4, weekends, 12:00-5:00 p.m.; July 5-October 31, Thursdays-Sundays, 12:00-6:00 p.m. Bear shows are at 1:00, 2:00, 3:00 & 4:00 p.m.; train runs before and after bear shows.

Fare: Adults $5.50, children (3-12) $3.50, children under 3 admitted free. Ticket includes park admission and railroad fare.

Rolling Stock/Equipment: 1934 D&O passenger car; work cars; ballast hopper car; handcar; others.

Special Events: Halloween Pumpkin Special, last two weeks of October. Christmas Week Special.

Location: Eight miles north of Honesdale. Take route 6 west through Honesdale to route 170 north, then follow signs for Big Bear Farm and the Ponderosa Pines Campground.

Contact: A. E. Burr
Manager

Mailing Address:
RD 3, Box 1352
Honesdale, PA 18431
Telephone: (717) 253-1794

Pennsylvania, Honesdale
R

GEORGE A. FORERO, JR.

STOURBRIDGE LINE
RAIL EXCURSIONS
Diesel, scheduled
Standard gauge

Ride/Operation: A 50-mile round trip from Honesdale to Hawley and Lackawaxen, through scenic Wayne and Pike Counties along the Lackawaxen River, closely following the route of the old Delaware & Hudson Canal.

Displays/Exhibits: Former gravity-railroad coach on display on Hawley; a replica of the "Stourbridge Lion" and a gravity-railroad coach on display in Honesdale.

Train: 1940s BL-2; five 1940s coaches, former Jersey Central, completely refurbished.

Schedule: Weekends, April 3-December 25.
Fare: Adults $17.50, children $8.00. Fares vary depending on type of excursion; please call or write for information.
Locomotives: No. 54, 1949 EMD BL-2, former Bangor & Aroostook.
Special Events: Easter Train. Hawley Limited. Great Train Robbery. Fall Foliage. Great Ghost Train. Santa Express.

Location: Northeastern Pennsylvania, about 24 miles from Scranton.

Contact: Annetta DeYoung
Executive Director

Mailing Address:
742 Main Street
Honesdale, PA 18431
Telephone: (717) 253-1960

RAIL TOURS, INC.
Steam, scheduled
Standard gauge

COURTESY OF RAIL TOURS, INC.

Ride/Operation: This line offers a 40-minute round trip to Nesquehoning and a 1 3/4-hour round trip to Lake Hauto. In October, 34-mile, 2 3/4-hour Flaming Foliage Rambles are made to Haucks, passing over scenic Hometown Trestle. All trips operate over a former Jersey Central branch.

Displays/Exhibits: An exhibit inside the Jim Thorpe depot features mining artifacts and other items of local history.

Schedule: 40-minute trip: weekends, May 6-September 4, 12:00, 1:00, 2:00 & 3:00 p.m.; weekends, September 9-24, plus holidays and July 3, 12:00, 1:00, 2:00, 3:00 & 4:00 p.m. 1 3/4-hour trip: weekends, May 27-September 3, 4:00 p.m. Flaming Foliage Rambles: September 30, October 1, 22 & 28-29, 1:15 p.m.; October 7-9, 14-15 & 21, 10:00 a.m. & 2:15 p.m.

Fare: 40-minute trip: Adults $5.00, children (2-11) $3.00, children under 2 ride free. 1 3/4-hour trip: Adults $7.00, children (2-11) $4.00, children under 2 ride free. Flaming Foliage Rambles: Adults $13.00, children (2-11) $7.00, children under 2 ride free.

Locomotives: 1913 D-10 4-6-0 No. 1098, former Canadian Pacific; 1937 SW-900 EMD F3A No. 11, former Maryland & Pennsylvania No. 83.

Passenger Cars: Coaches, former Reading and former Central of New Jersey.

Rolling Stock/Equipment: Various wood and steel cabooses; freight cars, former CNJ.

Location: At the former Jersey Central depot on U.S. 209 in downtown Jim Thorpe, 26 miles north of Allentown. Take the Mahoning Valley exit (No. 34) off the Northeast Extension of the Pennsylvania Turnpike (route 9) and travel six miles on U.S. 209.

Contact: John Eline
Sales and Customer Service

Mailing Address:
P.O. Box 285
Jim Thorpe, PA 18229
Telephone: (717) 325-4606

Pennsylvania, Johnstown-Altoona
R

"TRACKS THROUGH TIME"
HERITAGE RAIL EXCURSION
Diesel, scheduled
Standard gauge

Ride/Operation: The Pennsylvania Railroad main line across the Allegheny Mountains made it possible for communities and industry to flourish in this part of the country. The rich, diverse legacy of this region is best understood via the railroad, and "Tracks Through Time" gives visitors this opportunity. During a unique excursion over the mountains in Amtrak's *Pennsylvanian,* which travels east from Johnstown and west from Altoona on a 39-mile segment of the line, a National Park Service ranger provides narration and interpretive brochures describing the cultural history, changing landscape, and significant resources of the area. A 1 1/2-hour layover in Altoona allows travelers to visit the city and its Railroaders Memorial Museum.

Conrail operates approximately 60 trains per day over this historic route, but boarding the *Pennsylvanian* is currently the only way for visitors to ride through the famed Gallitzin tunnels and around spectacular Horsehoe Curve, where trains struggle to overcome grades of up to 2.2 percent.

Train: Amtrak Amcoaches and typically a dinette.

Schedule: Thursdays-Saturdays; lv. Johnstown 11:52 a.m., arr. Altoona 1:03 p.m.; lv. Altoona 2:33 p.m., arr. Johnstown 3:39 p.m.
Fare: $20.00 (round trip).

Location: Johnstown: 4 / Walnut Street. Altoona: 1231 11th Avenue.

Contact: Peter D. Barton
Executive Director
Railroaders Memorial Museum

Mailing Address:
1300 Ninth Avenue
Altoona, PA 16602
Telephone: (814) 946-0834
Amtrak: (800) 872-7245

Pennsylvania, Kempton
D-R

COURTESY OF WANAMAKER, KEMPTON & SOUTHERN, INC.

WANAMAKER, KEMPTON & SOUTHERN, INC.
Steam, scheduled
Standard gauge

Ride/Operation: A 6-mile, 40-minute round trip through scenic Pennsylvania Dutch country over part of the former Reading Company's Schuylkill & Lehigh branch. The steam train is supplemented by a unique gasoline-engine trolley, the "Berksy."

Displays/Exhibits: Restored stations relocated from Joanna and Catasauqua, Pennsylvania; original circa 1874 Wanamaker station; operating HO-gauge model layout (on steam Sundays).

Train: Open-window coaches; open gondola; caboose.

Schedule: Steam: Sundays, May, June & September; weekends, July, August & October; plus May 29 & September 4; 1:00, 2:00, 3:00, & 4:00 p.m. "Berksy": Saturdays, June & September; 1:00, 2:00, 3:00 & 4:00 p.m.

Fare: Adults $4.00, children (2-12) $2.00, children under 2 ride free.

Locomotives: No. 2, 1920 Porter 0-4-0T, former Colorado Fuel & Iron; No. 65, 1930 Porter 0-6-0T, former Safe Harbor Water Power; No. 35, 1927 Mack/SWMRR gas-electric switcher; No. 20, 1935 Whitcomb gas-mechanical switcher; No. 602, 1944 Whitcomb diesel-electric.

Passenger Cars: Coaches Nos. 1494 & 1474 and combine No. 408, all former Reading Company; coach No. 582, former Lackawanna.

Rolling Stock/Equipment: Assorted freight cars and caboose, former Lehigh & New England; steel and wood cabooses, former Reading.

Special Events: Mother's Day Specials, May 14. Sandman Special, June 17. Kids' Weekend, August 5-6. Harvest Moon Specials, October 6-7. Halloween Spooky Trains, October 28-29. Santa Claus Specials, December 9-10.

Location: Depot is located at Kempton on routes 143 or 737, a short distance north of I-78. The site is about 20 miles west of Allentown and 30 miles north of Reading.

Contact: Linda Hartman
Vice President, Advertising

Mailing Address:
P.O. Box 24
Kempton, PA 19529
Telephone: (610) 756-6469

250

Pennsylvania, Leesport
D-M

**READING COMPANY
TECHNICAL & HISTORICAL SOCIETY**
Railway museum
Standard gauge

COURTESY OF READING COMPANY TECHNICAL & HISTORICAL SOCIETY

Displays/Exhibits: Working LEMTU car, built for locomotive-engineer training; working stands for first- and second-generation diesels; working two-thirds-sized replica of a Reading A5A 0-4-0 switcher; museum car with many artifacts and working signals; rolling stock; gift shop in baggage car.

Schedule: <u>Weekends</u>, May-October, 12:00-5:00 p.m.

Admission: Donations welcomed.

Locomotives: No. 103, NW-2, fully restored; No. 5513, GP-30; No. 5308, Alco C-630; No. 900, FP7; No. 6300, U30C; No. 5204, Alco C424; No. 3640, GP-35; other locomotives in the yard or to be delivered.

Passenger Cars: Two baggage cars; No. 863, MU car; Blueliners Nos. 9111, 9113, 9118 & 9131; Nos. 9152 & 9162, last RDCs built; ten passenger cars, former Reading.

Rolling Stock/Equipment: Boxcars, gondolas, covered hopper, cabooses.

Special Events: <u>Annual Train Meet</u>, October 2.

Note: GP30 No. 5513 was featured at EMD's fiftieth anniversary celebration of the FT diesel locomotive at LaGrange, Illinois.

Location: Wall Street, at the railroad.

Contact: William L. Kline
Vice President

Mailing Address:
Box 15143
Reading, PA 19612-5143
Telephone: (800) 882-7797
Evenings: (610) 562-8677

251

Pennsylvania, Lewisburg
D-R

WEST SHORE RAIL EXCURSIONS
Diesel, scheduled
Standard gauge

Ride/Operation: This operation offers two narrated rides. The Lewisburg & Buffalo Creek Railroad is a 1 1/2-hour round trip over the former Reading Railroad through Victorian Lewisburg, past Bucknell University, and along the Susquehanna River and the cliffs of the Buffalo Mountains to the village of Winfield. The West Shore Railroad is a 2 1/2-hour round trip over the former Reading & Pennsylvania Railroad through the scenic Amish and Mennonite farms of the Buffalo Valley to Victorian Mifflinburg. A dinner train is available on Wednesdays during summer and fall.

Displays/Exhibits: Delta Place Station displays engines, passenger cars, a dining car, several cabooses, a train station, and scales.

Train: Steel coaches; cabooses; dining car.

Schedule: Weekends, April 1-June 19 & September 4-October 22; April-May, 2:00 p.m.; June-October, 11:30 a.m. & 2:00 p.m. Tuesday-Sunday, June 20-September 3, 11:30 a.m. & 2:00 p.m. Dinner Train: Wednesdays, May-October; May-September, 6:00 p.m.; October, 5:30 p.m. First Saturday of the month, May-October; May-September, 6:30 p.m.; October, 6:00 p.m. Reservations required for dinner train 48 hours in advance.

Admission: Lewisburg & Buffalo Creek: adults $7.00, senior citizens $6.50, children (3-11) $4.00. West Shore: adults $9.00, senior citizens $8.50, children (3-11) $5.00. Dinner train: Wednesday, $25.00; Saturday, $30.00. Group rates available on public excursions.

Locomotives: No. 9425, 1950 EMD SW-1 & No. 2233, 1963 EMD GP-30, both former PRR.

Passenger Cars: 1916 steel coaches, former Erie-Lackawanna; 1915 dining car, former Jersey Central; 1926 club car, former PRR.

Rolling Stock/Equipment: Cabooses, former PRR, Erie/Lackawanna, Reading, and Santa Fe.

Special Events: Easter Bunny Express. Armed Train Robberies. School Field Trips. Mother's

Day Dinner Train. Father's Day Dinner Train. Champagne Sunset Dinner Trains. Railcar Show. Antique Machinery Show. Fall Foliage Excursion. Haunted Train Rides. Santa Claus Express.

Location: Delta Place Station, on route 15 two miles north of Lewisburg.

Radio Frequency: 164.55

Contact: Dennis W. Confer
General Manager

Mailing Address:
RR 3, Box 154
Route 15 North
Lewisburg, PA 17837
Telephone: (717) 524-4337

KNOX & KANE RAILROAD
Steam, diesel, scheduled
Standard gauge

GEORGE A. FORERO, JR.

Ride/Operation: This line offers one round trip each operating day to Kane and the Kinzua Bridge over a former Baltimore & Ohio branch line. Passengers may board at Marienville for a 96-mile, 8-hour trip or at Kane for a 32-mile, 3 1/2-hour trip. The 2,053-foot-long, 301-foot-high Kinzua Bridge, built in 1882 to span the Kinzua Creek Valley, was at the time the highest bridge in the world. It is on the National Register of Historic Places and is a National Historic Civil Engineering Landmark.

Train: Steel coaches; open cars; two snack and souvenir cars.

Schedule: Friday-Sunday, June & September; Tuesday-Sunday, July & August; Wednesday-Sunday, beginning of October; weekends, October 15-16 & 22-23; lv. Marienville 8:30 a.m., lv. Kane 10:45 a.m.

Fare: From Marienville: adults $20.00, children $13.00. From Kane: adults $14.00, children $8.00. Advance reservations suggested. Box lunches available by advance order, $3.75.

Locomotives: No. 38, 1927 Baldwin 2-8-0, former Huntington & Broad Top Mountain; No. 44, Alco diesel; No. 58, Chinese 2-8-2 built in 1989; Porter Switcher No. 1.

Location: In northwestern Pennsylvania, about 20 miles north of I-80.

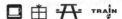

Mailing Address:
P.O. Box 422
Marienville, PA 16239
Telephone: (814) 927-6621

NEW HOPE & IVYLAND RAILROAD
Steam, diesel, scheduled
Standard gauge

NEW HOPE & IVYLAND RAILROAD

Ride/Operation: This line offers a 9-mile, 50-minute round trip from the historic 1891 New Hope depot to Lahaska over the former Reading Railroad. The narrated excursion takes passengers along the Delaware Canal, across the famous "Perils of Pauline" trestle, past a farmhouse that was used in the Underground Railroad, and through the rolling hills and valleys of Bucks County. Dinner, brunch, and wine-and-cheese trains operate year-round.

Train: 1920s former Reading steel coaches; air-conditioned parlor cars with snacks and beverages sold on board; air-conditioned dining cars.

Schedule: <u>Weekends</u>, year-round. <u>Daily</u>, mid April-November. <u>Dinner, brunch, and wine-and-cheese trains</u>: weekends. Number of trips per day varies with the seasons; please call or write for information.

Fare: Adults $7.95, senior citizens $6.95, children (2-11) $3.95, children (under 2) $1.00.

Locomotives: No. 40, 1925 Baldwin 2-8-0, former Lancaster & Chester; No. 3028, 1946 Alco 4-8-4, former National de Mexico; No. 1513, 1949 Alco RSC-2, former Seaboard Air Lines; No. 9423, 1950 EMD SW-1, former Pennsylvania.

Special Events: *Fireworks Express,* July 4. <u>Fall Foliage Trips</u>. <u>Haunted Halloween Trains</u>, 2 weeks before Halloween. *Santa Claus Express*, Thanksgiving through Christmas.

Location: West Bridge Street (route 179). Convenient access from I-95, routes 202 and 611, and the Pennsylvania Turnpike.

New York, Philadelphia, Princeton, Trenton

Contact: Irene Rumbas
Group Coordinator

Mailing Address:
P.O. Box 634
New Hope, PA 18938
Telephone: (215) 862-2332
Fax: (215) 862-2150

LAKE SHORE RAILWAY
HISTORICAL SOCIETY, INC.
Railway museum
Standard gauge

Displays/Exhibits: At this site, the restored former New York Central passenger station built by the Lake Shore & Michigan Southern Railway in 1899 houses extensive displays, including a Heisler demonstration model built in 1915. Other items include a 1908 wooden Bessemer & Lake Erie boxcar, three generations of refrigerator cars, a Whitcomb switcher, a fireless Heisler steam locomotive, the first NYC U25B diesel, a former South Shore "Little Joe" electric built by the nearby General Electric plant, standard sleepers, a baggage car, an operational diner, and an 1890 Lake Shore & Michigan Southern wooden business car. The museum is adjacent to Conrail (former NYC) and Norfolk Southern (former Nickel Plate) main lines.

Schedule: Wednesdays-Sundays and holidays, May 27-September 4; weekends, September 9-October 29; 1:00-5:00 p.m.

Admission: No charge; donations welcomed.

Location: At Wall and Robinson Streets. Fifteen miles east of Erie, the site is two miles north of exit 11 off I-90 and 3 blocks south of U.S. 20.

Erie

Mailing Address:
P.O. Box 571
North East, PA 16428-0571
Telephone: (814) 825-2724

Pennsylvania, Philadelphia
R

PENN'S LANDING TROLLEY
BUCKINGHAM VALLEY TROLLEY ASSN.
Electric, scheduled
Standard gauge

RICHARD RODEN

Ride/Operation: This line takes passengers on a 2 2/10-mile, 20-minute round trip along the Delaware River, Philadelphia's historic waterfront. Trolleys pass the Philadelphia Maritime Museum and the city's fleet of historic vessels, including the ship *Gazela Primeiro*, the lightship *Barriegat*, the submarine *Becuna*, and the historic U.S.S. *Olympia*.

Schedule: Weekends & holidays, April 15-July 5 & September 5-November 26. Thursdays-Sundays, July 6-September 4. Cars operate every 30 minutes or less, 11:00 a.m. to dusk.

Fare: All-day pass: adults $1.50, children (under 12) $.75. Tickets available from conductor on board car.

Electric Cars/Trolleys: No. 46, 1907 St. Louis Car Co. interurban, former Philadelphia & Western; No. 76, 1926 Brill center-entrance suburban/ interurban, former Philadelphia & West Chester; No. 80, 1931 Brill Master Unit, former Philadelphia Suburban Transportation.

Special Events: Santa Claus Specials, December 9-10&16-17.

Note: The Penn's Landing Trolley is operated by the Buckingham Valley Trolley Association, which has preserved a number of trolleys and interurban cars from the Philadelphia area.

Location: Cars may be boarded on Columbus Boulevard and on Dock, Spruce, and Market streets.

Contact: Charles Long
Treasurer

Mailing Address:
P.O. Box 7285
Philadelphia, PA 19101
Telephone: (215) 627-0807

Pennsylvania, Rockhill Furnace
D-R

EAST BROAD TOP RAILROAD
Steam, scheduled
36" gauge

JOHN J. HILTON

Ride/Operation: The East Broad Top Railroad, chartered in 1856, is the last operating narrow-gauge railroad east of the Mississippi. The road hauled coal, freight, mail, express, and passengers for more than eighty years. Today the East Broad Top offers passengers a 10-mile, 50-minute ride through the beautiful Aughwick Valley with its own preserved locomotives; the ride takes passengers from the historic depot at Rockhill Furnace to the picnic grove, where the train is turned. The railroad is a Registered National Historic Landmark.

Displays/Exhibits: Railroad yard with shops, operating roundhouse, and turntable. EBT freight cars, cabooses, work equipment, and gas-electric car can be seen.

Train: Wooden coaches; parlor cars; open cars.

Schedule: Summer operations are changed annually. Please call or write for the current schedule.

Admission: Please call or write for current information.

Locomotives: No. 12, 1911 Baldwin 2-8-2; No. 14, 1912 Baldwin 2-8-2; No. 15, 1914 Baldwin 2-8-2; No. 17, 1918 Baldwin 2-8-2; all original East Broad Top Railroad.

Special Events: Fall Spectacular, Columbus Day Weekend.

Note: Dates, times, and fares are subject to change; please call or write for latest information.

Location: At Rockhill Furnace, adjacent to Orbisonia on route 522. Take the Fort Littleton or Willow Hill exit off the Pennsylvania Turnpike.

Contact: Joe Kovalchick
President

Mailing Address:
Rockhill Furnace, PA 17249
or Box 279
Indiana, PA 15701
Telephone: (814) 447-3011

ROCKHILL TROLLEY MUSEUM
Electric, scheduled
Standard gauge

JOEL SALOMON

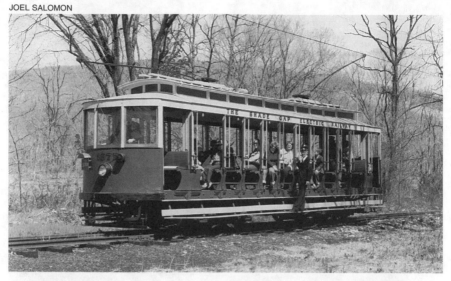

Ride/Operation: A nonprofit, educational museum incorporated in 1962, the Rockhill Trolley Museum is composed of volunteers who preserve, restore, and maintain a collection of two dozen electric rail vehicles, about twelve of which are in operating condition. Trolleys operate over dual-gauge trackage on the former Shade Gap Branch of the East Broad Top Railroad for a 2-mile, 20-minute round trip. Standard-gauge streetcars meet narrow-gauge steam trains. Walking tours are offered.

Displays/Exhibits: A small building at the site houses some artifacts, a few hands-on exhibits, and a collection of photographs of one hundred years of transit history.

Schedule: Weekends and holidays, May-October, 11:30a.m.-4:30p.m.

Fare: Adults $3.00, children (2-12) $1.00 if accompanied by an adult. Group rates by arrangement. Special fares during Fall Spectacular.

Locomotives/Trolleys: No. 163, 1924 Brill curveside car, former York Railways (Pennsylvania); No. 172, 1929 "Toonerville" type, former Porto, Portugal; No. 249, 1904 double-truck Brill semi-convertible; No. 311, 1923 double-truck Birney, former Johnstown, Pennsylvania; No. 315, 1909 Kuhlman, former Chicago, Aurora & Elgin interurban; No. 1875, 1912 St. Louis Car Co., summer car from Rio de Janeiro; No. 205, Philadelphia "Bullet" car. Liberty Liner *Independence Hall* (former *Electroliner* No. 803-804) operates by arrangement.

Rolling Stock/Equipment: Work car No. 402 and 1915 snowplow, both former Philadelphia & Western; 1898 snow sweeper; PCC car, former Washington, D.C.; 1910 snow sweeper, former Scranton, Pennsylvania; 1930 dropside work car; Philadelphia subway/bridge car No. 1009 (under restoration); Johnstown No. 355 (under restoration). Other cars in storage.

Special Events: Fall Spectacular, Columbus Weekend: all operable trolleys run, food service aboard *Independence Hall*, and full-course dinner served Saturday night. Halloween Trolley, October 28. Santa's Trolley, December 9-10.

Note: Since the museum relies on volunteers, operations are sometimes limited to 1 or 2 cars.

Location: On U.S. 522, 20 miles north of exit 13 of the Pennsylvania Turnpike. Adjacent to East Broad Top Railroad in Rockhill Furnace.

Contact: Sam Kuhn
Head of Operations

Mailing Address:
P.O. Box 203
Rockhill Furnace, PA 17249
Telephone: (814) 447-9576
(717) 263-3943

STEAMTOWN NATIONAL HISTORIC SITE
Railway museum
Standard gauge

Ride/Operation: A 27-mile round-trip steam excursion will operate between Scranton and Moscow, Pennsylvania, after July 1, 1995.

Displays/Exhibits: On July 1, 1995, this site presents the grand opening of its new facilities: two museums, a theater, a visitor center, restored portions of the roundhouse, and a bookstore. Roundhouse tours, locomotive-shop tours, preservation-shop tours, and various additional programs will be offered. Many locomotives and cars are on display in the buildings and in the historic Delaware, Lackawanna & Western Railroad yards.

Train: A five- to eight-car passenger train, powered by either former Canadian Pacific 4-6-2 No. 2317 or former Canadian National 2-8-2 No. 3254, is used for the main excursion. Yard duties are performed with Baldwin 0-6-0 No. 26.

Schedule: Daily, 9:00 a.m.-5:00 p.m. Closed Thanksgiving, Christmas, and New Year's Day.
Admission: Park: no charge. Excursion: adults $7.00, children (under 13) $3.00.
Locomotives: Many steam locomotives; three operate.
Passenger Cars: Electric trailers; suburban and day coaches; combines; business car; troop sleeper.
Rolling Stock/Equipment: Railway Post Office car, boxcars, cabooses, gondolas, hoppers, snowplows, baggage cars, and tank car.
Note: The park is finishing its development and will open its new buildings to the public in late spring 1995. Before July 1, 1995, the park will continue to operate from its existing facilities.

Location: Before July 1, 1995, entrance is at 150 South Washington Avenue; after July 1, 1995, entrance is off West Lackawanna Avenue

Contact: Calvin Hite
Assistant Superintendent

Mailing Address:
150 South Washington Avenue
Scranton, PA 18503
Telephone: (717) 961-2033

ROADSIDE AMERICA
Model railroad

Displays/Exhibits: Roadside America, an idea born in June 1903, is a childhood dream realized. From day to day and almost without interruption, this indoor miniature village has grown to be the largest and most beautiful of its type. More than sixty years in the making by Laurence Gieringer, it is housed in a new, modern, comfortable, air-conditioned building and covers more than eight thousand square feet of space. The display includes 2,570 feet of track for trains and trolleys and 250 railroad cars.   O-gauge trains and trolleys run among the villages.

Schedule: July 1-September 5; weekdays, 9:00 a.m.-6:30 p.m.; weekends, 9:00 a.m.-7:00 p.m. September 6-June 30: weekdays, 10:00 a.m.-5:00 p.m.; weekends, 10:00 a.m.-6:00 p.m.

Admission: Adults $3.75, senior citizens $3.50, children $1.25.

Location: Take exit 8 off I-78 between Allentown and Harrisburg.

Contact: Alberta Bernecker

Mailing Address:
P.O. Box 2
Shartlesville, PA 19554
Telephone: (215) 488-6241

CHOO-CHOO BARN & STRASBURG TRAIN SHOP
Model railroad

FRED M. DOLE

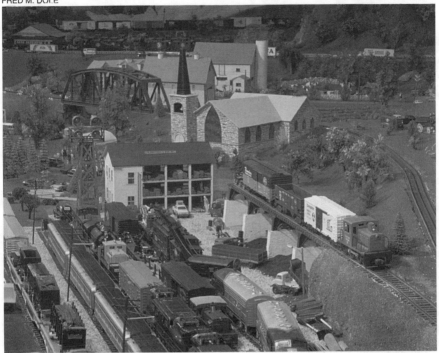

Displays/Exhibits: This hand-built operating display of Amish country covers seventeen hundred square feet and features 16 model trains and 130 animated scenes. Built by one family over a period of forty-nine years, this one-of-a-kind layout appeals to all ages. Journey from daybreak through nightfall in this miniature countryside while visiting a three-ring circus, seeing Amish friends raising a barn, and cheering with the crowd at the baseball game. Excellent detail and fascinating workmanship.

Schedule: Choo-Choo Barn: daily; June 1-August 31, 10:00 a.m.-6:00 p.m.; April 1-May 31 & September 1-December 31, 10:00 a.m.-5:00 p.m.; Strasburg Train Shop & Railroad Books and Videos: daily, June 1-August 31, 10:00 a.m.-6:00 p.m.; January 2-May 31 & September 1-December 31, 10:00 a.m.-5:00 p.m. Closed Thanksgiving, Christmas, and New Year's Day.

Location: Route 741 east.

♿ 🚻 🚗 🚐 ⊞ ✉ ⛟

Admission: Adults $3.00, children (5-12) $1.50, children under 5 admitted free. Groups rates available.

Note: The Choo-Choo Barn & Strasburg Train Shop are part of the large Shops of Traintown, which includes five specialty shops and Isaac's Deli, complete with an oak Victorian dining car.

Contact: Thomas C. Groff
President

Mailing Address:
Route 741 East, Box 130
Strasburg, PA 17579
Telephone: (717) 687-7911
(717) 687-0464

Pennsylvania, Strasburg
M

NATIONAL TOY TRAIN MUSEUM
Model railroad museum
Toy trains and accessories

COURTESY OF NATIONAL TOY TRAIN MUSEUM

Displays/Exhibits: Housed in a beautiful replica of a Victorian railroad station, this museum has one of the finest collections in the world of toy trains, dating from 1880 to the present. The collection includes items from such manufacturers as Ives, Lionel, American Flyer, LGB, and Marklin. Five operating layouts feature O-, S-, G-, HO-, and standard-gauge trains. A video on train subjects plays continuously.

Schedule: Daily, May 1-October 31; weekends and special holiday dates, April, November & December; 10:00 a.m.-5:00 p.m.

Admission: Adults $3.00, senior citizens (65+) $2.75, children (5-12) $1.50. Group discounts available.

Special Events: Junior Engineer Week, August 5-12.

Location: 300 Paradise Lane. From the Strasburg station, travel east on route 741, turn north onto Paradise Lane, and go past the Red Caboose Motel.

>>> Lancaster

Contact: Thelma Rapp

Mailing Address:
P.O. Box 248
Strasburg, PA 17579
Telephone: (717) 687-8976

Pennsylvania, Strasburg
M

RAILROAD MUSEUM OF
PENNSYLVANIA
Railway museum

COURTESY OF RAILROAD MUSEUM OF PENNSYLVANIA

Displays/Exhibits: The Railroad Museum of Pennsylvania was established by the commonwealth of Pennsylvania to collect, preserve, and interpret the history of railroading in the state. The museum displays one of the world's finest collections of steam, electric, and diesel-electric locomotives, passenger and freight cars, and related memorabilia. The 90,000-square-foot building covers six tracks, which exhibit equipment dating from 1825 to 1992. In the extensive yard (open during summer months, weather permitting) are more than twenty-five additional locomotives and cars. Interpretive exhibits help tell the story of railroading in Pennsylvania.

Schedule: Daily, May 1-October 31; Tuesday-Sunday, November 1-April 30; Monday-Saturday, 9:00 a.m.-5:00 p.m.; Sunday, 12:00-5:00 p.m. Closed on certain holidays.

Admission: Adults $6.00, senior citizens $5.00, youths (6-17) $4.00, children under 6 admitted free.

Locomotives: Indoors: the Pennsylvania Railroad Historical Collection, including K4s 4-6-2 No. 3750; L1s 2-8-2 No. 520; G-5 4-6-0 No. 5741; H3 2-8-0 No. 1187; B1 electric switcher; and GG-1 electric No. 4935. Also the "Tahoe," 1875 Baldwin 2-6-0, and all three major classes of logging locomotive: Shay, Heisler, and Climax. Outdoors: E-44 electric, former Pennsylvania Railroad; GG-1 No. 4800; Baldwin S-12 diesel switcher; others.

Rolling Stock/Equipment: 1855 wooden combine, former Cumberland Valley; 1895 combine No. 4639, former PRR; early PRR coaches and express, baggage, and mail cars; Pullman "Lotos Club"; business car No. 203, former Western Maryland; P-70 coach, former PRR; 1950s-era freight train.

Special Events: Grand Opening, New Museum Wing, May 19-21. Charter Day, March. Reading Weekend, July. Circus Days, August. Halloween Haunt, October. Christmas Program, "Home for the Holidays," December. Please write for schedules.

Location: On Pennsylvania route 741 opposite the Strasburg Rail Road.

Lancaster

Contact: Robert L. Emerson
Director

Mailing Address:
Box 15
Strasburg, PA 17579
Telephone: (717) 687-8628

Pennsylvania, Strasburg
D-R

STRASBURG RAIL ROAD
Steam, scheduled
Standard gauge

JOHN E. HELBOK

Ride/Operation: A 9-mile, 45-minute round trip from Strasburg to Paradise. Train travels through lush farmlands and turns around adjacent to the Amtrak main line.

Displays/Exhibits: The Strasburg Rail Road, one of the oldest and busiest steam tourist railroads in the country, displays a large collection of historic cars and locomotives.

Train: Open-platform wooden combine and coaches; "Hello Dolly" open observation car; first-class service including food and beverages aboard parlor "Marian." Lunch served on full-service diner "Lee Brenner" on hourly trains.

Schedule: <u>Daily</u>, April-October. Number of trips per day varies with the season, from four to fourteen. During July and August two trains operate, providing service every half-hour. Complete timetables are sent upon request. <u>Dinner Train Service</u>: Thursday-Sunday, July-August, 7:00 p.m.; weekends, September-December and May-June. Call for reservations and information.

Fare: Adults $7.00, children $4.00. <u>Group rates</u> available. <u>Parlor car</u>: adults $9.50, children $6.00. <u>Dining car (ride only)</u>: adults $8.00, children $5.00.

Locomotives: No. 31, 1908 Baldwin 0-6-0 & No. 89, 1910 Canadian 2-6-0, both former Canadian National; No. 90, 1924 Baldwin 2-10-0, former Great Western; No. 475, 1906 Baldwin 4-8-0, former Norfolk & Western.

Special Events: <u>Easter Bunny Trains</u>, Easter weekend. <u>Halloween Ghost Trains</u>, October 28. <u>Santa Claus Trains</u>, weekends, December 2-17.

Location: On Route 741 in Pennsylvania Dutch country, a short distance from Lancaster.

Lancaster

Radio Frequency: 161.235

Contact: G. Fred Bartels
President

Mailing Address:
P.O. Box 96
Strasburg, PA 17579
Telephone: (717) 687-7522

Pennsylvania, Titusville R

OIL CREEK & TITUSVILLE RAILROAD
Diesel, scheduled
Standard gauge

BEVERLY SNYDER

Ride/Operation: A 27-mile, 2 1/2-hour round trip over former Pennsylvania Railroad trackage through the Oil Creek valley, birthplace of the oil industry. The train makes its way through Oil Creek State Park, passing Petroleum Centre and Drake Well Park. Oil Creek State Park has picnic facilities, bicycle rentals, hiking trails, and a bike trail on the original (circa 1860) right-of-way of the Oil Creek Railroad. Drake Well Park has a working, steam-operated replica of the world's first oil well, plus the Drake Well Museum. The railroad is sponsored by the Oil Creek Railway Historical Society.

Train: Open-window coaches, former Delaware, Lackawanna & Western; *Wabash Cannon Ball* coach No. 1399; RPO; open car.

Schedule: Weekends, June 10-30 & September; lv. Titusville 11:45 a.m. & 3:15 p.m.; lv. Drake Well 12:00 & 3:30 p.m.; lv. Rynd Farm 1:15 & 4:30 p.m. (4:30 p.m. trip is one-way). Wednesday-Sunday, July, August & October 1-22. Wednesday-Friday, lv. Titusville 2:00 p.m.; lv. Drake Well 2:15 p.m.; lv. Rynd Farm 3:30 p.m. (3:30 p.m. trip is one-way). Weekends, lv. Titusville 11:45 a.m. & 3:15 p.m.; lv. Drake Well 12:00 & 3:30 p.m.; lv. Rynd Farm 1:15 & 4:30 p.m. (4:30 p.m. trip is one-way). Passengers may board at any of the three sites.

Fare: Adults $9.00, senior citizens $8.00, children (3-17) $5.00. One-way, group, car-rental, and train-rental rates available. Box lunches available with advance notice. MasterCard and Visa accepted.

Locomotives: No. 75, 1947 Alco S-2, former South Buffalo Railway.

Special Events: Peter Cottontail Express, April 8, 2:00 p.m. Murder Mystery Dinner Train, June 24, July 15, August 5 & 26, September 16 & 30. Moonlight Honky Tonk Excursion, August 11, 7:00 p.m. Applefest Special, September 29, 2:00 p.m.

Haunted Train Excursion, October 28, 6:00 p.m. Santa Train Excursion, December 9-10, 2:00 p.m. Passengers may board special-event trains in Titusville only.

Location: Easily accessible from I-79 and I-80. Trains depart from station at 409 South Perry Street in Titusville and at Rynd Farm, 3 1/2 miles north of Oil City on route 8.

Mailing Address:
P.O. Box 68
Oil City, PA 16301
Telephone: (814) 676-1733

265

PENNSYLVANIA TROLLEY MUSEUM
Electric, scheduled
5' 2 1/2" gauge, standard gauge

SCOTT R. BECKER

Ride/Operation: A 2 1/2-mile round trip along a portion of the former Pittsburgh Railways Washington-to-Pittsburgh interurban line and up the scenic Arden Valley along a former coal-mine railroad.

Displays/Exhibits: Trolleys from Pittsburgh, Philadelphia, Johnstown, Boston, New Orleans, and western Pennsylvania. In the museum's Visitors Education Center is the exhibit "Pennsylvania Trolleys and the Electric Age." Also on display are a 1930 Baldwin-Westinghouse diesel, a Bessemer & Lake Erie combine, and wooden trolley shelters from the Pittsburgh Railways; the Pittsburgh, Harmony, Butler & New Castle Railway; and the Pittsburgh & Butler Street Railway.

Schedule: Weekends, May, June, October, and December; May, June & October, 12:00-5:00 p.m.; December, 11:00 a.m.-5:00 p.m. Daily, July-August, 12:00-5:00 p.m.

Fare: Adults $5.00, senior citizens $4.00, children $3.00, family $14.00. Group rates available with advance reservation.

Locomotives/Trolleys: No. 3756, double-truck steel car, former Pittsburgh; No. 5326, double-truck steel car, former Philadelphia Rapid Transit; No. 832, double-truck steel car, former New Orleans; Nos. 66 & 73, double-truck center-door cars, former Philadelphia Suburban Transit; three other Philadelphia cars.

Location: Two miles from downtown on North Main Street Extension; take exit 8 off I-79. The site is on the former broad-gauge main line of the Pittsburgh-Washington interurban.

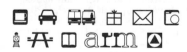

Contact: Scott R. Becker
Executive Director

Mailing Address:
1 Museum Road
Washington, PA 15301
Telephone: (412) 228-9256

266

Pennsylvania, Williamsport
M

TERRY WILD STUDIO

LYCOMING COUNTY HISTORICAL SOCIETY & MUSEUM
History museum
Toy trains

Displays/Exhibits: The Shempp toy-train collection is one of the finest in the country. More than 337 complete trains, one hundred individual engines (twelve are one-of-a-kind), and two working model layouts are on display. Exhibit includes items in L, TT, N, OO, HO, O, and I gauges; Lionel, American Flyer, Marx, Ives, and American Model Train Company pieces; an American Flyer Mayflower; a copper-and-gold-finished GG-1; and American Flyer S-gauge displays.

Schedule: May 1-October 31: Tuesday-Friday, 9:30a.m.-4:00p.m.; Saturday, 11:00a.m.-4:00p.m.; Sunday, 12:00-4:00p.m. November 1-April 30: Tuesday-Friday, 9:30a.m.-4:00p.m.; Saturday, 11:00 a.m.-4:00p.m. Closed major holidays.

Admission: Adult $3.50; seniors, AARP & AAA $3.00; children $1.50.

Location: 858 West Fourth Street.

   ♿ 🚗 🚌 ⊞ ✉ 📷 📖 🔺

Contact: Sara-Ann B. Briggs
Executive Director

Mailing Address:
858 West Fourth Street
Williamsport, PA 17701-5824
Telephone: (717) 326-3326

NEWPORT STAR CLIPPER
DINNER TRAIN
Diesel, scheduled
Standard gauge

Ride/Operation: Passengers on this train enjoy a 3-hour trip along the west coast of Aquidneck Island, overlooking Narragansett Bay. During the ride an elegant 5-course meal, prepared on board, is served by formally attired waitstaff.

Train: Center-cab, 65-ton, 1943 General Electric 400-horsepower diesel locomotive; 1952 former U.S. Army power car; three refurbished 1946 Budd coaches, two used as dining cars and one as a full kitchen, former Pennsylvania, former Seaboard, and former Atlantic Coast Line.

Schedule: Daily, year-round. Reservations required; please call or write for availability. Groups welcomed.
Fare: Lunch $29.95, dinner $45.00.
Special Events: Entertainment. Murder mysteries. Vocalists. Jazz.

Location: 19 America's Cup Avenue.

Contact: Reservations

Mailing Address:
102 Connell Highway
Newport, RI 02840
Telephone: (800) 462-7452
(401) 849-7550

Rhode Island, Newport
R

OLD COLONY & NEWPORT
SCENIC RAILWAY
Diesel, scheduled

GEORGE A. FORERO, JR.

Ride/Operation: The Old Colony & Newport Railway was established in 1863 to bring passengers from Boston, Massachusetts, to steamboats operating for New York and other parts of the eastern United States. After several mergers with other railroad companies, the OC&N reappeared in 1979 as one of the most scenic railways in New England. Passengers can take a 3-hour, 21-mile or a 1-hour, 10-mile round trip; the 3-hour ride includes a 1-hour stop at Green Animals Topiary Gardens (admission is extra; passengers may stay aboard the train if they choose). Both rides take passengers along picturesque Narragansett Bay and feature views of the Newport Naval Base, colorful ships sailing in the bay, and the beautiful rocky beaches that follow the 130-year-old right-of-way.

Train: 1912 open-platform coach, former Boston & Maine; 1895 open-platform parlor car, former Intercolonial Railway; P-70 heavyweight coach.

Schedule: Three-hour trip: May 7-November 26, Sundays & holidays, 12:30 p.m. One-hour trip: June 25-September 16; Wednesdays, Thursdays & Saturdays, 11:00 a.m., 12:30 & 2:15 p.m.

Fare: Three-hour trip: coach, adults $6.00, senior citizens $5.00, children (under 15) $4.00; parlor car, $9.00. One-hour trip: coach, adults $5.00, senior citizens $4.00, children (under 15) $3.00; parlor car, $7.00.

Locomotives: No. 84, 1945 45-ton General Electric; No. 64, 1942 45-ton General Electric.

Rolling Stock: 1938 steel caboose, former Pennsylvania Railroad; lightweight flatcars.

Special Events: Environmental guided trips. Fall Foliage trips. Christmas in Newport. Please call or write for schedules and fares.

Note: Historic buildings, gift shops, restaurants, and yachting centers are within walking distance.

Location: 19 America's Cup Avenue, next to the Newport Gateway and Visitor's Center in the heart of downtown Newport.

⊞(nearby) 🏠(nearby) ≫Providence

Radio Frequency: 160.395

Contact: Donald Elbert
Executive Director

Mailing Address:
P.O. Box 343
Newport, RI 02840
Telephone: (401) 849-0546
Charters: (401) 624-6951

269

South Carolina, Rockton
M-R

SOUTH CAROLINA
RAILROAD MUSEUM
Railway museum

Ride/Operation: This museum offers a 6-mile, 45-minute round trip between Rockton and Greenbrier. As track work progresses, the trip will be extended; please write for further details.

Displays/Exhibits: Founded in 1973, the museum features exhibits in some of its pieces of rolling stock.

Train: Open-air coach, former Strategic Air Command; cabooses, former Nickel Plate, Seaboard Coast Line, and Southern Railway.

Schedule: May 20-October 21, first and third Saturdays of the month.

Fare/Admission: Adults $4.00, children (2-12) $2.50, infants in arms ride free. Fares subject to change.

Locomotives: No. 44, 1927 Baldwin 4-6-0, former Hampton & Branchville (under restoration); No. 76, 1949 45-ton Porter diesel, and No. 82, 1941 45-ton General Electric, both former U.S. Army Transportation Corps; No. 33, 1946 44-ton General Electric, former Pennsylvania Railroad; No. 4, 1946 25-ton General Electric, former Tarmac/Lone Star Corporation.

Passenger Cars: 1910 office car "Norfolk", former Seaboard Air Lines; 1926 Pullman "Bizet"; 1927 RPO car; lightweight coach.

Rolling Stock/Equipment: Two baggage cars, former Southern; assorted boxcars; 1946 express refrigerator car, former SAL; tank cars; flatcars; dump cars; cabooses; maintenance-of-way equipment; motor cars; gang cars.

Special Events: Festival in the Park, October 14. Train Ride with Santa Claus, November 25.

Note: The museum is recruiting volunteers.

Location: Two miles south of Winnsboro, at the junction of highway 34 and U.S. 321, a short distance from I-77. The site is about 25 miles north of Columbia.

Columbia

Contact: Bill White
President

Mailing Address:
P.O. Box 7246
Columbia, SC 29202-7246
Telephone: (800) 968-5909
(Olde English Historical District)
For More Information: (803) 796-8540
(704) 393-0335

South Dakota, Hill City
D-R

BLACK HILLS CENTRAL RAILROAD
Steam, scheduled
Standard gauge

MICHAEL A. EAGLESON

Ride/Operation: A 20-mile, 2-hour round trip between Hill City and Keystone Junction, through forests and mountains near Mount Rushmore National Monument, over a four-percent ruling grade that was once part of the Burlington Railroad. This year marks the thirty-eighth year of operation of the Black Hills Central Railroad. The ticket terminal and a gift shop are located in a former Chicago, Burlington & Quincy station; a snack bar is located at the terminus.

Train: Vintage coaches; half-open coaches; open observation cars.

Schedule: Mid May-September; Monday-Friday, lv. Hill City 8:00 & 10:15 a.m. and 1:30 & 3:45 p.m., lv. Keystone 9:00 & 11:15 a.m. and 2:30 & 4:45 p.m. (4:45 trip is one-way); weekends, lv. Hill City 10:15 a.m., 1:30 & 3:45 p.m., lv. Keystone 11:15 a.m., 2:30 & 4:45 p.m. (4:45 trip is one-way). July-August, evening runs added. Early spring and fall, reduced schedule. Please call for more information.

Fare: Adults $13.00, children (4-14) $8.50, children under 4 ride free when not occupying a seat. Prices include tax and are subject to change.

Locomotives: No. 7, 1919 Baldwin 2-6-2, former Prescott & Northwestern; No. 104, 1926 Baldwin 2-6-2, former Peninsula Terminal Railroad.

Note: No. 7 and some of its cars have appeared in "Gunsmoke," the Disney film *Scandalous John,* and the television movie *Orphan Train.*

Location: In the western part of South Dakota, near Mt. Rushmore National Monument.

Contact: Robert Warder
President

Mailing Address:
P.O. Box 1880
Hill City, SD 57745
Telephone: (605) 574-2222
Fax: (605) 574-4915

271

South Dakota, Madison
D-R

PRAIRIE VILLAGE
Steam, irregular
Standard gauge, 24" gauge

DAVE SANFORD

Ride/Operation: Prairie Village is a collection of turn-of-the-century buildings assembled from area towns. There are many steam traction engines on display, along with gas tractors and all types of farm equipment. Passengers may take a two-mile ride around the grounds; part of the loop is from the original Milwaukee line that ran from Pipestone, Minnesota, to Wessington Springs, South Dakota. One-third of a mile of 24-inch-gauge track surrounds the old Wentworth, South Dakota, depot.

Displays/Exhibits: Junius, South Dakota, depot; former Chicago & North Western turntable from Sioux Falls, South Dakota (scheduled to be installed in 1995); chapel car "Emmanuel"; Russell snowplow; tank car; two former REA/Santa Fe express refrigerator cars; track tamper; motorized way cars.

Train: No. 29, 0-6-0, and No. 11, 0-4-0; former REA/Santa Fe express refrigerator car converted to coach; 1909 former C&NW combination coach/baggage car No. 7403 (with original seats and lights); coaches, former Deadwood Central; former Illinois Central caboose.

Schedule: Village Museum: daily, May 29-September 4. Train: June 4 & 18, July 2 & 16, August 6 & 20, and during Fall Jamboree.

Fare/Admission: Museum: $4.00. Two-mile ride: $2.50. One-third-mile ride: $1.00 Fall Jamboree: $5.00.

Locomotives: No. 29, 1944 Lima 0-6-0, former Army, former Bay City Terminal, former Iron & Steel Processing, former Duluth & Northeastern; No. 11, Alco 0-4-0T, former Cadillac & Lake City, former Deadwood Central; No. 5, 1927 Orenstein & Koppel 0-4-0T used in Germany until after World War II.

Special Events: Prairie Village Fall Jamboree, August 25-27. Fourth of July Dinner Train with parade and fireworks.

Location: Two miles west of Madison. From Sioux Falls, take I-29 north to the Madison/Coleman exit, then travel west on highway 34.

Contact: Bill Nolan

Mailing Address:
Prairie Village: P.O. Box 256
Madison, SD 57042-0256
Telephone: (605) 256-3644
Train information: P.O. Box 302
Madison, SD 57042-0302
Telephone: (605) 256-6177

南

South Dakota, Milbank
D-R

TRAINFEST '95
Diesel, scheduled
Standard gauge

COURTESY OF TRAINFEST

Ride/Operation: A 21-mile, 2 1/2-hour round trip from Milbank to Corona over a former branch of the Milwaukee Road, with dinner available. A 10-mile valley trip is also available. The train is operated by the common-carrier Sisseton Milbank Railroad in conjunction with the Milbank Chamber of Commerce.

Displays/Exhibits: In the National Guard Armory are fifteen operating model railroads, including HO, G, N, and O27 gauge; railroad antiques; slide shows; videos; and railroad collectibles. A free shuttle is offered between the armory and the depot.

Train: 1911-1934 Soo Line, Great Northern, and Milwaukee Road heavyweight coaches.

Schedule: Please call for information.

Fare/Admission: Corona trip: adults $12.00, children $9.00. Valley trip: adults $7.00, children $5.00. Display: adults $1.00, children admitted free. Reservations required for "Dinner in the Diner."

Locomotives: No. 627, 1954 EMD SW-1200, former Milwaukee, the last Milwaukee Road engine to leave Tacoma, Washington.

Passenger Cars: No. 2705, 1934 combine, and 1940 caboose, both former Milwaukee. No. 993, 1911 coach; No. 2111, 1913 coach; and No. 756, 1911 diner; all former Soo line.

Special Events: The United States Post Office issues a special cancellation during these trips; mail is canceled aboard the train.

Note: Train robberies occur on every train, conductors dress in uniform, and hobos ride the rails.

Location: In northeastern South Dakota, 126 miles north of Sioux Falls, South Dakota, 180 miles west of Minneapolis, Minnesota, and 126 miles south of Fargo, North Dakota.

Fargo, North Dakota

Contact: Neil Bagaus
Director of Passenger Operations

Mailing Address:
Chamber of Commerce
203 South Main Street
Milbank, SD 57252
Telephone: (800) 675-6656

273

CHATTANOOGA CHOO CHOO
Railway display

Ride/Operation: Opened in 1909 as the Southern Railway's Terminal Station, this depot welcomed thousands of travelers during the golden age of railroads. Today, the restored station is the heart of the Chattanooga Choo Choo Holiday Inn, a thirty-acre complex with a full range of entertainment. Forty-eight passenger cars are part of the 360-room hotel; three passenger cars serve as a bar, formal restaurant, and meeting/banquet room. A 1924 former New Orleans trolley takes passengers on tours of the historic property.

Displays/Exhibits: Terminal Station, listed on the National Register of Historic Places; HO-gauge model railroad, 174 feet long and 33 feet wide, featuring 3,000 feet of track, 150 switches, 120 locomotives, 1,000 freight cars, 80 passenger cars, and 320 structures. On display in the formal gardens, a former train yard, is a former Cincinnati Southern steam locomotive.

Fare: Trolley: $.50. Model Railroad: adults $2.00, children $1.00.

Location: 1400 Market Street.

Contact: Joe Kilgore
Director of Marketing

Mailing Address:
1400 Market Street
Chattanooga, TN 37402
Telephone: (800) 872-2529
(615) 266-5000

274

Tennessee, Chattanooga
D-R

TENNESSEE VALLEY RAILROAD
Steam, scheduled
Standard gauge

R. W. LYNDALL

Ride/Operation: A 6-mile, 45-minute round trip, much on original ET&G roadbed, across Chickamauga Creek and Tunnel Boulevard and through 986-foot-long Missionary Ridge Tunnel to East Chattanooga Depot, where a shop, turntable, displays, and active steam-locomotive repair shop are located.

Displays/Exhibits: Tour of caboose, display car, theater car, diner, Pullmans, and various steam and diesel locomotives; Grand Junction Depot; large gift shop; audio-visual show; outside exhibits.

Train: Heavyweight coaches with adjustable windows; air-conditioned lightweight coaches Nos. 661 & 907, former Central of Georgia; diner No. 3158.

Schedule: <u>Daily</u>, May, September & October, 10:00 a.m.-2:00 p.m.; <u>daily</u>, June-August, 10:00 a.m.-5:00 p.m.; <u>Saturdays</u>, April-November, 10:00 a.m.-5:00 p.m.; <u>Sundays</u>, April-November, 12:00-5:00 p.m.; lv. East Chattanooga 10:30 & 11:40 a.m., 12:55, 2:20, 3:35 & 4;35 p.m.; lv. Grand Junction 11:00 a.m., 12:15, 1:35, 2:45, 4:00 & 5:00 p.m. (5:00 p.m. train is one-way). *Downtown Arrow* service to Chattanooga Choo-Choo hotel complex: weekends, June-August, with food service and extra-fare seating. <u>Schedules subject to change.</u>

Fare: <u>Regular fare:</u> adults $8.00, children (3-12) $4.00. *Downtown Arrow:* adults $13.00, children (3-12) $9.00. <u>Group rates and charters</u> available.

Locomotives: No. 610, 1952 Baldwin 2-8-0, and Nos. 8669 & 8677, Alco RSD-1 diesels, former U.S. Army; No. 349, 1891 Baldwin 4-4-0, former Central of Georgia; No. 509, 1910 Baldwin 4-6-0, former Louisiana & Arkansas; No. 630, 1904 Alco 2-8-0, and No. 4501, 1911 Baldwin 2-8-2, both former Southern Railway; No. 913, Alco RS-1, former Hartford & Slocomb; No. 36, Baldwin VO1000, former U.S. Air Force; ACT-1, DOT experimental electric train.

Special Events: <u>North Georgia Specials</u>, some powered by steam locomotive No. 4501. <u>Others</u>. Please call or write for information.

Location: 4119 Cromwell Road, near the Jersey Pike exit of Tennessee highway 153 and 1 1/2 miles west of the I-75/highway 153 interchange (exit 4).

Radio Frequency: 160.425

Contact: Robert M. Soule
President

Mailing Address:
4119 Cromwell Road
Chattanooga, TN 37421-2119
Telephone: (615) 894-8028
Fax: (615) 894-8029

275

COWAN RAILROAD MUSEUM
Railway museum

COURTESY OF COWAN RAILROAD MUSEUM

Displays/Exhibits: The CSX line from Nashville to Chattanooga (once Nashville, Chatta-nooga & St. Louis, later Louisville & Nashville) climbs over Cumberland Mountain south of Cowan. The grades are steep enough to require helpers in each direction; they are added to southbound trains at Cowan. The former station is now a museum housing a re-creation of a turn-of-the-century telegraph operator's office, various artifacts, and an HO-scale model of the Cowan Pusher District.

Train: Steam locomotive, flatcar, caboose.

Schedule: Thursday-Saturday, May-October, 10:00 a.m.-4:00 p.m. Sunday, May-October, 1:00-4:00 p.m.

Admission: No charge, donations welcomed.

Note: Food is available in Cowan; lodging can be found in Winchester, seven miles west.

Location: Take exit 135 off I-24; 12 miles west on U.S. 41A and 64 and about 15 miles north of the Alabama border.

Contact: Howard Coulson
President

Mailing Address:
P.O. Box 53
Cowan, TN 37318
Telephone: (615) 967-7365

SOUTHERN APPALACHIA
RAILWAY MUSEUM
Railway museum
Standard gauge

Ride/Operation: This museum, a nonprofit corporation, is dedicated to the preservation of rail equipment pertinent to the region. Although a permanent site has not been established, members continue an ongoing effort to restore and maintain equipment. Once restored, the equipment is available for lease to individuals or organizations.

Displays/Exhibits: Coaches; combine; RPO; sleepers; collection of railroad artwork and artifacts.

Schedule: Weekends, by appointment. Only escorted visits are available, because of ongoing restoration.

Admission: Donations welcomed.

Rolling Stock: Boxcar, former Boston & Maine; caboose No. 6847, former Louisville & Nashville; coach No. 664, "Fort Oglethorpe," 1947 Budd, former Central of Georgia; sleeper-lounge "General Beauregard," 1942 Pullman, former Illinois Central; diner-lounge No. 1550, "Oklahoma City," former Frisco; baggage cars No. 1608, 1926 Pullman, and No. 1625, 1928 Pullman, both former Atlantic Coast Line; coach No. 619, 1947 Milwaukee, former Milwaukee Road. Sleeper No. 2206, "Roanoke Valley," 1949 Pullman; 22-seat combine No. 720, 1914 Pullman; coaches Nos. 826 and 827, 1949 Budd, No. 1075, 1922 Pullman, and No. 846, 1958 Pullman; and RPO No. 34, 1928 American Car & Foundry; all former Southern.

Note: The museum welcomes new members.

Location: Middlebrook Industrial Park.

Contact: John E. Humphrey

Mailing Address:
P.O. Box 5870
Knoxville, TN 37928
Telephone: (615) 691-4147

Tennessee, Nashville
R

THE BROADWAY DINNER TRAIN
Diesel, scheduled
Standard gauge

COURTESY OF THE BROADWAY DINNER TRAIN

Ride/Operation: This line offers a 2 1/2-hour, 35-mile trip through historic middle Tennessee in restored streamlined passenger cars, with a four-course meal served during the trip.

Train: E8A locomotive; RPO/power car; private car "Hollywood Beach"; coach; pleasure dome; dining cars; round-end tavern-lounge observation car.

Schedule: Thursday-Saturday; other times as required.

Fare: Adults $42.95; does not include tax and gratuity. Alcoholic beverage service is available.

Locomotives: Nos. 5764 and 5794, EMD E8As, former Pennsylvania Railroad, former MBTA, former Conrail.

Passenger Cars: No. 514, RPO (power car), former Rock Island; "Hollywood Beach"; sun lounge/sleeper No. 800129 and dining cars Nos. 245 and 6507, all former Seaboard; 52-seat coach No. 4967, former PRR; No. 504, former Santa Fe Pleasure Dome; diners Nos. 1493 and 1494, former Santa Fe; tavern lounge-observation car, former Florida East Coast.

Special Events: Hour-long trips, spring and fall. Story-telling trips for children. Valentine's Day Special. Mother's Day Special. Halloween Special. Santa Special.

Location: 108 First Avenue South, at Riverfront Park.

Radio Frequency: 160.365

Contact: Dianne Turnage
Secretary/Treasurer

Mailing Address:
108 First Avenue South
Nashville, TN 37201
Telephone: (800) 274-8010

DOLLYWOOD ENTERTAINMENT PARK
Steam, scheduled

GEORGE A. FORERO, JR.

Ride/Operation: The *Dollywood Express,* located in the Village area of Dollywood, takes visitors on a 5-mile journey through this scenic park, known as "the friendliest town in the Smokies." As passengers ride on the authentic, coal-fired steam train, they can catch a glimpse of the different areas of Dollywood: Daydream Ridge, Rivertown Junction, The Village, Craftsman's Valley, Country Fair, Showstreet, and the new Jukebox Junction. The *Dollywood Express* also takes visitors through replicas of a typical turn-of-the-century mountain village and logging community. During Christmas Festivals, the train is decorated with lights and features a special Christmas message for visitors.

Train: The train has been part of the park since June 1, 1961, when the park was known as Rebel Railroad. It has been known as the *Dollywood Express* since May 1986, when the park became Dollywood. The Dollywood Express, with seven open-air passenger cars, is pulled by ninety-ton 2-8-2 Baldwin steam locomotives.

Schedule: One 30-minute ride is offered every hour during park operating hours.

Fare/Admission: Train fare is included with Dollywood admission: adults $22.99 + tax, senior citizens (60+) $19.99 + tax, children (4-11) $15.99 + tax. Group rates available for groups of 20 or more.

Locomotives: "Klondike Katie," 1943 Baldwin 2-8-2, former U.S. Army No. 192; "Cinderella," 1939 Baldwin 2-8-2, former U.S. Army No. 70.

Passenger Cars: Seven open-air passenger cars.

Special Events: Annual Fall Festival, October. Smoky Mountain Christmas Festival, mid November-December. School field trips.

Location: Please call for specific directions.

Contact: Ellen Long
Publicist

Mailing Address:
1020 Dollywood Lane
Pigeon Forge, TN 37863-4101
(615) 428-9488

AUSTIN STEAM TRAIN ASSOCIATION, INC.
Steam, scheduled
Standard gauge

GEORGE A. FORERO, JR.

Ride/Operation: A 6-hour, 68-mile round trip through the scenic Texas hill country, over the former Southern Pacific route built in 1881 to bring pink granite stone to build the state capitol. The route crosses the beautiful South San Gabriel River.

Train: Mikado No. 786; steam-era coaches; other special cars as needed.

Schedule: Weekends; one train each day. Please call or write for information and reservations.

Fare: Regular coach: adults $24.00, children (under 13) $10.00. Air-conditioned coach: adults $32.00, children (under 11) $16.00. First-class air-conditioned coach: $38.00. Senior-citizen and group discounts available.

Locomotives: Mikado No. 786, 1960 Alco, former Southern Pacific, former Texas & New Orleans.

Passenger Cars: Six 1920 P-70 coaches, former Pennsylvania Railroad; air-conditioned coaches chartered as needed.

Special Events: Wildflower Specials, spring. Christmas Specials. Call for information.

Location: Four miles northwest of Austin in Cedar Park (intersection of U.S. 183 and Farm Road 1431).

   Austin

Radio Frequency: 160.550

Contact: Ness Meredith
Marketing Director

Mailing Address:
Box 1632
Austin, TX 78767-1632
Telephone:
Reservations: (512) 477-8468
Office/Administration: (512) 477-6377

AGE OF STEAM RAILROAD MUSEUM
Railway museum
Standard gauge

BOB LAPRELLE

Displays/Exhibits: Operated by the Southwest Railroad Historical Society since 1963, this museum offers a nostalgic journey back to the days of steam locomotives and name passenger trains, featuring some of the world's largest steam, diesel-electric, and electric locomotives. A superlative collection of heavyweight passenger equipment includes dining car "Gollad," former Missouri-Kansas-Texas; business car "Texland," former Fort Worth & Denver; and newly restored parlor-club car No. 3231, former Santa Fe. Also at the site are chair and Pullman cars, vintage freight cars and cabooses, Dallas's oldest train station, and many railroad artifacts. Come blow the steam locomotive whistles and enjoy one of the nation's foremost railroad collections. Former Santa Fe "doodlebug" M-160 and former Western Railroad VO-1000 No. 1107 operate periodically within the museum site.

Schedule: Weekends, 11:00 a.m.-5:00 p.m. Thursdays-Fridays, 10:00 a.m.-3:00 p.m.

Admission: Adults $3.00, children (under 13) $1.50.

Locomotives/Trolleys: "Big Boy" No. 4018, 1942 Alco 4-8-8-4 & "Centennial" No. 6913, EMD DDA40X, both former Union Pacific; No. 1625, 1918 Alco 2-10-0, former Eagle-Picher Mining Co.; No. 4501, 1942 Baldwin 4-8-4, former Frisco; No. 7, 1923 Baldwin 0-6-0, former Dallas Union Terminal Co.; No. 4906, Amtrak GG-1 electric, former Pennsylvania Railroad No. 4903; M-160, diesel-electric "Doodlebug," former Santa Fe; No. 1107, Baldwin VO-1000 diesel-electric, former Western Railroad Co., former Colorado & Wyoming; No. 115, 1956 Fairbanks-Morse H12-44, former Southern Pacific No. 2379.

Special Events: Open daily during State Fair of Texas, October, 10:00 a.m.-6:00 p.m.

Location: Two miles east of downtown at 1105 Washington Street, on the north side of the State Fair of Texas grounds at Fair Park. From I-30 eastbound, take exit 47A to Parry Avenue, turn left and travel 3 blocks to the entrance. From I-30 westbound, take exit 47A right onto Exposition Avenue, then turn left on Parry Avenue.

Dallas

Contact: Bob LaPrelle
Executive Director

Mailing Address:
P.O. Box 153259
Dallas, TX 75315-3259
Telephone: (214) 428-0101

MCKINNEY AVENUE TRANSIT AUTHORITY
Electric, scheduled
Standard gauge

GEORGE A. FORERO, JR.

Ride/Operation: A 3-mile, 30-minute round trip in restored vintage streetcars between the downtown Arts District and the shops, galleries, and restaurants of McKinney Avenue. More than half of the route (along McKinney and Cole Avenues) is original Dallas Railway & Terminal trackage, a line that began service in 1890. The system is operated with volunteer labor by the nonprofit McKinney Avenue Transit Authority.

Displays/Exhibits: Carbarn tours are available upon request.

Schedule: Daily; Sunday-Thursday, 10:00 a.m.-10:00 p.m.; Friday-Saturday, 10:00 a.m.-midnight. Frequency of service varies from 15 to 30 minutes, depending on the number of cars in service.

Fare: Round trip: adults $1.50, senior citizens $.50, children $1.00. Day passes and tokens are also sold. Charters available.

Trolleys: In operation are four closed streetcars: No. 122, "Rosie," 1906 single-truck Brill, former Oporto, Portugal; No. 186, "The Green Dragon," 1913 Stone and Webster "turtle roof," and Birney No. 636, "Petunia," both former Dallas, Texas; No. 369, "Matilda," Australian class W-2. Interurban No. 332, former North Texas Traction, is under restoration. In storage and awaiting restoration are Stone and Webster Nos. 183, 189, and 323, former Dallas.

Special Events: Couples-only Love Trolleys, Valentine's Day. Shamrock Fest, weekend nearest St. Patrick's Day. Free rides for Moms and Dads on their holidays. Free cake to all riders on weekend nearest MATA birthday in mid-July. Halloween Special. Christmas Special.

Location: Two main terminals: McKinney Plaza on McKinney Avenue between Bowen and Hall, one-half mile west of North Central Expressway (U.S. 75); and St. Paul by Ross, 2 blocks south of Woodall Rodgers Freeway in the Arts District. More than 20 additional stops are along the route.

Mailing Address:
3153 Oak Grove Avenue
Dallas, TX 75204
Telephone: (214) 855-0006
Fax: (214) 855-5250

TARANTULA TRAIN
Steam, scheduled

GEORGE A. FORERO, JR.

Ride/Operation: A 10-mile, 1 1/2-hour round trip over the Fort Worth & Western Railroad freight line through the heart of Fort Worth, crossing both legs of the Trinity River over massive timber and steel trestles and offering spectacular vistas of the Fort Worth skyline. The Tarantula follows the route of the Chisholm Trail between Eighth Avenue Yard and the historic Fort Worth stockyards. Stockyards Station is the largest train station in the Southwest. The Tarantula may be boarded at either end of the railroad.

Displays/Exhibits: Historic Fort Worth stockyards district and operating turntable.

Train: Fully restored 1896 Cooke 4-6-0; four open-window passenger coaches; two open-air touring coaches.

Schedule: Daily. Please call or write for timetable.

Fare: Adults $10.00, senior citizens (55+) $8.00, children (3-12) $5.50. One-way tickets available.

Locomotives: No. 2248, 1896 Cooke 4-6-0, and No. 1744, 1901 Baldwin 2-6-0, both former Southern Pacific; No. 938, 1910 Alco 4-6-2, former Rock Island.

Special Events: Chisholm Trail Days, June. Railroad Days, July. Pioneer Days, September.

Location: 140 East Exchange Avenue, in the stockyards; or 2318 Eighth Avenue, southwest of downtown Fort Worth.

Fort Worth

Mailing Address:
140 East Exchange Avenue
Fort Worth, TX 76106
Telephone: (817) 625-RAIL (7245)
(800) 952-5717

GULF COAST RAILROAD MUSEUM
Gulf Coast Chapter,
National Railway Historical Society
Railway museum

Displays/Exhibits: This museum, located near the Southern Pacific's Sunset Route in northeastern Houston, features historic locomotives and passenger and freight cars of regional significance, many in operable condition. The recently completed visitor center is housed in former Santa Fe 1928 end-door baggage-express car No. 1890, which also contains a collection of railroad artifacts.

Schedule: April 1-October 31, Saturdays, 11:00 a.m.-4:00 p.m. Group tours available at other times by appointment.

Admission: Adults $3.00, children (under 13) $1.50.

Locomotives: No. 14, 1949 Alco, former Houston Belt & Terminal; No. 510, 1949 Baldwin DS44-750, former Texas Mexican.

Passenger Cars: Streamlined sleeper "Verde Valley," 1942 Pullman, former Santa Fe; all-stainless chair car "New Braunfels," 1955 Pullman, former Missouri-Kansas-Texas, built for the *Texas Special;* tavern-lounge-observation "Good Cheer," 1940 Pullman, former Kansas City Southern, built for the streamlined *Southern Belle;* 1947 streamlined parlor car "Alton," former Gulf, Mobile & Ohio; streamlined baggage-RPO No. 3401, 1938 Budd, former Santa Fe; heavyweight baggage car No. 50, Barney & Smith, former Spokane, Portland & Seattle.

Rolling Stock/Equipment: Caboose No. 6, 1949 MKT (Dennison) shops, former MKT; 1979 bay-window caboose No. 4696, former Southern Pacific; 1927 riveted steel tank car No. 2198, former Cities Service Oil.

Special Events: National Model Railroad Month Open House, November, features layouts from area model railroad clubs in the museum's cars. Occasional main-line steam and diesel excursions as fund-raisers. Various local railroad-related tours and day trips.

Location: 7390 Mesa Drive, about 1 1/2 miles north of McCarty Road (U.S. highway 90) off North Loop 610.

🚋 🚌 🚐 ⊞ ✉ 📷

🎪 ▲ ♿(limited)

Contact: Museum Director

Mailing Address:
P.O. Box 457
Houston, TX 77001-0457
Telephone: (713) 631-6612

COURTESY OF *TEXAS LIMITED*

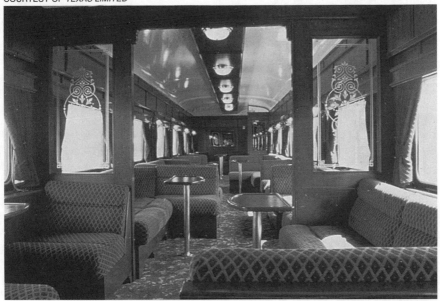

Ride/Operation: This excursion train travels on a charter basis from Houston to historic Galveston Island, with a stop at League City Park in the NASA/Clear Lake area.

Displays/Exhibits: The Galveston terminal is the historic Center for Transportation and Commerce, which includes a large collection of locomotives, cars, and other railroad artifacts. NASA, Space Center Houston, and the Gulf Greyhound Park are located in League City-NASA/Clear Lake.

Schedule: Charter only. Please call or write if you are interested in arranging a trip.
Fare: Please call or write for information.
Locomotives: Two EMD F-7s.
Passenger Cars: Seven restored passenger cars from the 1930s, 1940s, and 1950s.

Location: Houston Eureka Station, 567 T.C. Jester.

Houston

Contact: April Smith

Mailing Address:
3131 West Alabama Street
Suite 309
Houston, TX 77098
Telephone: (713) 522-8895

ROSSTYNE TROLLEY LINE
Electric, scheduled
24" gauge

COURTESY OF ROSSTYNE TROLLEY LINE

Ride/Operation: An eight-horsepower gas-driven motor car operates on five hundred feet of track, with two stops. At the end of track, the one-car train is turned on a turntable to return to the point of origin. Loading stations are at each end.

Displays/Exhibits: The trolley is housed inside the Pastime Museum building for winter protection. The museum features railroad antiques, an anvil, a large vise, and an old blacksmith shop.

Train: Trolley carries three adults (including motorman) or five children (ages 3-9).

Schedule: Ride: May-October, Saturdays, 9:00 a.m.-12:00 p.m. Museum: Year-round, Monday-Saturday.

Admission: Ride: $.50.

Trolleys: Open-air trolley.

Rolling Stock/Equipment: Two standard-gauge handcars; fire hydrant; standard-gauge switch

Special Events: Sam Bass Days, July 15, with parade, beef dinner and fiddling music.

Location: Eighteen miles west of Valley View, off I-35 north.

Dallas

Contact: Jim Penton
Owner

Mailing Address:
Box 633 or 643
Rosston, TX 76263
Telephone: (817) 768-2792
Historical General Store: (817) 768-2239
286

TEXAS STATE RAILROAD
Steam, scheduled
Standard gauge

GEORGE A. FORERO, JR.

Ride/Operation: A 4-hour, 50-mile round trip over a major segment of the original Texas State Railroad, built in 1896. Trains make one trip each day through the heart of East Texas from the Victorian-style depots of both Rusk and Palestine. A locomotive tour is given before the morning departure.

Train: Steel combine; six coaches.

Schedule: Weekends, March 12-May 29, August 6-October 30, plus September 6; Thursday-Monday, May 30-July 31; lv. Rusk for Palestine 11:00 a.m., return 3:00 p.m., lv. Palestine for Rusk 11:00 a.m., return 3:00 p.m.

Fare: Round trip: adults $15.00, children (3-12) $9.00, children under 3 ride free. One way: adults $10.00, children (3-12) $9.00; children under 3 ride free. Reservations recommended.

Locomotives: No. 201, 1901 Cooke 4-6-0, former Texas & Pacific No. 316; No. 300, 1917 Baldwin 2-8-0, former Texas Southeastern No. 28; No. 400, 1917 Baldwin 2-8-2, former Magma Arizona No. 7; No. 500, 1911 Baldwin 4-6-2, former Santa Fe No. 1316; No. 610, 1927 Lima 2-10-4, former Texas & Pacific No. 610.

Location: Rusk Depot is 2 1/2 miles west of Rusk on U.S. 84; Palestine Depot is 4 miles east of Palestine on U.S. 84.

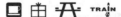

Contact: Curtis Pruett
Park Superintendent

Mailing Address:
P.O. Box 39
Rusk, TX 75785
Telephone: (903) 683-2561
In Texas: (800) 442-8951

TEXAS TRANSPORTATION MUSEUM
Railway museum

COURTESY OF TEXAS TRANSPORTATION MUSEUM

Ride/Operation: Passengers enjoy a one-third-mile caboose ride on the "Longhorn & Western Railroad" behind a Baldwin 0-4-0T or a 44-ton diesel. The ride will soon be extended to one mile.

Displays/Exhibits: Santa Fe business car No. 404; heavyweight Pullman "McKeever"; Missouri Pacific transfer caboose; Union Pacific caboose; Southern Pacific station from Converse, Texas, with railroad displays and pictures; G-gauge garden railroad; five-thousand-square-foot display building with one-hundred-foot model railroad; fire trucks; antique vehicles; transportation toys; technology display.

Train: One locomotive; one or two cabooses. Steam operates if available; Fairmont motor-car rides available at other times during regular hours.

Schedule: <u>Museum</u>: Thursday and weekends, 9:00 a.m.-4:00 p.m., weather permitting. <u>Train</u>: Sundays, 1:00-3:30 p.m.; train departs every 20 minutes. <u>Steam locomotive</u>: first Sunday of each month.

Fare/Admission: <u>Suggested donation</u>: adults $3.00, children and students $1.00. Includes admission and all rides.

Locomotives: No. 6, 1911 Baldwin 2-8-0, former Moscow, Camden & San Augustine; No. 1, 1925 Baldwin 0-4-0T, former Comal Power Company; 1942 44-ton General Electric switcher, former U.S. Air Force; 12- and 14-ton 36-inch-gauge Plymouth diesels.

Special Events: <u>Open house</u>, first Sunday of each month, weather permitting, with all divisions of the museum operating as much equipment as possible. <u>With advance reservation</u>, the museum is available for groups, with train and fire-truck rides.

Location: McAllister Park, north of San Antonio International Airport, at 11731 Wetmore Road.

 San Antonio

Contact: Frank Brogan
Marketing Director

Mailing Address:
11731 Wetmore Road
San Antonio, TX 78247-3606
Telephone: (210) 490-3554

288

RAILROAD AND PIONEER MUSEUM
Railway museum

FRED M. SPRINGER

Displays/Exhibits: Early Santa Fe and Missouri-Kansas-Texas station equipment and furniture, including a working telegraph for train orders, as well as segregated waiting rooms. The museum houses a large collection of railroad artifacts and displays of woodworking, ranching, farming, blacksmithing, and local history. Also displayed is a large collection of railroad timetables and passes, photographs, and papers from around the world.

Schedule: Tuesday-Friday, 1:00-4:00 p.m.; Saturday, 10:00 a.m.-4:00 p.m.

Admission: Adults $2.00, senior citizens and children $1.00, children under 5 admitted free.

Locomotives: No. 3423, 1921 Baldwin 4-6-2, former Santa Fe; No. 2301, 1937 Alco, the oldest surviving Santa Fe diesel.

Rolling Stock/Equipment: Steel caboose No. 1556, former Gulf, Colorado & Santa Fe; three section cars; steel caboose No. 140, former MKT; handcar, caboose, and boxcar, all former Missouri Pacific; World War II Pullman troop sleeper.

Special Events: Texas Train Festival, September 16-17, includes model train show, one-eighth-gauge operating models, full-sized Santa Fe operating equipment, living history demonstrations, and arts and crafts. Special exhibits.

Note: The museum has acquired the former MKT Temple depot, the last mission-style MKT depot in Texas, and is planning to restore it and open it as a railroad research center.

Location: 710 Jack Baskin (31st Street and Avenue H). Temple is in central Texas, between Austin and Waco; take the Avenue H exit off I-35.

Temple

Contact: Mary Irving
Director

Mailing Address:
P.O. Box 5126
Temple, TX 76505
Telephone: (817) 778-6873

HEBER VALLEY RAILROAD
Steam, diesel, scheduled
Standard gauge

STEVEN W. BELMONT

Ride/Operation: A 32-mile, 3 1/2-hour round trip through the high mountain meadows of the Heber Valley, across rivers and streams and into the deep canyon of the Provo River to Vivian Park.

Displays: Various freight cars, maintenance-of-way equipment, and related machinery. The railroad is operated by the Heber Valley Railroad Authority, a nonprofit organization formed r jointly by Heber City, Wasatch County, and the state of Utah. During 1994, repairs were completed to former Union Pacific No. 618, one of the first standard-gauge steam locomotives in the U.S. to be removed from static display and placed in operation on a tourist railroad.

Train: Former Lackawanna commuter coaches; former Louisville & Nashville heavyweight; former Union Pacific combination car; former UP steel caboose or former Kennecott Copper caboose; various "mountain observation" cars.

Schedule: <u>Daily</u>, May 27-October 2; <u>weekends</u>, January 7-March 5, May 13-21, October 7-29, and November 25-December 30. Please call or write for complete schedule.

Fare: Adults $16.00, seniors $14.00, children (10 & under) $12.00, children (2 years & under) not occupying a seat ride free.

Locomotives: No. 618, 1907 Baldwin 2-8-0, and No. 1011, 1940 EMD NW-2, both former UP; No. 1218, 1953 Davenport 44-ton diesel, former U.S. Army.

Note: Trains will be operated by either No. 1011 or No. 1218 when No. 618 is having its monthly service inspection.

Location: Heber City Depot, 450 South 600 West. Heber City is 46 miles east of Salt Lake City on U.S. 40.

Salt Lake City

Radio Frequency: 150.995

Contact: Gloria Montgomery
Executive Director

Mailing Address:
P.O. Box 641
Heber City, UT 84032
Telephone: (801) 654-5601

OGDEN UNION STATION
UTAH STATE RAILROAD MUSEUM
Railway museum

COURTESY OF OGDEN UNION STATION

Displays/Exhibits: This museum features a model railroad, films on the Union Pacific "Big Boy," and various railroad artifacts. Other special exhibits include the Browning National Firearms collection, Browning-Kimball antique automobiles, the Golden Spike Gem/Mineral/Historic Museum, and the Myra Powell Art Gallery.

Schedule: Not available at press time. Please call or write for information.

Admission: Adults $2.00, senior citizens (65+) $1.50, children (under 12) $1.00.

Locomotives: GP-9 No. 3769, former Southern Pacific; "Centennial" No. 6916, former UP; gas turbine, A and B units, former UP.

Rolling Stock/Equipment: Four cabooses; three former UP, one former Southern Pacific.

Location: Forty minutes north of Salt Lake City.

Contact: Bob Geier
Executive Director

Mailing Address:
2501 Wall Avenue
Ogden, UT 84401
Telephone: (801) 629-8444

GOLDEN SPIKE NATIONAL HISTORIC SITE
Railway museum
Standard gauge

Displays/Exhibits: This is the spot where the famous Golden Spike ceremony was held on May 10, 1869, completing the nation's first transcontinental railroad. Exact operating replicas of the original locomotives are on display; these locomotives run to the Last Spike Site on their own power each morning (from May to the first weekend in October) and return to the enginehouse in early evening. In the Visitor Center are color movies and many exhibits. Park rangers are on hand to explain the importance of the railroad and the significance of the ceremony of 1869.

Schedule: <u>Daily</u>; May 27-September 4, 8:00 a.m.-6:00 p.m.; September 5-May 26, 8:00 a.m.-4:30 p.m. Closed Thanksgiving, Christmas, and New Year's Day.

Admission: $4.00 per car, $2.00 per adult (17-61).

Locomotives: Full-sized operating replicas of Union Pacific 4-4-0 No. 119 and Central Pacific 4-4-0 No. 60, the "Jupiter."

Rolling Stock: 1891 class CA caboose, former Union Pacific, under restoration.

Special Events: <u>Annual Celebration</u>, May 10, features re-enactments. <u>Annual Railroader's Festival</u>, August 12, includes games, contests, and re-enactments. Admission is free on both days.

Note: Ranger Talks, Big Fill Walk, self-guided auto tours, afternoon locomotive demonstrations, and other activities are available. Check the activities board in the Visitor Center.

Location: 32 miles west of Brigham City.

Contact: Randy Kane
Chief Ranger

Mailing Address:
P.O. Box 897
Brigham City, UT 84302
Telephone: (801) 471-2209

PACIFIC LIMITED GROUP
Steam, diesel, irregular
Standard gauge

Ride/Operation: This group sponsors excursions powered by historic Union Pacific steam and diesel locomotives over the UP's lines; most trips feature one or more photo stops. A highlight for 1995 is a trip from Denver to the Pacific Northwest in September and October to celebrate the 50th anniversary of the inaugural of the streamliner *City of Portland*. Those interested can travel on one or several segments of the trip, which includes layovers at major cities such as Laramie, Wyoming; Boise, Idaho; Spokane, Washington; and Portland, Oregon. This trip features travel over the Granger cutoff, which has not seen passenger service in 20 years; a ride along the Snake River, crossing it on 3,900-foot-long Joso Bridge; rare mileage on the Montana Division from Pocatello, Idaho, to Butte, Montana; and the Columbia River Gorge.

Schedule: Excursions this year are scheduled to run in California, Oregon, Washington, Colorado, Idaho, Montana, Wyoming, Nebraska, and Kansas. Please call or write for information.

Fare: Varies depending on trip. Reservations required; please call or write for ticket information and availability.

Locomotives: No. 3985, 1943 Alco 4-6-6-4, largest operating steam locomotive in the world; No. 844, 1944 Alco 4-8-4, last steam locomotive purchased by the UP; Nos. 951, 963B & 949, 1955 EMD A-B-A E-9s; No. 6936, DD40AX, largest diesel built; all currently UP.

Passenger Cars: Original UP streamliner fleet cars, rebuilt to current standards.

Note: The Pacific Limited Group is responsible for ticket sales, advertising, staffing, and the safe operation of excursions. All railroad equipment and locomotive crews are provided by the Union Pacific Railroad. The PLG is made up of the Central Coast Chapter, NRHS; the Promontory Chapter, NRHS; the Union Pacific Historical Society; and the Feather River Rail Society.

Mailing Address:
P.O. Box 27081
Salt Lake City, UT 84119
Telephone: (801) 355-5871

TOOELE COUNTY RAILROAD MUSEUM
Railway museum

COURTESY OF TOOELE COUNTY RAILROAD MUSEUM

Ride/Operation: A short ride on the Tooele Valley Mini-Railroad, a one-and-one-half-inch-scale railroad circling the museum grounds.

Displays/Exhibits: Open since 1983, this museum preserves the history of railroading, mining, and smelting in Tooele. The centerpiece of the collection is former Tooele Valley Railway No. 11, a 1910 Alco 2-8-0 used on the railway until 1963; it now rests on the only remaining segment of TVR trackage, in front of the restored TVR depot. Also on display are a former Denver & Rio Grande Western wooden caboose; a former TVR outside-wood-braced caboose; a former TVR water car with a snowplow attached; two former Atchison, Topeka & Santa Fe coaches; a former Union Pacific boxcar; motor cars; and railroad-related equipment, such as a water column and coaling crane. Tooele County historical displays are located in the equipment. Inside the depot are displays depicting the TVR in its heyday, as well as scale models and photos of the smelter the railroad was built to serve. Outside the museum is a small replica of a coal mine.

Train: Replicas of Central Pacific steam locomotive No. 173, an Amtrak diesel, and a Union Pacific diesel.

Schedule: May 30-September 5, Tuesday-Saturday, 1:00-4:00 p.m.
Fare/Admission: Donations welcomed.

Location: 35 North Broadway. Tooele is 40 miles southwest of Salt Lake City.

Salt Lake City

Mailing Address:
90 North Main Street
Tooele, UT 84074
Telephone: (801) 882-2836
(801) 882-8133

294

GREEN MOUNTAIN RAILROAD
GREEN MOUNTAIN FLYER
Diesel, scheduled
Standard gauge

Ride/Operation: A 26-mile, 2-hour round trip from Bellows Falls to Chester. Ludlow foliage specials feature a 6-hour round trip. The former Rutland Railroad trackage goes through three river valleys, offering many scenic highlights. The Green Mountain Railroad is a working freight line.

Train: Restored open-window coaches, former Rutland Railroad and Jersey Central.

Schedule: Summer: June 17-18 & 24-25; July 1-September 4, Tuesday-Sunday. Fall: September 16-October 15, daily. Ludlow Trip: September 30, October 1, 7, 8, 14 & 15.

Fare: Round trip: adults $10.00, children $6.00, children under 3 not occupying a seat ride free. One way: adults $6.00, children $4.00. Please call or write for schedules and fares for special-event trains.

Locomotives: Alco RS-1 No. 405, former Rutland; EMD GP-9 No. 1849, former Burlington Northern; EMD GP-9 No. 1850, former Chesapeake & Ohio; EMD GP-9 No. 1848, former Bangor & Aroostook; EMD GP-9R No. 1851, former Norfolk Southern.

Note: Tickets are sold at Bellows Falls Union Station, on all trains, and in Chester at Cummings Hardware.

Special Events: Valentine's Day, February 12. Sugar on Snow, March 25-26. Easter Bunny, April 15. Mother's Day, May 14. Memorial Day, May 27-29.

Location: The railroad station is located on Depot Street at the junction of the Green Mountain and Boston & Maine railroads. Take exit 5 or 6 off I-91. Bellows Falls is in southern Vermont, on the New Hampshire border.

Bellows Falls

Contact: Barbara Adams

Mailing Address:
P.O. Box 498
Bellows Falls, VT 05101
Telephone: (802) 463-3069

JOHN E. HELBOK

Displays/Exhibits: This museum displays an extensive and internationally renowned collection of Americana housed in thirty-seven historic buildings on a forty-five-acre site. The railroad exhibit features the restored 1890 Shelburne depot with a Central Vermont steam locomotive and the private car "Grand Isle." Nearby is former Woodstock Railroad steam inspection car "Gertie Buck." There is also a wooden replica of Baldwin's "Old Ironsides" of 1832 and a collection of railroad memorabilia. Other exhibits at the museum include a 220-foot sidewheel steamer, the S.S. *Ticonderoga*, which was moved overland from Lake Champlain, and collections of antiques, quilts, carriages, art, decoys, and tools.

Schedule: <u>Daily</u>, late May-late October, 10:00 a.m.-5:00 p.m. <u>Guided tours</u>: late October-late May, 1:00p.m.

Admission: Admission ticket valid for two consecutive days (daily season only). <u>Group rates</u> available for groups of 15 or more.

Locomotives: No. 220, 1915 Alco 4-6-0, former Central Vermont.

Note: Limited handicapped accessibility.

Location: On U.S. route 7, seven miles south of Burlington.

Contact: Collections Department

Mailing Address:
P.O. Box 10
Shelburne, VT 05482
Telephone: (802) 985-3346
Fax: (802) 985-2331

U.S. ARMY TRANSPORTATION MUSEUM
Railway display

SGT. MALCOLM WILLIAMS

Displays/Exhibits: This military-history museum displays items of transportation dating from 1776 to the present. Inside the fifteen-thousand-square-foot museum are dioramas and exhibits; on five acres outside are rail rolling stock, trucks, jeeps, amphibious marine craft, helicopters, aircraft, and an experimental hovercraft.

Schedule: Daily, 9:00 a.m.-4:30 p.m. Closed all federal holidays except Memorial Day, July Fourth, and Labor Day.

Admission: No charge.

Locomotives: No. 607, Lima 2-8-0; narrow-gauge Vulcan 0-6-0.

Passenger Cars: U.S. Army medical ambulance car; Berlin duty train sleeper.

Rolling Stock/Equipment: Caboose, Jordan spreader, snowplow, steam crane, tank car, World War II ammunition car, flatcar, all former U.S. Army; German caboose and tank car; French 40 & 8 boxcar.

Location: Off I-64 at route 105 and Fort Eustis Boulevard (exit 250A), 20 miles south of Williamsburg.

     ♿ 🚗 🚐 ⊞ ▢ arm

TRAIN

 Williamsburg or Newport News

Contact: Barbara Bower

Mailing Address:
Building 300
Besson Hall
Fort Eustis, VA 23604-5260
Telephone: (804) 878-1115

OLD DOMINION RAILWAY MUSEUM
Railway museum

COURTESY OF OLD DOMINION RAILWAY MUSEUM

Displays/Exhibits: This museum's collection includes a caboose, freight equipment, and track-maintenance equipment; a Richmond, Fredericksburg & Potomac baggage car contains exhibits on telegraphy, passenger depots, and Railway Express Agencies.

Schedule: Weekends; Saturday, 11:00 a.m.-4:00 p.m.; Sunday, 1:00-4:00 p.m.
Admission: Donations requested.
Locomotives: Porter saddletank 0-4-0.
Rolling Stock/Equipment: 1959 boxcar and 1969 caboose, both former Seaboard; 1937 baggage car, former RF&P; track-inspection car.
Special Events: Floodwall Guided Walking Tours, second Sunday of each month. Children's Day, mid-September.

Note: The museum is a public-service project of the Old Dominion Chapter of the National Railway Historical Society.

Location: 102 Hull Street, near the downtown tourist area, adjacent to the former Southern Railway Hull Street station and the Richmond Floodwall Promenade.

Richmond

Contact: Michael P. Bonner
Director

Mailing Address:
P.O. Box 8583
Richmond, VA 23226
Telephone: (804) 233-6237

VIRGINIA MUSEUM OF TRANSPORTATION
Railway museum
Standard gauge

COURTESY OF VIRGINIA MUSEUM OF TRANSPORTATION

Displays/Exhibits: Founded in 1963 as the Roanoke Transportation Museum, Inc., the VMT was designated as the official transportation museum of the commonwealth of Virginia in 1983, in recognition of the quality and diversity of its collection. On exhibit at the site, a 1917 former Norfolk & Western freight station, are a number of steam, diesel, and electric locomotives and an extensive collection of passenger cars, freight cars, cabooses, trolleys, and memorabilia. Other displays include a PCC car from Washington, D.C.; a former N&W dynamometer car; the first N&W diesel; a former Illinois Terminal Railroad business car; antique automobiles and trucks; and former N&W class J 4-8-4 No. 611.

Schedule: March-December: daily. January-February: Tuesday-Sunday. Monday-Saturday, 10:00a.m.-5:00p.m.; Sunday, 12:00-5:00p.m. Closed Thanksgiving, Christmas, New Year's Day, and Easter.

Admission: Adults $4.00, senior citizens $3.00, youths (13-18) $2.00, children (3-12) $1.75, children under 3 admitted free. Group rates available.

Locomotives: No. 4, 1910 Baldwin class SA 0-8-0, former Virginian Railway; No. 6, 1897 Baldwin class G-1 2-8-0, former N&W; No. 763, 1944 Lima class S-2 2-8-4, former Nickel Plate; No. 34, 1923 Baldwin 0-6-0T, former E.J. Lavino Co.

Special Events: Annual Roanoke Railway Festival, October. Western Virginia Railfair, featuring the sale and display of model railroad items and railroad memorabilia. Please call or write for details.

Location: 303 Norfolk Avenue, S.W.

♿ 🚗 🚌 ✉ 🪑 📖 🔺

Contact: Katherine F. Houck
Executive Director

Mailing Address:
303 Norfolk Ave., S.W.
Roanoke, VA 24016
Telephone: (703) 342-5670
Fax: (703) 342-6898

ANACORTES RAILWAY
Steam, scheduled
18" gauge

COURTESY OF ANACORTES RAILWAY

Ride/Operation: This railway offers a 3/4-mile scenic train ride from the historic Great Northern Depot to downtown Anacortes along the city's waterfront and tree-lined parkways. In operation since 1986, this family-owned tourist line is one of the world's smallest narrow-gauge passenger railroads (as distinguished from a miniature railway). Turntables at each end of the line rotate the locomotive for its return trip. Limited cab rides are allowed.

Displays/Exhibits: Railroad artifacts and photographs in the depot; Tangley air calliope.

Train: Maine/Wales-style narrow-gauge train of four passenger cars, pulled by a Forney-type steam locomotive. The cars, acclaimed for their beauty and luxurious comfort, feature cherry-wood interiors, red velvet cushions, plush carpeting, and a marble fireplace.

Schedule: <u>Weekends and holidays,</u> June 17-September 4; frequent departures, 12:00-4:30 p.m.

Fare: $1.00.

Locomotives: Forney-type steam locomotive, rebuilt from a 1909 H.K. Porter compressed-air 0-4-0 mining locomotive, fueled with fir bark.

Passenger Cars: One observation-parlor car, two roofed open summer cars, one baggage-parlor car.

Rolling Stock/Equipment: Includes seven steel flatcars formerly used at the Asarco Smelter in Tacoma and one gondola (wood-sided for ballast service).

Special Events: <u>Waterfront Festival,</u> May 20-21. <u>Anacortes Arts and Crafts Festival,</u> August 5-6.

Note: Nearby attractions include an adjacent maritime museum, an art gallery, and the ferry to the San Juan Islands.

Location: 7th Street and R Avenue.

Everett or Seattle

Contact: Thomas G. Thompson, Jr.
President

Mailing Address:
387 Campbell Lake Road
Anacortes, WA 98221
Telephone: (206) 293-2634

Washington, Chehalis
R

CENTRALIA *DAILY CHRONICLE*

CHEHALIS-CENTRALIA
RAILROAD ASSOCIATION
Steam, scheduled
Standard gauge

Ride/Operation: A 12-mile, 1 3/4-hour round trip over Weyerhaeuser trackage (former Milwaukee Road) between South Chehalis and North Centralia, under contract with the Mt. Rainier Scenic Railroad. An extended trip to Ruth (nine miles west of Chehalis), offered on Saturdays, passes through scenic rural farmlands and a river valley. Longer trips on selected Sundays feature dinner stops at area restaurants; please call or write for information.

Displays/Exhibits: Restored Union Pacific C-5 cabooses serve as the ticket office and gift shop.

Train: Two open-window heavyweight coaches, former UP; open-air observation car.

Schedule: Weekends and holidays, May 28-September 5; lv. Chehalis 1:00 & 3:00 p.m.; lv. Centralia 2:00 & 4:00 p.m. (4:00 p.m. trip is one way). Ruth trip: Saturdays; lv. Chehalis 5:00 p.m.

Fare: Round trip: adults $7.00, children (3-16) $5.00. One way: adults $3.50, children (3-16) $2.50. Ruth trip: adults $11.00, children $9.00.

Locomotives: No. 15, 1916 Baldwin 90-ton 2-8-2, former Cowlitz, Chehalis & Cascade, former Puget Sound & Cascade No. 200. This engine had been displayed for thirty years in a local park; restoration was completed in 1989 by Mt. Rainier Scenic Railroad shop and volunteers.

Rolling Stock/Equipment: Z-frame 40-foot wood boxcar used as shop/supply car, former Milwaukee; steel 40-foot boxcar used as movable billboard, former Burlington Northern, former Chicago, Burlington & Quincy.

Location: Between Seattle, Washington, and Portland, Oregon. Chehalis: On Main Street; take exit 77 off I-5 and travel one block east to the railroad tracks. Centralia: Take exit 82 east off I-5 onto Harrison Avenue and travel to the intersection of Main Street and the railroad tracks.

Centralia

Radio Frequencies: 161.385, 160.635

Contact: Harold Borovec

Mailing Address:
1945 South Market Boulevard
Chehalis, WA 98532
Telephone: (206) 748-9593

301

MT. RAINIER SCENIC RAILROAD
Steam, scheduled
Standard gauge

J. S. DAVID WILKIE

Ride/Operation: A 14-mile, 1 1/2-hour round trip over a secluded right-of-way on the south slope of Mt. Rainier; the train goes through farms, forests, and tree farms, over rivers and creeks, up hills and down. Live musical entertainment is featured on board, and there is a 20-minute layover at Mineral Lake; passengers may stay there to visit or picnic and return on a later train. The *Cascadian Dinner Train* makes a 4-hour round trip to either Morton (40-mile trip) or Eatonville (25-mile trip) and offers a five-course prime rib dinner served aboard a restored Union Pacific dining car, along with live music in the lounge-observation car.

Displays/Exhibits: A 1912 Heisler, the first successful 3-truck Heisler built (former Pickering Lumber).

Train: Steam power on all runs; closed coaches with bench seats; open-air cars.

Schedule: <u>Daily</u>, June 15-September 5; <u>weekends</u>, May 30-end of September; 11:00 a.m., 1:15 & 3:30 p.m. <u>Dinner train:</u> spring and fall, 1:00 p.m.; summer, 5:30 p.m.

Fare: Adults $8.50, senior citizens $7.50, juniors (12-17) $6.50, children (under 12) $5.50, babes in arms ride free. <u>Dinner train:</u> $55.00, reservations required.

Locomotives: Operable: No. 5, 1924 Porter 2-8-2, former Port of Grays Harbor; No. 10, 1928 3-truck Climax, former Hillcrest Lumber Co.; No. 11, 1929 3-truck Shay; No. 91, 1930 West Coast Special Heisler, former Kinzua Pine Mills; No. 17, 1929 Alco 2-8-2T; No. 41, 1941 Alco RSD-1, former Dept. of Transportation; No. 7012A, 1956 EMD F-9, former Northern Pacific Railroad; No. 30, 1940 Alco S-1, former NPT Co.; No. 42, 1942 Alco S-1; No. 500, 1942 80-ton General Electric; others under restoration.

Passenger Cars: Two commuter coaches; open-air car; dining car, former Union Pacific; lounge/observation car, former Alaska Railroad.

Rolling Stock/Equipment: Log trains, work trains, freight trains.

Special Events: <u>Steam excursions</u>, spring or fall. <u>Wedding charters</u>. <u>Limited photo days</u>.

Location: On highway 7, 42 miles southeast of Tacoma.

Tacoma

Radio Freqency: 160.635

Contact: Jack Anderson
Owner

Mailing Address:
P.O. Box 921
Elbe, WA 98330
Telephone: (360) 569-2588

302

Washington, Snoqualmie
D-R

PUGET SOUND RAILWAY
HISTORICAL ASSOCIATION
Diesel, scheduled
Standard gauge

COURTESY OF PUGET SOUND RAILWAY HISTORICAL ASSOCIATION

Ride/Operation: This group offers a ride between Snoqualmie and North Bend.

Displays/Exhibits: The 1890 Snoqualmie depot houses the Puget Sound Railroad Museum.

Train: Wood and steel heavyweight passenger cars pulled by Alco or Fairbanks-Morse diesel locomotives.

Schedule: <u>Weekends</u>, May 27-September 4; <u>Sundays</u>, May 7-May 21 & September 10-October 29.

Fare/Admission: <u>Train</u>: adults $6.00, senior citizens $5.00, children $4.00. <u>Museum</u>: no charge.

Locomotives: No. 201, Alco RSD-4, former Kennecott Copper Corp.; No. 1, Fairbanks-Morse H12-44, former Weyerhaeuser Timber Co.; No. 7320, General Electric 45-ton diesel switcher, former U.S. Navy.

Rolling Stock/Equipment: Miscellaneous pieces.

Special Events: <u>Santa Train</u>, December 2-3 & 9-10.

Contact: Richard Wilkens

Mailing Address:
P.O. Box 459
Snoqualmie, WA 98065
Telephone: (206) 746-4025

ERIC NELSON

YAKIMA VALLEY RAIL AND STEAM MUSEUM
Diesel, scheduled
Standard gauge

Ride/Operation: This museum operates freight and passenger service on the former Northern Pacific White Swan branch line. Passenger excursions are 20-mile round trips from Harrah to White Swan.

Displays/Exhibits: The restoration of the 1911 Toppenish former NP railroad depot, which serves as the museum and gift shop, is nearing completion. The freight house has been converted to an engine house, where steam locomotive No. 1364 is being restored. The former NP section foreman's house is adjacent to the depot.

Train: Pending completion of the steam-locomotive restoration, the two former Pennsylvania Railroad heavyweight cars are pulled by a diesel.

Schedule: Train: April-October; Saturdays, 11:00 a.m.; Sundays, 1:00 p.m. Museum: daily, summer; weekends, winter.

Fare/Admission: Train: adults $8.00, children $5.00, family $25.00. Museum: adults $2.00, senior citizens & children (under 18) $1.00. Charters available.

Locomotives: No. 1364, 1902 Baldwin 4-6-0, former NP; No. B-2070, 1953 120-ton Alco, former U.S. Army.

Passenger Cars: Two 1920s P-70 heavyweights, former PRR; No. 588, 1947 coach, former NP; combine, former New Haven.

Location: 10 Asotin Avenue.

Contact: Douglas Shearer
Public Relations

Mailing Address:
P.O. Box 889
Toppenish, WA 98948
Telephone:
Museum: (509) 865-1911
Chamber of Commerce: (509) 865-3262

LAKE WHATCOM RAILWAY
Steam, diesel, scheduled
Standard gauge

DAVID WILKE

Ride/Operation: A 7-mile, 1 1/2-hour round trip over a former Northern Pacific branch line originally constructed as the Bellingham Bay & Eastern Railroad in 1902. The train climbs a 2.3-percent grade along highway 9, then heads through a tunnel, along Mirror Lake, and through a forest inhabited by beavers. Passengers may also tour the steam locomotive and ride an old hand-pump car.

Displays/Exhibits: Varies; business car "Madison River," former NP; 1923 Shell Oil Co. tank car; 1900-1923 boxcars, former Great Northern; handcar; track motor car; cabooses (wooden, former NP; steel, former Spokane, Portland & Seattle).

Train: Steam locomotive; 86-seat coach, originally Pullman parlor car "Dunlop"; coffee-shop coach; 88-seat coach, originally Pullman parlor car "Clearview."

Schedule: Nonreserved trains and motor-car rides: Saturdays and Tuesdays, July 1-August 29; trains, 11:00 a.m. & 1:00 p.m.; motor cars, 3:15 p.m. Special trains, by reservation only: October 21, December 2, 9, 16 & 23. Please call or write for weekday schedules.

Fare: Trains: Adults $10.00, children (2-17) $5.00. Motor-car rides: $1.50. Charters on regularly scheduled trains: business car or 32-seat coach, $250; 86-seat coach, $600. Please call or write for special charter prices.

Locomotive: No. 1070, 1907 Alco (Manchester) 0-6-0, former NP.

Passenger Cars: Coach No. 627, originally 1910 Pullman parlor car "Dunlop"; 1912 coach No. 634, Pullman "Clearview"; coffee-shop coach No. 1681, originally 1925 Pullman coach; 1926 Pullman business car "Madison River," built for the *North Coast Limited;* and baggage car; all former Northern Pacific.

Special Events: Autumn Train, October 21. Santa Claus Train, December 2, 9, 16 & 23, including live music. Reservations required.

Location: 10 1/2 miles north of Sedro Woolley on highway 9.

Seattle or Everett

Mailing Address:
Box 91
Acme, WA 98220
Telephone: (360) 595-2218

YAKIMA ELECTRIC RAILWAY MUSEUM
Electric, scheduled
Standard gauge

DENNIS L. DILLEY

Ride/Operation: A 90-minute round trip through city streets, past orchards, and along the Naches River and the shoulder of Yakima Ridge through Selah Gap, over a route established by the former Yakima Valley Transportation Company in 1907.

Schedule: Weekends and holidays, April 30-October 16; lv. Yakima 10:00 a.m., 12:00, 2:00 & 4:00 p.m.; lv. Selah Terminal 10:45 a.m., 12:45, 1:45 & 4:45 p.m. Fridays, July-August; lv. Yakima 7:00 p.m.; lv. Selah Terminal 7:45 p.m. Please call to confirm the Friday evening trip.

Fare: Adults $4.00, senior citizens and children (6-12) $3.50, family rate (two adults and two children 6-12) $14.00, children under 6 not occupying a seat ride free. Group charters available.

Locomotives/Trolleys: Line Car "A," 1909 Niles 26-ton boxcab converted to line-car use in 1922 (in continuous service since 1909); freight motor No. 298, General Electric 50-ton steeple-cab; Nos. 21 & 22, 1930 double-truck Brill Master Units that originally operated in Yakima from 1930 to 1947; Nos. 1776 & 1976, single-truck Brill cars from Oporto, Portugal (the same type that operated in Yakima from 1907-1929); others.

Note: Self-guided tours of the Car Barn Museum are available during public-ride hours at no charge; donations are welcomed.

Location: Passengers may board at the shop of the Yakima Electric Railway Museum at 3rd Avenue and Pine or at the Selah Terminal.

⊞ 𝕒𝕣𝕞 ◭

Contact: Mel LaBoyne
President

Mailing Address:
P.O. Box 649
Yakima, WA 98907-0649
Telephone: (509) 575-1700

CASS SCENIC RAILROAD STATE PARK
Steam, scheduled
Standard gauge

JOHN HELBOK

Ride/Operation: This railroad, a reconstruction of a logging railroad that saw sixty years of service, features two switchbacks and climbs grades as steep as eleven percent, providing overlooks and panoramas of mountain scenery. Passengers may choose either a 22-mile, 4 1/2-hour round trip to the top of Bald Knob (elevation 4,842 feet) or an 8-mile, 1 1/2-hour round trip to Whittaker Station.

Displays/Exhibits: Modern steam-locomotive shop, open on weekdays.

Train: Restored logging cars converted for passenger use.

Schedule: Daily, May 27-September 4; weekends, September 8-October 30. Bald Knob: Tuesday-Sunday, 12:00 p.m. Whittaker: daily, 11:00 a.m., 1:00 & 3:00 p.m. Dinner train: Reservations required. Please call or write for information.

Fare: Bald Knob: adults $13.00, children $7.00. Whittaker: adults $9.00, children $5.00. Dinner train: adults $25.00, children $15.00. Special group rates available, Tuesday-Friday. Charter rates available upon request. Prices include admission to museums and historical presentation.

Locomotives: No. 2, 1928 Lima 3-truck Shay; No. 4, 1922 Lima 3-truck Shay; No. 5, 1905 Lima 3-truck Shay; No. 6, 1929 3-truck Heisler; No. 6, 1945 Lima 162-ton 3-truck Shay, former Western Maryland No. 6; No. 7, 1921 Lima 3-truck Shay; No. 8, 1919 3-truck Climax; No. 612, 1943 Baldwin 2-8-0; No. 20, 1941 45-ton General Electric.

Special Events: Fall Color Runs, October.

Note: Reservations are accepted.

White Sulphur Springs

Radio Frequency: 31.98

Contact: Superintendent

Mailing Address:
P.O. Box 107
Cass, WV 24927
Telephone: (304) 456-4300
(800) CALL-WVA

West Virginia, Harpers Ferry
M-R

HARPERS FERRY TOY TRAIN MUSEUM
& JOY LINE RAILROAD
Railway museum

COURTESY OF HARPERS FERRY TOY TRAIN MUSEUM & JOY LINE RAILROAD

16" gauge

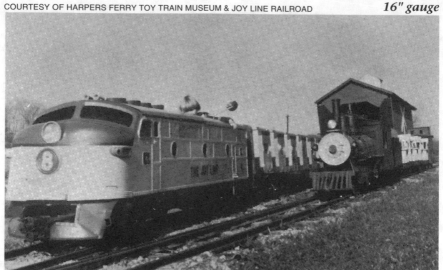

Ride/Operation: Passengers ride around the 1,780 feet of track aboard a 1953 waist-high train, traveling over a trestle and past an authentic railroad station brought to Harpers Ferry from Hagerstown, Maryland. The museum houses pre-World War II toy trains.

Displays/Exhibits: Two full-sized section cars; railroad tools.

Train: Two 1953 amusement-park trains.

Schedule: <u>Weekends</u>, April-November.
Fare/Admission: $1.00.
Locomotives: F-7; steam-type Miniature Train Company locomotive; gas-powered shop-made locomotive.
Passenger Cars: Four 12-person cars.
Rolling Stock/Equipment: Four flatcars; stock car; caboose; snowplow.

Location: One mile west of Harpers Ferry National Park, on Bakerton Road.

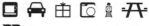 Harpers Ferry

Contact: Christian Wallich
General Manager

Mailing Address:
Route 3, Box 315
Harpers Ferry, WV 25425
Telephone: (304) 535-2291
(304) 535-2521

COURTESY OF POTOMAC EAGLE

Ride/Operation: Diesel-powered, open-window coach trains take passengers on a 3-hour, 15-minute round trip through the beautiful South Branch Trough. Riding the rails along the clear waters of the Potomac River's South Branch, passengers can watch for American Bald Eagles (seen on ninety percent of Potomac tours during the 1993 season) that have made this remote region their home.

Train: Open-window coaches; open-top sightseeing car; temperature-controlled lounge car offering Classic Club Service (luxury lounge seating and luncheon).

Schedule: May 27-September 4: weekends, 1:00 p.m. September 5-30: weekends; Saturdays, 10:00 a.m. & 2:00 p.m.; Sundays, 1:00 p.m. October 1-29: daily; Monday-Friday, 1:00 p.m.; weekends, 10:00 a.m & 2:00 p.m. All-day round trip to Petersburg: April 29, June 24, July 29, August 26, September 30, October 28; 9:00 a.m.

Fare: May-September: adults $16.00, senior citizens (60+) $15.00, children (3-10) $10.00, children under 3 ride free, season pass (coach; May 27-September 4) $75.00, Classic Club $35.00. October: adults $19.00, senior citizens (60+) $17.00, children (3-10) $12.00, children under 3 ride free, Classic Club $42.00. All-day round trip: adults $32.00, senior citizens (60+) $28.00, children (3-10) $15.00, Classic Club $65.00; one way, adults & senior citizens (60+) $20.00, children (3-10) $10.00.

Locomotives: GP-9s, former Baltimore & Ohio; Alco FPA-4; F-units, former CSX.

Passenger Cars: 1920s open-window coaches, former Canadian National; 1950-era lounge car, former Chesapeake & Ohio.

Special Events: All-day Excursion to Moorefield,

May 6. Excursion to Sycamore Bridge, May 7 & 20. Railfan Day, May 13. Memorial Day & Labor Day, coach tickets $10.00. Ronald McDonald Days, June 10-11. Hampshire Heritage Days, September 9-10. Hardy Heritage Weekend, September 23.

Location: Route 28, one mile north of Romney.

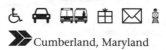
Cumberland, Maryland

Contact: Ann Parsons
Passenger Agent

Mailing Address:
P.O. Box 657
Romney, WV 26757
Telephone: (304) 822-7464
(800) 22-EAGLE

EAST TROY ELECTRIC RAILROAD
WISCONSIN TROLLEY MUSEUM
Electric, scheduled
Standard gauge

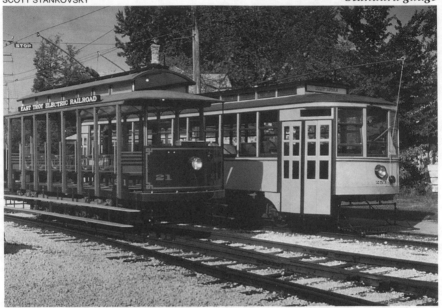

Ride/Operation: This museum offers the longest ride of its type in the country; trolleys take passengers on a 10-mile round trip over original trackage of the famed Milwaukee Electric Railway & Light Company. This line, completed in 1907, is the last remnant of a network of more than two hundred miles of interurban trackage that used to serve southeastern Wisconsin.

Displays/Exhibits: An extensive collection of Milwaukee Electric photos and artifacts. Cars undergoing restoration include former Chicago North Shore & Milwaukee No. 228 and former WP&L No. 26.

Schedule: <u>Weekends</u>, May 30-October 23.

Admission: Adults $7.00, children (4-11) $3.50.

Trolleys: Nos. 9, 11 & 30, former Chicago South Shore & South Bend; diner No. 25, former East Troy Electric; open car No. 21; Nos. L8 & L9, former MER&L; No. 4420, former Chicago Transit Authority.

Rolling Stock/Equipment: Crane No. L6 and line car No. D23, both former MER&L.

Special Events: <u>Railfan Weekend</u>, May 6-7. <u>Dinner Trains</u>, May 14, June 18, August 12, October 14&21.

Location: 2002 Church Street. East Troy is 30 miles southwest of Milwaukee. Take the highway 20 exit off I-43 in East Troy, head west to CTH ES, travel south on ES to Church Street, and turn right.

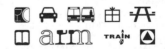

Contact: President
Mailing Address:
P.O. Box 436
East Troy, WI 53120
Telephone:
Operating Hours: (414) 642-3263
All Other Times/Group & Party Reservations: (414) 542-5573

NATIONAL RAILROAD MUSEUM
Railway museum
Standard gauge

Ride/Operation: Visitors to this museum can take a 20-minute train ride in vintage equipment, enjoy the "Rails to America" theater show, and embark on guided or self-guided tours of the equipment displays. On the train, the uniformed conductor talks about hobo history, the museum, and local points of interest. "Rails to America" is a 20-minute, 9-projector multimedia show that presents an outline of railroad history.

Displays/Exhibits: Established in 1958, this museum holds more than seventy historic locomotives and railroad cars, as well as railroad memorabilia, archives, a research library, and a 30- by 70-foot model-railroad display.

Schedule: Museum: daily, 9:00 a.m.-5:00 p.m. Train: May 1-October 15. Guided tours: May 29-September 4. Closed Easter, Thanksgiving, Christmas, and New Year's Day.

Fare/Admission: May 1-October 15: adults $6.00, senior citizens $5.00, students (6-15) $3.00, children under 6 admitted free, family rate $16.00. October 16-April 30: Half-price. Group rates available.

Locomotives: No. 4017, 4-8-8-4, former Union Pacific; No. 24, 2-8-0, former Lake Superior & Ishpeming; No. 2718, 4-6-2, former Soo Line; No. 2736, 2-8-4, former Chesapeake & Ohio; No. 5017, 2-10-4, former Santa Fe; No. 506, 2-10-2, former Duluth, Missabe & Iron Range; No. 101, 2-8-0 "General Pershing," former U.S. Army; No. 29, Pullman 0-4-0; No. 5, Shay; No. 315, Alco C-430, former Green Bay & Western; No. 38A, E-9, former Milwaukee; *Aerotrain* No. 2, former Rock Island; GP-30 No. 715, former Wisconsin Central; No. 706, Fairbanks-Morse H-10-44; others.

Passenger Cars: General Eisenhower's WWII Command Train "Bayonet"; observation car "Silver Spirit," former Chicago, Burlington & Quincy; sleeper "Poplar River," former Great Northern; dome diner No. 8003, former UP; No. 2330, Railway

Post Office, former CB&Q; others.

Special Events: NMRA Division Meet, April 29. Heritage Bicycle Tour, May 21. Railfest, June 24-25. Fall Color Excursion, September 23. Haunted Train, October 19-30. Christmas Train, December 2-3.

Location: 2285 South Broadway. Take highway 172 to Ashland Avenue (business highway 41); travel north to Cormier Avenue and east three blocks.

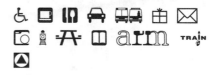

Contact: Raymond Sauvey

Mailing Address:
2285 South Broadway
Green Bay, WI 54304
Telephone: (414) 437-7623

Wisconsin, Laona
D-R

PAUL SWANSON

CAMP FIVE MUSEUM FOUNDATION, INC.
Logging museum
Railway displays

Ride/Operation: Camp Five offers visitors a unique mix of history, steam railroading, and ecology. Visitors may ride the *Lumberjack Special* steam train to the museum complex; once there, they may take a guided surrey tour through beautiful forests managed on a perpetual-cycle basis and an ecology walk through a natural arboretum. A pontoon ride on the Rat River is also offered,

Displays/Exhibits: Logging museum with an early-transportation wing and an active blacksmith shop; half-hour steam engine video; nature center with northern Wisconsin wildlife diorama; petting corral; large outdoor display of logging artifacts.

Schedule: Daily, June 21-August 26, 10:30 & 11:00 a.m., 12:00, 1:00 & 2:00 p.m. Fall Weekend Color Tours, mid September-mid October.

Fare/Admission: Family rates and group discounts available.

Locomotive: 1916 Vulcan 2-6-2.

Passenger Cars: Cupola cabooses.

Location: U.S. highway 8, just west of Laona.

Contact: Mary R. Connor
Executive Director

Mailing Address:
Summer: RFD #1
Laona, WI 54541
Telephone: (715) 674-3414
(800) 774-3414
Winter: 1011 8th Street
Wausau, WI 54403
Telephone: (715) 845-5544

312

Wisconsin, North Freedom
D-R

WILLIAM RAIA

MID-CONTINENT RAILWAY
HISTORICAL SOCIETY
Steam, scheduled
Standard gauge

Ride/Operation: Mid-Continent, which has operated steam trains at North Freedom since 1963, is dedicated to preserving turn-of-the-century railroading. Its line and equipment are historic, all a part of the "golden age of railroading." The 7-mile, 50-minute "Experience 1900" round trip takes passengers on a former Chicago & North Western branch line built in 1903 to serve iron mines. Trains depart from a restored 1894 C&NW depot.

Displays/Exhibits: The museum is nationally known for its wooden passenger and freight cars; restored equipment is displayed in the Coach Shed. The collection also includes locomotives, snowplows (including a 1912 steam rotary), and steam wreckers. Artifact and photography exhibits are in the depot and the Coach Shed.

Train: Open-platform cars from the Delaware, Lackawanna & Western; freight or mixed trains often run for special events.

Schedule: Daily, May 19-August 27; weekends, April 29-May 14 & September 2-October 29; 10:30 a.m., 12:30, 2:00 & 3:30 p.m.

Fare: Adults $8.00, senior citizens $7.00, children (3-15) $4.50, family (2 adults, 2 or more children) $22.00. Group discounts available. Higher fares may apply at some special events.

Locomotives: No. 1385, 1907 Alco 4-6-0, former C&NW; No. 2, 1912 Baldwin 2-8-2, former Saginaw Timber; No. 9, 1884 Baldwin 2-6-0, former Dardanelle & Russellville; No. 1, 1913 Montreal 4-6-0, former Western Coal & Coke Co.; No. 2645, 1900 Brooks 4-6-0, former Soo (Wisconsin Central); No. 440, 1901 Baldwin 2-8-0, former Union Pacific; No. 49, 1929 Alco 2-8-0, former Kewaunee, Green Bay & Western; No. 31, 1925 EMC gas-electric car, former Montana Western; No. 988, 1947 Alco RSC-2, former Milwaukee Road.

Special Events: Autumn Color, October 7-8 & 14-15. Santa Express, November 25-26. Snow Train, February 16-18, 1996.

Location: In Sauk County, seven miles west of Baraboo. Follow route 136 west to PF, then turn south to North Freedom. The depot is one-half mile west of the four-way stop in North Freedom.

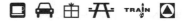

Mailing Address:
P.O. Box 358
North Freedom, WI 53951-0358
Telephone: (608) 522-4261

313

KETTLE MORAINE RAILWAY
Steam, scheduled
Standard gauge

DONALD M. MURPHY

Ride/Operation: A leisurely, nostalgic, 8-mile round trip over a former Milwaukee Road branch line. The train departs from the 1889 depot in North Lake, travels up 2-percent grades and through two moraine cuts, and crosses the Oconomowoc River on a 125-foot timber trestle.

Displays/Exhibits: No. 1000, EMD gas-electric car, former Chicago Great Western; restored 1889 railroad depot.

Train: Steel coaches; combination car; "hobo car"; caboose.

Schedule: Sundays, June 4-September 24, plus September 4, 12:30, 2:00 & 3:30 p.m. Autumn Color Trips: October 1, 7-8 & 14-15; Saturdays, 12:30, 2:00 & 3:30 p.m.; Sundays, 11:00 a.m. train added. Subject to change when necessary to meet operating conditions.

Fare: Adults $7.50, children (3-11) $4.00, children under 3 ride free when not occupying a seat. Charter and group rates available.

Locomotives: No. 9, 1901 Baldwin 2-6-2, former McCloud River; No. 3, 1917 65-ton Heisler, former Craig Mountain Railroad; No. 3, 1943 Davenport gas-powered 0-4-0 switcher, former Heil Co. & U.S. Air Force.

Special Events: Please call or write for schedule.

Location: North Lake is at the junction of Highways VV (formerly 74) and 83, northwest of Milwaukee. The site is on route 83, 9 miles north of exit 287 off I-94, south of Holy Hill, south of Hartford, and north of Hartland.

Milwaukee

Contact: Richard M. Hinebaugh
President

Mailing Address:
Box 247
North Lake, WI 53064
Telephone: (414) 782-8074

314

OSCEOLA & ST. CROIX VALLEY RAILWAY
MINNESOTA TRANSPORTATION MUSEUM
Steam, diesel, scheduled
Standard gauge

ART NETTIS

Ride/Operation: Visitors experience the beautiful St. Croix River Valley on a 90-minute round trip between Osceola, Wisconsin, and Marine-on-St. Croix, Minnesota. A 45-minute round trip through fields and woods between Osceola and Dresser, Wisconsin, is also available. First-class service is available in September and October.

Displays/Exhibits: U.S. Railway post Office exhibits aboard Northern Pacific triple combine No. 1102; regular demonstrations of mail and order catches "on the fly" at the Osceola depot.

Schedule: Weekends and holidays, May 27-October 29; Marine-on-St. Croix, 11:00 a.m. & 2:00 p.m.; Dresser, 12:45 & 3:45 p.m. Thursdays, May 25-October 26, and Tuesdays, September, for group reservations and charters.

Fare: Marine-on-St.-Croix: adults $10.00, senior citizens (65+) $8.00, children (5-15) $6.00, family $30.00, first-class $15.00. Dresser: adults $7.00, senior citizens (65+) $5.00, children (5-15) $3.00, family $20.00, first-class $10.00. Group rate: $8 per seat for groups of 15 or more. Charter rates available.

Locomotives: No. 328, 1907 Alco 4-6-0, former NP; No. 102, 1948 EMD NW2, and No. 105, 1958 EMD SW1200, both former Lake Superior Terminal & Transfer.

Passenger Cars: Suburban coaches Nos. 2604 & 2608, former Rock Island; streamlined coaches Nos. 1096 & 1097, former Chicago & North Western; former Great Northern; No. 1213, built for GN's *Empire Builder;* triple combine No. 1102, former NP; suburban coach No. 2232, former Delaware, Lackawanna & Western.

Special Events: Fourth of July Fireworks Special. Wisconsin Fall Festival and Osceola Wheels and Wings Celebration, September.

Note: The O&SCV is a nonprofit organization of the Minnesota Transportation Museum, the Osceola Historical Society, and local communities. The

MTM provides equipment/train crews; trains operate on Wisconsin Central track between Withrow, Minnesota, and Amery, Wisconsin, through a special agreement.

Location: The historic Osceola Depot on Depot Road, just off state highway 35. Osceola is on the Minnesota/Wisconsin border, about an hour northeast of the Twin Cities.

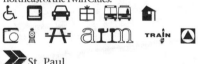

Contact: John W. Diers
Chairman

Mailing Address:
P.O. Box 17240
Nokomis Station
Minneapolis, MN 55417-0240
Telephone: Charter & group info/reservations: (800) 643-7412
Recorded info: (612) 228-0263

COURTESY OF PARK LANE MODEL RAILROAD MUSEUM

Displays/Exhibits: This museum features a collection of more than two thousand models of all ages, ranging from tiny Z gauge through N, HO, S, O, and Buddy L gauges. Several operating model railroad layouts can also be seen.

Schedule: <u>Daily</u>, mid May-mid September; Monday-Saturday, 10:00 a.m.-5:00 p.m; Sunday, 10:00 a.m.-3:00 p.m.

Admission: Adults $3.50, children (6-12) $1.75, children under 6 admitted free with paying adult.

Note: The museum is located 11 miles from the Circus World Museum in Baraboo and 20 miles from the Mid-Continent Railway Museum in North Freedom.

Location: In the Wisconsin Dells area, near exit 89 of I-90 and I-94. The museum is at the intersection of state route 23 and Herwig Road.

Contact: Alexander Zmuda
Director

Mailing Address:
S-2083 Herwig Road
Reedsburg, WI 53959
Telephone: (608) 254-8050

Wisconsin, Wisconsin Dells
D-R

GEORGE A. FORERO, JR.

RIVERSIDE & GREAT NORTHERN RAILWAY
Steam, scheduled
15" gauge

Ride/Operation: Elmer and Norman Sandley purchased the right-of-way of the former LaCrosse & Milwaukee Railroad (1854-1902) in 1952 and operated the 15-inch-gauge Riverside & Great Northern Railway from 1954 to 1982. The R&GN is now being restored by the Riverside & Great Northern Preservation Society, Inc., with two of the original locomotives operating on a 2 1/2-mile round trip through scenic rock cuts and wooded areas. The Soo Line (former Milwaukee Road) main line, which parallels the R&GN right-of-way, sees frequent operations.

Displays/Exhibits: Sandley Light Rail Equipment Works being restored; expanded gift shop and museum in car shop building.

Schedule: Daily, May 27-September 4; weekends, September 9-October 8; 10:00 a.m.-6:00 p.m. Subject to change; please call or write for information.

Fare/Admission: Train: adults $5.00, children (4-15) $3.00, family maximum $14.00. Museum: no charge.

Locomotives: No. 82, 1957 4-4-0, former Milwaukee County Zoo; vertical-boilered "Tom Thumb."

Passenger Cars: Five 12-passenger cars.

Rolling Stock/Equipment: Several 4-wheel work-train cars; 8-wheel ballast hopper.

Special Events: Please call or write for information.

Location: One mile north of Wisconsin Dells. Take U.S. 16 north from Crossroads to county road A and travel to the Soo Line overpass; depot is on the east side of the Soo Line tracks. Or take Stand Rock Road from Broadway west of the Soo Line Wisconsin River bridge and travel one mile north to the Soo Line overpass on county road A.

Wisconsin Dells

Contact: Bill Koster

Mailing Address:
P.O. Box 842
Wisconsin Dells, WI 53965
Telephone: (608) 254-6367

CHEYENNE PARKS & RECREATION DEPARTMENT
Railway display
Standard gauge

COURTESY OF CHEYENNE PARKS & RECREATION

Displays/Exhibits: No. 4004, the 4-8-8-4 "Big Boy," is the world's largest steam locomotive. Built in 1941, this engine and the twenty-four others of its class were designed by the Union Pacific Railroad especially for use on its rugged run from Cheyenne to Odgen, Utah. The engine weighs in at 1,208,750 pounds; is 132 feet, 9 3/4 inches long; and has a fuel capacity of 28 tons and a water capacity of 25,000 gallons. It was retired in October 1958 after running 440,545 miles.

Admission: No charge.   **Location:** Holliday Park, Cheyenne.

Cheyenne

Contact: Jerry Logemann
Assistant Director

Mailing Address:
610 West 7th Street
Cheyenne, WY 82007
Telephone: (307) 637-6423

Wyoming, Laramie
R

GEORGE A. FORERO, JR.

WYOMING SCENIC RAILROAD
Diesel, scheduled
Standard gauge

Ride/Operation: This railroad offers a full-day excursion from the Wyoming Territorial Park through some of the most scenic areas in the region. Heading west out of Laramie, the train travels through a fairly flat area, in sharp contrast to the winding climb that begins as it turns south toward the Snowy Range Mountains. After passing through the historic gold-mining town of Centennial, the train encounters several "muleshoe" curves as it winds into high country, going by the tiny town of Albany before finally reaching the turnaround point at Lake Owen, whose elevation is more than 9,000 feet. This route is one of the highest standard-gauge lines in the country.

Schedule: May-October, weather permitting; Tuesdays, Thursdays, and weekends; 10:00 a.m.

Fare: Adults $32.95, senior citizens (65+) $29.95, children (under 12) $17.95. First class: $49.95. Prices include lunch, admission to the Territorial Park, and applicable sales tax. Charter and group rates available. Tour groups and travel agents commissionable.

Locomotives: Streamlined 1953 FP-7s Nos. 1510 & 1512, former Alaska Railroad.

Special Events: Color tours, September.

Location: The Laramie station is on 975 Snowy Range Road, one-half mile off I-80 and one-half mile east of the Wyoming Territorial Park. Laramie is 2 1/2 hours from Denver, Colorado, and 45 miles west of Cheyenne, Wyoming.

Contact: Mollie Smith
Excursion Manager

Mailing Address:
P.O. Box 1653
Laramie, WY 82070
Telephone: (307) 742-9162

HERITAGE PARK HISTORICAL VILLAGE
Steam, electric, scheduled
Standard gauge

COURTESY OF HERITAGE PARK HISTORICAL VILLAGE

Ride/Operation: With more than one hundred restored buildings and exhibits assembled from many parts of western Canada, Heritage Park is an authentic living memorial to pre-1914 western settlement. A visit begins with a 7-minute streetcar ride from the Fourteenth Street entrance over a winding route to the park's main gate. Inside, a steam train operates continuously on a 20-minute schedule.

Displays/Exhibits: Original stations from Bowell, Laggan, Midnapore, and Shepard; water tank; sand tower; six-stall roundhouse; railway car shop; single-track engine shed; No. 76, 1882 business car, used at Last Spike ceremonies on completion of the Canadian Pacific Railroad, November 7, 1885; No. 100, 1901 private car, former Dominion of Canada No. 100 (Prime Minister's car); No. 5, 1902 business car "Pacific"; No. 141, 1907 suburban coach; Canadian Pacific wooden colonist cars, coaches; freight cars; work equipment.

Train: Two 1885 open-platform coaches; former Canadian National observation car No. 15097.

Schedule: Daily, May 20-June 16; weekdays, 10:00 a.m.-4:00 p.m.; weekends, 10:00 a.m.-5:00 p.m. Daily, June 16-September 4, 10:00 a.m.-5:00 p.m. Weekends and holidays, September 9-October 9, 10:00 a.m.-5:00 p.m.

Fare/Admission: Adults $7.50, senior citizens (65+) $6.50, children (3-16) $4.50, children under 3 admitted free. Streetcar: $.50 each way between parking area and main gate.

Locomotives/Trolleys: No. 2023, 1942 Alco 0-6-0, former U.S. Army No. 4012 (operating); No. 2024, 1944 Lima 0-6-0, former U.S. Army No. 4078 (operating); No. 5931, 1949 Montreal 2-10-4, former Canadian Pacific No. 5934; No. 4, 1905 Angus Shops 0-6-0, former CP No. 2144; No. 7019, 1944 Alco S-2, former CP; double-truck closed cars Nos. 14 & 15, 1910 Ottawa Car, former Calgary Municipal.

Location: In southwest Calgary at Heritage Drive and 14th Street S.W.

Contact: Rick Smith
General Manager

Mailing Address:
1900 Heritage Drive S.W.
Calgary, AB T2V 2X3
Telephone: (403) 259-1900

Alberta, Edmonton
R

FORT EDMONTON PARK
Steam, scheduled
Standard gauge

Ride/Operation: Nestled in Edmonton's river valley, Fort Edmonton Park is brought to life by costumed staff reenacting life as it was in Edmonton from its fur-trading days of the 1840s through its development into a bustling city of the 1920s. The train takes visitors from the present day through four historical eras.

Displays/Exhibits: More than seventy period buildings staffed with historical interpreters dressed in period costumes.

Schedule: Daily, May 21-September 4; Sundays, September; train runs continuously.

Fare: Adults $6.50, senior citizens and youths (13-16) $5.00, children (6-12) $3.25, family $19.50. Prices include tax and train ride.

Locomotives: No. 107, 1919 Baldwin 2-6-2, former Oakdale & Gull Railway (restored to a 1905 appearance).

Passenger Cars: Three passenger cars.

Special Events: Please call or write for calendar.

Location: Whitemud Freeway and Fox Drive, 10 minutes from downtown.

Contact: Jan Repp
Communications Officer

Mailing Address:
P.O. Box 2359
Edmonton, AB T5J 2R7
Telephone: (403) 496-8787

Alberta, Stettler
D-R

ALBERTA PRAIRIE RAILWAY EXCURSIONS
Steam, scheduled
Standard gauge

COURTESY OF ALBERTA PRAIRIE RAILWAY EXCURSIONS

Ride: Round-trip tours of several varieties are featured from Stettler to a combination of rural lineside communities: Meeting Creek, Donalda, Big Valley, Rumsey, Rowley, and Morrin. Excursions are operated on a former Canadian National branch line through picturesque parkland and prairies in central Alberta and on a former Canadian Pacific branch line past Stettler to Castor. All excursions include full-course roast-beef buffet dinner and on-board entertainment and commentary.

Displays/Exhibits: Restored railway stations, community museums, historical sites, and curio shops.

Train: 1920 Baldwin 2-8-0; coaches, from various dates; leased vintage diesel power.

Schedule: Weekends and selected weekdays, late May-August. Weekends, September-mid October.

Fare: Adults $48.00, senior citizens $45.00, students $36.00, children $29.50.

Locomotives: No. 41, 1920 Baldwin 2-8-0, former Jonesboro Lake City & Eastern No. 41, former Frisco No. 77, former Mississippian No. 77, former Huntsville Depot No. 9.

Passenger Cars: Two 1925 Pullman coaches, former Erie Lackawanna lightweight self-propelled coaches; 1920 and 1931 heavyweight sleepers, former CP; 1930s day coaches, 1919 combination coach/baggage, four 1920s-era day coaches, open-air observation car, caboose, all former CN.

Special Events: Murder Mysteries. Canada Day Special. Train Robberies. Overnight Camp-out. Casino Train. Family Specials. Entertainment is featured on selected routes and in selected communities.

Location: Stettler is a 2 1/2-hour drive on main highways from both Edmonton and Calgary.

Contact: R. C. Willis
General Manager

Mailing Address:
Postal Bag 800
Stettler, AB T0C 2L0
Telephone: (403) 742-2811
Fax: (403) 742-2844

322

WALTER LANZ

CANADIAN MUSEUM
OF RAIL TRAVEL
Railway museum
Standard gauge

Ride/Operation: This static display portrays the elegant lifestyle aboard trains of the past. Plans call for five complete train sets, under cover, by 1998. Several pieces for these future consists are now in storage.

Displays/Exhibits: The centerpiece is an entire set of the Canadian Pacific Railway's 1929 "flag train," the *Trans-Canada Limited,* featuring restored inlaid woods, brass fixtures, plush upholstery, and wool carpets; cars include solarium-lounge "River Rouge"; day parlor No. 6751; sleepers "Rutherglen," "Glencassie," and "Somerset"; dining car "Argyle"; and baggage-sleeper No. 4489. Also on display are 1928 business car "British Columbia"; former CPR baggage car No. 4481, containing an operating HO-gauge model railway; 1927 former CPR executive night car "Strathcona"; modernized sleeper "Redvers," former *Soo-Spokane Train DeLuxe*; 1907 observation-library-buffet-sleeper "Curzon." The 1900-era Elko Station is the visitor center and gift shop. The dining car is often open for tea, coffee, and light refreshments.

Schedule: Daily; summer, 10:00 a.m.-6:00 p.m.; winter, 12:00-5:00 p.m.

Admission: Various categories; Grand Tour tickets strongly recommended. Large groups and bus tours should make advance arrangements.

Special Events: School Programs, September-May; ask about the overnight option for out-of-town classes. Special Railway Gala Christmas Dinners, early December, feature gourmet dining and lodging aboard the restored cars. Bus tours and other groups can book luncheons, dinners, or the museum's famous tea and scones service during their stop.

Location: 1 Van Horne Street (downtown on highway 3/95), Cranbrook.

Contact: Barry McNamar
Marketing/Collections Care
or Mark McDonald
Office/Visitor Services

Mailing Address:
Box 400
Cranbrook, BC V1C 4H9
Telephone: (604) 489-3918
Fax: (604) 489-5744

British Columbia, Duncan
M-R

COURTESY OF BRITISH COLUMBIA FOREST MUSEUM

Ride/Operation: A 1 1/2-mile steam-train ride through forested areas and over a long, curved, wooden trestle, passing a logging camp and historic machinery.

Displays/Exhibits: Standard-gauge Shay and Climax locomotives; railroad equipment, including log cars and engines; logging museum on the site of the first community building in the Cowichan Valley (1863); logging camp with tours and films.

Train: Steel open-platform coaches; open cars.

Schedule: <u>Daily</u>, late April-late September, 9:30 a.m.-6:00 p.m.; train leaves every half hour.

Fare/Admission: Adults $7.00, senior citizens and students (13-18) $6.00, children (5-12) $4.00, children under 5 admitted free, family day pass (2 adults and up to 3 children) $20.00. Includes train ride and admission to park. <u>Group rates</u> available. Fares subject to change. Prices do not include 7% GST.

Locomotives: No. 1, 1921 Lima 2-truck Shay; No. 9, 1925 class B 45-ton 2-truck Climax; No. 24, 1900 Vulcan 12-ton side-tank 0-4-0T; No. 25, Vulcan 18-ton saddletank 0-4-0T; No. 22, 1926 Plymouth gas locomotive; No. 26, 10-ton Plymouth; No. 27, 8-wheeled logging crew speeder; No. 1, narrow-gauge diesel, former White Pass & Yukon.

Rolling Stock/Equipment: Rail cars; tank cars; track crew car; dump cars; flatcar; jiggers; other construction/industrial equipment.

Special Events: <u>Opening Day</u>, May. <u>National Forestry Week</u>, May 1-7. <u>Classic Tractors of Vancouver Island Picnic</u>, June 18. <u>Canada Day and Pioneer Day</u>, July 1. <u>Fords & Friends Picnic</u>, July 16. <u>B.C. Day</u>, August 1. <u>Closing Day</u>, September.

Location: On Vancouver Island, on highway 1 about one mile north of Duncan and 55 minutes from Victoria.

Contact: Christine Brant
Operations Supervisor

Mailing Address:
RR #4
Trans Canada Highway
Duncan, BC V9L 3W8
Telephone: (604) 746-1251
Fax: (604) 746-1487

324

British Columbia, Fort Steele
D-R

EAST KOOTENAY RAILWAY
Steam, scheduled
Standard gauge

COURTESY OF EAST KOOTENAY RAILWAY

Ride/Operation: Passengers enjoy a 2 3/10-mile, 25-minute ride through the grounds of Fort Steele Heritage Town. The double-loop track climbs to the Kootenay River Lookout, where riders may disembark to enjoy the majestic scenery. The conductor gives a brief talk on local history and railroading before the train returns to the station. The availability of the ride is determined each year; please call ahead to find out if railway is in full operation.

Displays/Exhibits: Caboose, former Canadian Pacific; snowplow used on coal lines; the Highland Railway private carriage belonging with the "Dunrobin."

Train: Coach, former British Railways; open-air car with benches.

Schedule: Daily, June 25-September 5; 11:00 a.m.-4:00 p.m.

Fare: Adults $4.00, senior citizens (65+) and youths (13-18) $3.00, children (6-12) $2.00, children under 6 ride free, family $10.00; includes sales tax. Fares subject to change.

Locomotives: 1895 Sharp, Stewart 0-4-4T "Dunrobin," built for the Duke of Sutherland in Scotland; No. 1077, 2-6-2, 1923 Montreal Locomotive Works.

Note: Guided tours are available with advance notice.

Location: Train leaves from the shed-roofed station at Fort Steele Heritage Town in southeastern British Columbia. Fort Steele is located near Cranbrook on route 93-95 and is on the Crow's Nest Pass line of the Canadian Pacific Railway.

Contact: Grant Kvemshagen

Mailing Address:
c/o Fort Steele Heritage Town
General Delivery
Fort Steele, BC V0B 1N0
Telephone: (604) 489-3351

BC RAIL LIMITED
Steam, diesel, scheduled
Standard gauge

JOHN HELBOK

Ride/Operation: BC Rail operates two passenger trains. The Royal Hudson Steam Excursion is an 80-mile, 6-hour round trip from North Vancouver to Squamish, including a 2-hour layover during which optional tours are available. The highly scenic route hugs the seashore along island-dotted Howe Sound Fjord, surrounded by the towering, glacier-capped peaks of the Coast Mountain Range. Passengers may travel in one direction by train and in the other by boat. The Cariboo Dayliner covers a 460-mile route through five distinct climates and some of North America's most spectacular vistas, offering passengers a range of options for day trips or extended journeys to destinations between North Vancouver and Prince George, including the resort areas of Whistler and the Cariboo.

Train: Royal Hudson: baggage car; thirteen coaches; two food-service cars. Cariboo Dayliner: Budd RDC-3s (combination baggage/galley/42 seats); Budd RDC-1s (food kiosk/64 seats). Consists vary from one to seven cars.

Schedule: Royal Hudson: Wednesday-Sunday and Monday holidays, June 3-September 10, plus September 15-17, 10:00 a.m. Cariboo Dayliner: daily round trip to Whistler and Lillooet, 7:00 a.m. Extends north to the Cariboo and Prince George on Sundays, Wednesdays, and Fridays and returns south on Mondays, Thursdays, and Saturdays.

Fare: Royal Hudson: Train only: Adults $35.00, senior citizens and youths $30.50, children $10.00. Train and boat: Adults $59.92, senior citizens and youths $50.29, children $18.19. Cariboo Dayliner: Please call or write for information. Parlor and business cars on the Royal Hudson are available for charter.

Locomotives: No. 2860, 1940 Montreal 4-6-4 H1e "Royal Hudson," former Canadian Pacific: No. 3716, 1912 Montreal 2-8-0, former CP, used for charters and as backup.

Special Events: Royal Hudson Season Inaugural, June 3. Occasional double-headed steam runs.

Location: North Vancouver Station, 1311 West First Street (at the south foot of Pemberton Avenue).

Contact: Cathy Thomson
Director

Mailing Address:
P.O. Box 8770
Vancouver, BC V6B 4X6
Telephone: (604) 631-3500

British Columbia, North Vancouver
R

ROCKY MOUNTAINEER RAILTOUR
Electric, scheduled
Standard gauge

Ride/Operation: A two-day, all-daylight railtour aboard the *Rocky Mountaineer* between Vancouver, British Columbia, and Banff/Calgary or Jasper, Alberta (eastbound), or the same routes westbound. It includes two breakfasts and two lunches, an overnight stay in a comfortable hotel in Kamloops, British Columbia, and transfers to and from the hotel in Kamloops. The tour can be combined with attractions and hotels in eleven independent package tours or rail/Alaska cruise programs.

Train: Two locomotives; two baggage cars; eighteen coaches; steam-generating unit; one bilevel dome coach (new for 1995).

Schedule: Alternating Sundays, Thursdays, and Tuesdays, (three times every 2 weeks), May 16-October 9. Value Season: May 16-June 1 & September 24-October 6.

Fare: *Regular Season*: Banff/Jasper, one way: single $449, double $410, triple $402, child $269. Banff/Jasper, round trip: single $807, double $737, triple $725, child $484. Calgary, one way: single $491, double $452, triple $445, child $312. Calgary, round trip: single $885, double $815, triple $800, child $562. *Value Season*: Banff/Jasper, one way: single $371, double $332, triple $324, child $230. Banff/Jasper, round trip: single $667, double $597, triple $585, child $413. Calgary, one way: single $413, double $374, triple $367, child $273. Calgary, round trip: single $745, double $675, triple $659, child $491. All prices are in U.S. dollars and do not include 3.5% GST. Child rate applies to children ages 2 to 11 sharing a room with adults. Children under 2 ride free; they are not entitled to a seat, but they will receive meals.

Locomotives: Nos. 7488 and 7498, 1980 General Electric B-36 Dash 7 locomotives, former Santa Fe, rebuilt in 1990.

Passenger Cars: Seventeen 48-seat coaches, 1954 Canadian Car and Foundry, rebuilt 1972 and 1985-1988; 48-seat No. 5749, 1949 Pullman.

Location: Suite 104, 340 Brooksbank Avenue.

Contact: Eric Bellanger

Mailing Address:
Suite 104
340 Brooksbank Avenue
North Vancouver, BC V7J 2C1
Telephone: (800) 665-7245

British Columbia, Port Alberni
D-R

COURTESY OF ALBERNI VALLEY MUSEUM

WESTERN VANCOUVER ISLAND INDUSTRIAL HERITAGE SOCIETY
Steam, scheduled
Standard gauge

Ride/Operation: A 3-mile round trip along the industrial waterfront.

Displays/Exhibits: Restored CP Rail station; 1947 Hayes logging truck; Fairmont speeder; other restoration work in progress.

Schedule: Weekends and statutory holidays, July 1-September 4, 11:00 a.m.-4:00 p.m., on the hour.

Fare: Adults $2.00, children $1.00.

Locomotives: No. 2, "Two Spot," 1912 Lima 42-ton 2-truck Shay; No. 7, 1928 Baldwin 90-ton 2-8-2 ST; No. 11, 1942 General Electric 45-ton diesel-electric; No. 1, 1928 Westminster Iron Works Buda gas switcher; No. 8427, Montreal Locomotive Works/Alco RS-3 diesel.

Rolling Stock/Equipment: Two modified cabooses, former Canadian National; early 1900s Victoria Lumber & Manufacturing Co. crew car.

Special Events: Santa Claus Run.

Location: The restored CP Rail station at Harbour Quay in Port Alberni on Vancouver Island. The Alberni Valley is a one-hour drive from Nanaimo, the B.C. Ferry terminal to the mainland.

▢ 🚗 ⊞ ⛐ ▲

Contact: Hugh Grist
Treasurer

Mailing Address:
"The Station"
3100 Kingsway Avenue
Port Alberni, BC V9Y 3B1
Telephone: (604) 724-3441

CENTRAL BRITISH COLUMBIA RAILWAY & FOREST INDUSTRY MUSEUM SOCIETY
Railway museum

Displays/Exhibits: This museum houses a large collection of railway buildings, rolling stock, and equipment, complemented by the Fire Hall, housing a 1929 Reo fire truck, a 1948 fire truck, and a horse-drawn fire sleigh. The pioneer building contains a large telephone display and an operating telegraph system. A turn-of-the-century bunkhouse shows how the Yelanka, a local ethnic group, lived while working on the railway. Logging displays include a 1930 band saw, a 1950 gang saw, and several pieces of logging road equipment.

Schedule: May 21-September 18, 10:00 a.m.-5:00 p.m.

Admission: Adults $2.50, senior citizens and children $1.00, family (up to 5) $5.00.

Locomotives: No. 1520, 1906 4-6-0, and No. 9169, EMD F7A, both former Canadian National; No. 586, RS-10, former BC Rail; No. 101, 44-ton General Electric, and 65-ton Atlas diesel, both former U.S. Navy.

Passenger Cars: 1913 business car "Nechako," former GTP; "Endeavour," former BC Rail; sleeper; coach; combine.

Rolling Stock/Equipment: Head-end power car from *American Freedom Train;* baggage car; road repair car; 1903 snowplow; operating 1913 100-ton steam crane; boxcars; cabooses; tank cars; work cars; operating 88-foot, 10-inch turntable.

Special Events: Will be held on the third Sunday of each month during the season.

Location: 850 River Road, just north of Canadian National yards, close to downtown, and adjacent to Cottonwood Island Nature Park.

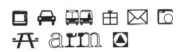

Contact: Roy Smith

Mailing Address:
P.O. Box 2408
Prince George, BC V2N 2S6
Telephone: (604) 563-7351

WEST COAST RAILWAY
HERITAGE PARK
Railway displays

Displays/Exhibits: This site offers a static display of more than 50 locomotives and pieces of rolling stock as well as artifacts related to the railway history of British Columbia. Features of the display include 1890 former Canadian Pacific business car "British Columbia"; former Pacific Great Eastern RSC-3 No. 561; former PGE interurban sleeper "Clinton"; museum display car "Cowichan River"; and 2-6-2 No. 2, the first steam locomotive on the PGE.

Schedule: <u>Daily</u>, May 1-October 30, 10:00 a.m.-4:00 p.m.

Admission: Adults $3.50, children (under 13) $2.50, family (2 adults with children under 13) $10.00.

Locomotives: No. 551, 65-ton, former PGE; No. 53, former CP; No. 960, former B.C. Electric; 2-8-2 No. 16, former Comox Logging & Railway; others.

Passenger Cars: Colonist car No. 2514 and observation No. 598, both former CP; cafe-observations Nos. 1090 & 1057, both former Great Northern; diner "Dunraven," former Canadian National.

Rolling Stock/Equipment: Snowplow No. 55365, former CN; Jordan spreader No. 402846 and steam crane No. 414330, both former CP; cabooses Nos. 1817 & 1821, former PGE; transfer caboose, former GN; others.

Note: Guided tours of the park can be arranged at any time of the year for tour groups and trade associations.

Location: 33547 Government Road.

Contact: Grant Ferguson
Vice President

Mailing Address:
P.O. Box 2387
Squamish, BC V0N 3G0
Telephone: (604) 898-9336

PRAIRIE DOG CENTRAL
Steam, scheduled
Standard gauge

V. MARTIN

Ride/Operation: A 36-mile, 2-hour round trip to Grosse Isle over the Oakpoint Subdivision of the Canadian National Railways. Vintage wooden cars are pulled by a beautiful American Standard locomotive that was in service on the Canadian Pacific from 1882 to 1918.

Displays/Exhibits: On display in the city of Winnipeg are former Canadian National 2-8-0 No. 2747 and 4-8-2 No. 6043.

Train: Wood combination car; four wood coaches.

Schedule: Sundays, June-September, 11:00 a.m. & 3:00 p.m.

Admission: Adults $13.00, senior citizens and youths (12-17) $11.00, children (2-11) $7.00, children under 2 not occupying a seat ride free. Fares and schedules subject to change without notice.

Locomotives: No. 3, 1882 Dubs & Co. (Glasgow) 4-4-0, former Canadian Pacific, former City of Winnipeg Hydro.

Passenger Cars: Coaches, former Keweenaw Central, former Canadian Northern, former CP; business car, former CP (awaiting restoration).

Rolling Stock/Equipment: Boxcars; bunk car; caboose; flatcar.

Location: Train departs from the CN St. James Station near 1661 Portage Avenue, just west of St. James Street.

Contact: K. G. Younger
Secretary-Treasurer

Mailing Address:
The Vintage Locomotive Society, Inc.
P.O. Box 33021
RPO Polo Park
Winnipeg, Manitoba R3G 3N4
Telephone: (204) 832-5259

New Brunswick, Hillsborough
D-R

BOB MITCHELL

SALEM & HILLSBOROUGH
RAILROAD
Steam, diesel, scheduled
Railway display

Operation: This operation, a project of the New Brunswick Division of the Canadian Railroad Historical Association, features a museum, static display, and gift shop. On September 16, 1994, a fire destroyed the railroad's shops and offices, as well as considerable rolling stock. The line normally featured 1-hour, 10-mile excursions, 3 1/2-hour, 22-mile dinner excursions, and chartered excursions. Please call ahead for the 1995 operating schedule.

Schedule: Museum: Daily, July 1-September 4, 10:00a.m.-6:00p.m.

Admission: $1.00.

Locomotives: No. 29, 1897 4-4-0, former Canadian Pacific (damaged in fire); No. 1009, 1912 4-6-0, and No. 8245, 1958 MLW MS-10p, both former Canadian National.

Passenger Cars: Coaches dating from 1911 to 1942.

Rolling Stock/Equipment: Cabooses; double-ended snowplow; 1920 Jordan spreader; 100-ton 1913 steam wreck crane; 1921 tank car; others.

Location: On highway 114, on the way to The Rocks Provincial Park and Fundy National Park, 12 miles south of Moncton.

VIAMoncton

Radio Frequency: 172.305

Contact: E. F. Bowes
Director

Mailing Address:
P.O. Box 70
Hillsborough, NB E0A 1XO
Summer: (506) 734-3195
Off-season: (506) 734-3100

RAILWAY SOCIETY
OF NEWFOUNDLAND
Railway displays

COURTESY OF RAILWAY SOCIETY OF NEWFOUNDLAND

Displays/Exhibits: Two trains are on display at this site: a passenger train headed by steam locomotive No. 593 and a snowplow train powered by diesel No. 931, a narrow-gauge six-motor road switcher.

Schedule: Display: open for exterior viewing year-round. Full tour with tour guides on the trains: mid June-August 31, 10:00 a.m.-6:00 p.m.

Admission: No charge.

Locomotives: No. 593, 1920 Baldwin 4-6-2; No. 931, 1956 General Motors.

Passenger Cars: Baggage car; express car; day coach dining car; sleeper.

Rolling Stock/Equipment: Snowplow No. 3460; caboose No. 6072; side-dump car; gang track-force speeder with two speeder trailers.

Location: The former Newfoundland Railway Terminal at Humbermouth, Corner Brook East.

Contact: R. J. Hickey
President

Mailing Address:
P.O. Box 673
Corner Brook, NFLD A2H 6G1
Telephone: (709) 634-6089

SYDNEY & LOUISBURG
RAILWAY MUSEUM
Railway museum

INSERT PHOTO CREDIT HERE

Displays/Exhibits: This museum, located in the original 1895 Louisburg railway station, features exhibits describing the history of the S&L, railway technology, and local and marine history. Several model trains are included, and a model of the complete S&L line is now under construction. Outside, visitors can see the restored original freight shed, rolling stock, and the newly constructed "roundhouse," which houses some of the rolling stock in the winter.

Schedule: <u>Daily</u>; June 1-June 30 & September 1-mid October, 9:00 a.m.-5:00 p.m.; July 1-August 31, 9:00 a.m.-7:00 p.m. <u>Other times</u> by appointment. <u>Bus and school tours</u> welcome.

Admission: No charge; donations welcomed.

Locomotives: No. 593, 1920 Baldwin 4-6-2; No. 931, 1956 General Motors.

Passenger Cars: 1884 passenger car; 1914 passenger car.

Rolling Stock/Equipment: Caboose; tank car; freight car; small handcar; maintenance equipment.

Special Events: <u>100th Anniversary Celebration</u>, June 16-18, commemorates the June 17, 1895, first run of the railway and features a concert in the roundhouse and an open house with interpreters in period costumes. <u>In 1995 the town observes</u> the 250th anniversary of its taking by the New England Army and the British Navy, and the roundhouse will be used for many events. <u>Annual Reunion</u>, second Sunday in September each year.

Location: Main Street, at the entrance of town. Louisbourg is 22 miles from Sydney on highway 22.

Contact: Bill Bussey
President

Mailing Address:
P.O. Box 225
Louisbourg, NS B0A 1M0
Telephone: (902) 733-2720

334

Ontario, Cochrane
M

COCHRANE RAILWAY & PIONEER MUSEUM
Railway museum

COURTESY OF COCHRANE RAILWAY & PIONEER MUSEUM

Displays/Exhibits: This museum preserves a three-dimensional picture of the pioneer railway and homesteading days, as a tribute to the men and women who opened northern Ontario, an empire bigger than the territories of many United Nations members. A model train display aboard a former Canadian National coach introduces the main railway exhibits, which include a telegraph operator's corner, a ticket office, a document display, an insulator collection, and uniforms. There is also a large, varied display of photographs. Many of the pictures are from the large collection assembled by the Rev. W. L. L. Lawrence around 1912, for which the museum is now trustee.

Schedule: Mid June-mid September, daily, 10:00 a.m.-8:00 p.m.

Admission: Adults and students $1.50; senior citizens and children $1.00.

Locomotives: No. 137, 2-8-0, former Temiskaming & Northern Ontario.

Passenger Cars: Caboose and three coaches, former CN.

Rolling Stock/Equipment: Interpretive car.

Special Events: Museum Days, two days in August; free hot dogs and soda served. Please call or write for specific dates.

Note: Lodging and a restaurant are available at Union Station, adjacent to the museum.

Location: 210 Railway Street, northeast of Cochrane Union Station.

Contact: Paul LaTondress
Curator

Mailing Address:
P.O. Box 490
Cochrane, ON P0L 1C0
Telephone: (705) 272-4361

335

FORT ERIE RAILROAD MUSEUM
Railway museum

Displays/Exhibits: This museum displays railroad-related exhibits in two train stations, one built in 1910 and another built in 1873; also on display are maintenance-of-way equipment, a steam engine, a caboose, and a fireless engine.

Schedule: Daily, May 23-September 5, 9:00 a.m.-5:00 p.m. Weekends, September 6-October 8, 9:00 a.m.-5:00 p.m. Subject to change; please call or write to confirm.

Admission: Adults $2.00, children $.50. Includes admission to the town's two other museums, the Fort Erie Historical Museum and the Ridgeway Battlefield Museum.

Locomotive: No. 6218, former Canadian National 4-8-4; Porter fireless locomotive.

Location: Central Avenue, near Gilmore Road.

Contact: Jane Davies
Curator

Mailing Address:
P.O. Box 339
Ridgeway, ON L0S 1N0
Telephone: (905) 894-5322

KOMOKA RAILWAY MUSEUM
Railway museum
Standard gauge

JOHN KANAKOS

Displays/Exhibits: Housed in Komoka's former Grand Trunk station, which was built in 1880 and was moved to its present site across the tracks when purchased in 1974, this museum preserves the railroad history of Ontario. Many railroad items are available for close examination, such as telegraph keys, spike hammers, spike pullers, switch lanterns, steam gauges, a railroad safe, and a baggage sleigh; there are also Fairmont motor cars and a three-wheel velocipede. The museum's pride is a 1913 Shay steam logging locomotive, now undergoing restoration in its own building. When restored, a pre-1939 steel-sided baggage car will house a model railroad display and a theater for multimedia presentations. Visitors may also view the tiny (8-foot by 9-foot) Longwoods flagstop station, and researchers are welcome to browse the extensive library of books, photos, and newspaper clippings.

Schedule: June 1-September 30: Tuesday and Thursday, 7:00-9:00 p.m.; Saturday, 9:00 a.m.-12:00 p.m.; Sunday, 1:00-4:00 p.m. Group tours and off-peak visits may be arranged in advance.

Admission: $2.00 donation.

Special Events: Day trips to other local railroad museums. Pancake breakfast, held in conjunction with the annual Thames Valley Central Modular Railroad Club's model railroad flea market, mid April. "Shunpikers" Tour, fall. Toy Miniatures Flea Market and Show, November.

Location: 133 Queen Street, adjacent to the Komoka Community Center. Komoka is 10 minutes west of London and halfway between Detroit and Toronto.

Contact: Ronald Davis
Curator

Mailing Address:
P.O. Box 22
133 Queen Street
Komoka, ONT N0L 1R0
Telephone: (519) 657-1912

NATIONAL MUSEUM OF
SCIENCE & TECHNOLOGY
Science museum
Railway displays

Displays/Exhibits: This museum features all types of transportation from Canada's earliest days to the present, along with many other types of exhibits relating to science and technology. There are four steam locomotives on display in the huge Railroad Hall; the cabs of some are accessible, and sound effects give the feeling of live locomotives. The engines are meticulously restored, with polished rods and lighted number boards and class lights. The scene is enhanced by station benches, platform lights, signs, and memorabilia.

Schedule: May 1-September 4: Friday-Wednesday, 9:00 a.m.-5:00 p.m.; Thursday, 9:00 a.m.-9:00 p.m. September 5-April 30: Closed Mondays except statutory holidays. Closed Christmas Day.

Admission: Adults $5.00, seniors citizens and students $4.00, children (6-15) $1.75, children under 6 admitted free, family rate (2 adults and children under age 16) $10.00, groups of 15 or more (without a guide) $2.25 per person, school groups (children's tours) $1.75 per person. Tour leader and bus driver admitted free. No admission charge from 5:00 to 9:00 p.m. on Thursdays.

Locomotives: No. 6400, 1936 Montreal 4-8-4, former Canadian National, displayed at the 1939 New York World's Fair. No. 926, 1912 4-6-0; No. 2858, 1938 Montreal "Royal Hudson" 4-6-4; No. 3100, 1928 Montreal 4-8-4; all former Canadian Pacific.

Passenger Cars: 1892 business car "Terra Nova," former Newfoundland Railway.

Location: At 1867 St. Laurent Boulevard in southeast Ottawa.

Contact: Jean-Guy Monette
Public Relations Officer

Mailing Address:
1867 St. Laurent Blvd.
P.O. Box 9724
Ottawa, ON K1G 5A3
Telephone: (613) 991-3044

PORT STANLEY TERMINAL RAIL
Diesel, scheduled
Standard gauge

BRAD JOLLIFFE

Ride/Operation: This line offers three different rides originating from the station in Port Stanley, on the harbor next to the lift bridge. Trains pass over two bridges and head north up to seven miles through the Kettle Creek Valley. Port Stanley is a commercial and fishing village on the north shore of Lake Erie.

Displays/Exhibits: Equipment includes cabooses; heavyweight coaches; open coaches; baggage cars; boxcars; flatcars; hopper cars; a snowplow; tank cars; Borrocranes; and more. Ticket office and displays are in the former London & Port Stanley station.

Train: Open excursion cars; cabooses, former Canadian National, modified into enclosed coaches; standard coaches, former VIA. The "Little Red Caboose" can be chartered for birthday parties and other events with advance reservation.

Schedule: Union: Sundays, January-April & November-December; weekends, May-June & September-October; daily, July-August. Whites: weekends, May-June & September-October; daily, July-August. St. Thomas: Sundays, May-June & September-October; weekends, July-August.

Fare: Union: adults $6.50, senior citizens (65+) $5.75, children (2-12) $3.25. Whites: adults $8.00, senior citizens (65+) 7.00, children (2-12) $5.50. St. Thomas: adults $11.00, senior citizens (65+) $10.00, children (2-12) $5.50. Fares do not include GST tax. For group and charter rates call Shirley Liggett at (519) 672-7953.

Locomotives: No. L-1, 1952 25-ton General Electric; No. L-2, 1950 Canadian Locomotive Co.; and No. L-5, "Albert," 1947 50-ton Whitcomb; all former Consolidated Sand & Gravel Co., Paris, Ontario; General Electric 44-ton "Winnie."

Special Events: Easter Bunny, April. Wild Flowers, May. Santa Claus Trains, December.

Note: This site offers fair exchange on U.S. funds.

Location: On highway 4 south of London, about 20 minutes from highway 401.

Contact: Al Howlett
Marketing

Mailing Address:
309 Bridge Street
Port Stanley, ON N5L 1C5
Telephone: (519) 782-3730
Fax: (519) 782-4385

HALTON COUNTY RADIAL RAILWAY
Electric, scheduled
4' 10 7/8" gauge

J. D. KNOWLES

Ride/Operation: Located on the right-of-way of the former Toronto Suburban Railway, Canada's first operating railway museum offers a 2-mile ride through scenic woodlands. Two loops are in service.

Displays/Exhibits: Many pieces of electric-railway rolling stock from lines in Ontario, ranging from early wooden cars to PCC cars from Toronto. Also on display are a line car, a crane car, a sweeper, an electric locomotive, a caboose, and boxcars.

Schedule: Weekends and holidays, May, September, and October; Wednesday-Sunday, June; daily, July-August; 10:00 a.m.-5:00 p.m.

Fare: Adults $6.00, senior citizens and students (13-17) $5.00, children (3-12) $3.50, family rate (2 over 18 and up to 3 under 18) $16.50. Night shows: adults $4.50, senior citizens and students (13-17) $3.75, children (3-12) $3.00. Different rates apply on special-event days. Charters and group tours available for groups of 20 or more during the week with advance reservation: adults $4.75, senior citizens and students (13-17) $4.25, children (3-12) $3.00. Prices do not include tax.

Trolleys: No. 327, 1893 4-wheel open car (rebuilt 1933); No. 55, 1915 Preston single-truck closed car; No. 2890, 1923 small Peter Witt, Ottawa; No. 2424, 1921 large Peter Witt; and No. 4000, 1938 PCC; all former Toronto Transportation Commission. No. 107, 1912 Montreal & Southern Counties interurban; No. 1326, 1910 Toronto Railway Co.; No. 8, 1915 Jewett Car Co. heavy interurban, former London & Port Stanley; No. 732, trolley coach, former Hamilton Street Railways.

Special Events: Summer Extravaganza, June 25. Work Car Extra Special Day, July 23. Night Shows, August 19, December 9 & 16. Roaring Twenties Fall Picnic, September 3. Fall Extravaganza, October 1. Christmas Fiesta, December 3.

Location: Take exit 312 (Guelph Line) off highway 401 and travel north nine miles.

Contact: Joan Johns
Curator

Mailing Address:
RR #2
Rockwood, ON N0B 2K0
Telephone: (519) 856-9802

Ontario, Smiths Falls
M-R

SMITHS FALLS RAILWAY
MUSEUM CORP.
Diesel, irregular
Standard gauge

COURTESY OF SMITHS FALLS RAILWAY MUSEUM

Ride/Operation: Extensive renovations have been carried out since 1982 to restore the Smith Falls station. Inspection-car rides are offered daily.

Displays/Exhibits: 1914 former Canadian Northern station, now a national historic site; agent's bay; railroad and artifacts display in Main Waiting Room. Train display includes a diesel locomotive, coaches, and a caboose; other displays include steam locomotive No. 1112, former Canadian Northern; a 1947 Cadillac railcar; a 1913 dental car; Wickham inspection cars, work cars, ballast cars, and assorted freight equipment.

Schedule: April-November, 10:00 a.m.-4:00 p.m.

Fare: Adults $1.50, students $.50, children under 13 admitted free.

Locomotives: No. 6591 MLW S-3, former Canadian Pacific No. 6591; former CN 4-6-0 No. 1112, undergoing restoration.

Passenger Cars: No. 5019, 1923 Canadian Car & Foundry coach, former Canadian National No. 5019; No. 5013, 1919 CC&F coach, former CN No. 5013; Wickham car No. 23, former CN; Wickham car No. M-26, former CP

Rolling Stock/Equipment: 1941 caboose No. 437183, former CP.

Special Events: Great Canadian Handcar Race, July. Please call or write for information.

Note: A number of coaches and other railway equipment not listed are undergoing restoration at the museum.

Location: 90 William Street West; signs in town indicate museum location. From Ottawa, take highway 15 south; from Kingston, take highway 15 north; from Brockville, take highway 29 north.

Contact: Julia Brady
Curator

Mailing Address:
P.O. Box 962
Smiths Falls, ON K7A 5A5
Telephone: (613) 283-5696

341

ELGIN COUNTY RAILWAY MUSEUM
Railway museum

Displays/Exhibits: St. Thomas was once a bustling railway town with yards and service facilities for the Pere Marquette, the New York Central, and the Wabash, along with connections for the Canadian Pacific, the London & Port Stanley, and the Canadian National. Established to preserve this rich heritage, this museum houses its displays in the vintage Michigan Central Railway shops. The highlight of the collection is former CN steam locomotive No. 5700, which was formerly displayed in the Museum of Science and Technology. The newest addition is operable General Electric 43-ton diesel switcher No. 51, "Tillie," former Wabash, which was in service until July 1994. Other displays include an 1880s Howard Regulator clock; a "Railway Hall of Fame" paying tribute to those who made their living on the railroad, and artifacts and memorabilia.

Schedule: Mondays, Wednesdays & Saturdays, mornings. Also one Sunday per month. Tours can be arranged any time. Please call or write for more information.

Admission: No charge; donations welcomed.

Passenger Cars: 1939 Pullman sleeper "Cascade Lane," former NYC.

Rolling Stock/Equipment: 1953 baggage car, former CN; gas cars; handcars; yard crane, former Chesapeake & Ohio.

Special Events: Nostalgia Weekend, first weekend in May each year. Heritage Weekend, last weekend in August each year. These events feature vendors, live entertainment, and other attractions.

Location: Wellington Street, downtown. Take exit 4 south off highway 401 and travel fifteen minutes. St. Thomas is midway between Detroit and Toronto.

Contact: Shari J. Boland
Secretary

Mailing Address:
R.R. 6
St. Thomas, ONT N5P 3T1
Telephone: (519) 631-0936

SOUTH SIMCOE RAILWAY
Steam, scheduled

COURTESY OF SOUTH SIMCOE RAILWAY

Ride/Operation: An 8-mile, 50-minute round trip over a scenic portion of the former Canadian National line from Hamilton to Allandale. Former Canadian Pacific No. 136, an 1883 4-4-0, or former CP No. 1057, a 1912 4-6-0, hauls 1920s-vintage cars.

Train: Former Canadian Pacific 82-seat steel day coach and 32-seat steel combine; former Toronto, Hamilton & Buffalo 74-seat steel coach.

Schedule: Sundays, May 21-October 8, plus May 22, August 7, September 4 & October 9, 10:00 a.m.-4:00 p.m., on the hour. Mondays-Wednesdays, July-August, September 25-27, & October 2-4, plus July 1; 10:30 & 11:30 a.m., 1:00 & 3:00 p.m.

Fare: Adults $7.00, senior citizens $6.00, students (12-18) $6.00, children (3-11) $3.00. Family ticket (2 adults and up to 3 children) $18.00.

Locomotives: 1883 4-4-0 No. 136, 1939 diesel-hydraulic No. 22, ; and 1912 4-6-0 No. 1057, all former CP; 1960 "Blue Goose" diesel switcher, former GM; diesel switcher No. 10, former Pilkington Glass.

Passenger Cars: Six cars from the 1920s, undergoing or awaiting restoration.

Rolling Stock/Equipment: A variety of vintage freight equipment in various stages of restoration.

Special Events: Railfan Day, July 2, with a special program of events. Please call or write for details.

Location: On Simcoe County Road 10, 2 1/2 miles north of highway 9, between highway 50 and highway 27.

Radio Frequency: 172.95

Contact: Al Wilkinson
Marketing Manager

Mailing Address:
P.O. Box 186
Tottenham, ON L0G 1W0
Telephone: (905) 936-5815

HULL-CHELSEA-WAKEFIELD
STEAM TRAIN
Steam, diesel, scheduled

COURTESY OF HULL-CHELSEA-WAKEFIELD

Standard gauge

Ride/Operation: This line offers a 36-mile, 5-hour round trip through the Gatineau Hills, Chelsea, and Farm Point with a 2-hour stop at the picturesque village of Wakefield in the Gatineau Valley. A tour guide on each coach gives the history of the line, the train, and the region. In Wakefield, passengers can watch the engine being turned on the hand-powered turntable and filled at the water tower.

Train: 1907 Swedish steam engine; nine 1940 open-window coaches, one with a snack bar.

Schedule: Weekends, May; Tuesdays, Wednesdays & weekends, June, September & October; daily, July-August; 1:30 p.m.

Fare: Adults $23.00, senior citizens $21.00, students $20.00, children $11.00; one-way $19.50. Taxes not included. Group rates and charters available.

Locomotives: No. 909, 2-8-0; No. 244, 1962 General Motors.

⬜ 🚗 🚌 ⊞ 🗖 ⛢

&(partially)

Contact: Marc Beaulieu
General Manager

Mailing Address:
165 Deveault Street
Hull, PQ J8Z 1S7
Telephone: (819) 778-7246
(800) 871-7246
Fax: (819) 778-5007

CANADIAN RAILWAY MUSEUM
Railway museum
Standard gauge

COURTESY OF CANADIAN RAILWAY MUSEUM

Ride/Operation: A 1 1/2-mile ride through the museum grounds. Streetcar operates daily; train operates Sundays and holidays.

Displays/Exhibits: The largest railway museum in Canada, the CRM owns a collection of more than 120 pieces of rolling stock, including steam and diesel locomotives, passenger and freight cars, streetcars, and interurbans.

Train: No. 30, 70-ton General Electric, former Canadian National; No. 1002, MLW S-3, former Port of Montreal; No. 20, MLW RS-2, former Roberval & Saguenay; No. 1959, Montreal Tramways streetcar; No. 3, Montreal Tramways open observation car; "John Molson," operating replica of an 1850s steam locomotive.

Schedule: Daily, May 1-September 4; weekends, September 9-October 15; 9:00 a.m.-5:00 p.m.

Admission: Adults $4.50 ($5.25 Sundays and holidays), senior citizens (60+) and students $3.50 ($4.25 Sundays and holidays), children $2.00 ($2.75 Sundays and holidays), family rate (2 parents and up to 3 children) $12.00, children under 5 admitted free. Taxes not included. Group discounts available for 20 or more people. Reservations required.

Location: Thirty minutes from downtown Montreal on route 209, one mile south of route 132.

Locomotives/Trolleys: Included are the oldest existing Canadian-built steam locomotive, former Canadian Pacific No. 144; No. 77, the oldest surviving diesel-electric; the "Rocket," the first electric streetcar to operate in Montreal, in 1892.

Passenger Cars: First-class coach, former CP; business car "Saskatchewan."

Contact: Ms. Marie-Claude Reid
Director

Mailing Address:
120 St. Pierre Street
Saint-Constant, PQ J5A 2G9
Telephone: (514) 632-2410

RUSTY RELICS MUSEUM
Railway museum
Standard gauge

COURTESY OF RUSTY RELICS MUSEUM

Displays/Exhibits: This museum, which is primarily a museum of pioneer days in Saskatchewan, is housed in a former Canadian National Railway station. A 1943 former Canadian Pacific caboose and a former CN motor car are on display outside; a former CN tool shed, containing railroad tools, is located in the yard. A new attraction is a 1905 one-room country school, complete with artifacts. The museum, which is located near the Moose Mountain Provincial Park and White Bear Lake, serves as Carlyle's tourist information center.

Schedule: Daily, June-September, or by appointment.
Admission: Adults $2.00, students $1.00, preschool children admitted free.

Location: At Railway Avenue and 3rd Street West. Carlyle is in southeast Saskatchewan about 60 miles north of the U.S. border and 40 miles west of the Manitoba border.

Contact: Delores Cutler
Administrator

Mailing Address:
Box 840
Carlyle, SASK S0C 0R0
Telephone: (306) 453-2266
Off-season: (306) 453-2987

Index

351

Index to Advertisers

Notes

Notes

$9.95
list 11.95